Pages from Tarusa

(ТАРУССКИЕ СТРАНИЦЫ)

THE POND

V. E. Borisov–Musatov. Watercolor. No date. Borisov–Musatov was
a well-known artist who worked in Tarusa, where he died in 1905. His
paintings, while realistic in manner, have strong symbolist and
psychological overtones. Many, including this one, were reproduced
in *Pages from Tarusa* for the first time.

Published simultaneously in Canada
by Little, Brown & Company (Canada) Limited

PRINTED IN THE UNITED STATES OF AMERICA

Pages from Taru

New Voices in Russian Writ

* * * *

Edited with an Introduction by

ANDREW FIELD

LITTLE, BROWN AND COMPANY · BOSTON · TORONT

For Audrey

Introduction

❊ ❊ ❊ ❊

There is a well-known passage in *War and Peace* in which Tolstoy, bearing down hard on his pen, describes the role of Napoleon at the battle of Borodino. After recounting (and savagely ridiculing) the theories put forward by leading historians concerning the significance of Napoleon's actions at Borodino, Tolstoy summarizes his attitude towards individuals in the historical process with the statement that the course of events in this world is determined beyond the province of individuals and that the influence of some Napoleon or other upon the sequence of these events is only extrinsic and illusory. Even though we need not accept Tolstoy's judgment uncritically, there is a compelling logic in his basic proposition.

It is my contention that Western accounts of Soviet literature since Stalin's death have been far too simplistic, and that, in the attention which they give to the superficial, the sensational and the inferior, our Soviet experts, like Tolstoy's historians, frequently convey insufficiently and even falsely the reality which they purport to describe. Their accounts belong to a subdivision of the game we call Kremlinology. The fundamental characteristic of such critical reportage is its concern with incident, inside and outside of literature, rather than with writing as such. The primary interest of the approach is its fascinating terminology: "protest" has been followed by "dissonant" which, in turn, has been superseded by such curious appellations as — the actual title of an article by one of our pillars of Sovietology — "the coffee break in Soviet literature."

It is instructive to compare the manner in which Evgeny

Evtushenko, the laureate of facile imagery and easy rhyme, is still being widely lauded in the West, even while, in the Soviet Union, he is now being criticized from the liberal position and on purely literary grounds. This criticism is a good measure of the hardheaded maturity of the Russian intelligentsia; and there are other signs, too. Soviet literary criticism in general has become interesting to read for the first time in decades. To cite but one instance, a study of Ivan Goncharov's classic novel, *Oblomov*, published by the Soviet Academy of Sciences, delves into the novel's rich sexual symbolism and even makes reference to American New Criticism. Many heretofore forbidden or consciously disregarded poets — aesthetes, decadents, symbolists — have been rehabilitated, and poets with highly sensitive political backgrounds, such as Boris Pasternak, Nikolai Gumilyov and Sergei Esenin, have also been published, the latter in a five-volume scholarly edition of the sort that American university presses ordinarily reserve for nineteenth-century poets. This astonishingly diverse publishing activity has been occurring not only in Leningrad and Moscow, but also (and the book in hand bears witness to this) in many provincial centers. Clearly, there is a widespread upheaval — renaissance might be the better word — taking place in Soviet culture. When seen against this background, the battles won and lost by a Evtushenko, though by no means insignificant, are far less important than they are taken to be.

Pages from Tarusa is uniquely qualified to give the Western reader a fair and inclusive representation of the important currents in contemporary Soviet literature. Tarusa is a small town on the Oka River, situated not far from Moscow in the province of Kaluga. It was, even in the nineteenth century, a center for artists. Now, however, the town is better known for its large number of writers who live and work there and periodically make the boat trip or short bus ride to Moscow with their manuscripts.

The dominant mood of *Pages from Tarusa* is one of youth. Although the two works are quite dissimilar in most respects, Boris Balter's long story, "Three from a Town," performs much the same function as Salinger's *Catcher in the Rye* did in America in capturing the essence of one aspect of Soviet youth. The Tarusa writers strongly feel the need to record and come to terms with that life which has had no one to tell its story during the dreary years of Socialist Realism. This tale is now being told with sensitivity and forthrightness. It was the Tarusa writers, especially Koblikov and Okudzhava, who, more than a year before Solzhenitsyn's celebrated novel, broke the first ground in the movement away from the Victorianism of Soviet literary language.

As might be expected, *Pages from Tarusa* has its political story. The anthology appeared in a printing of 75,000 copies in late 1961. Advance word of the volume had spread widely, and, when it was placed on sale in Moscow, buyers at once rushed to the bookstores to obtain it. There had, however, been some irregularities in the publication of the book, and that, together with the book's "liberal" tone, caused some bureaucrat (or Bureaucrat) to issue an order for the book's withdrawal. Fortunately, the courage of Konstantin Paustovsky, one of the most widely respected individuals among older Soviet writers, in placing his own reputation behind the book averted any serious reprisals against the Tarusa writers. This must be said — only a Babbitt or his Soviet equivalent, a Drozdov, could have issued such a withdrawal order, for *Pages from Tarusa* is at all times within the context of the very highest aspirations and ideals of Communist society.

According to the most reliable estimates, only a few thousand copies actually reached buyers. No matter — the book was out, and copies rapidly went from hand to hand. Stories are told of single copies being passed through dormitories, clubs and residential buildings and thereby reaching hundreds of readers. Its poets and writers had bestowed upon them the sobriquet "lads from Tarusa" (*tarusskie rebyata*), a phrase which contains more implicit approval and warmth of feeling than any English translation can possibly suggest. The "spirit of Tarusa" has, in fact, acquired such emblematic significance that it is now frequently understood as a general term which includes many fine writers who, by mere chance, do not happen to live there. Tarusa has come to symbolize what is honest and, above all, *literary* in Soviet literature.

Perhaps the most striking feature of the Tarusa stories is their old-fashioned realistic manner. The reason for this is that, lacking an adequate contemporary literary language and tradition, young Soviet writers are turning to the classics of Russian literature. Yury

Kazakov's outstanding stories, for example, may be considered, in both style and scope, to be modern versions of Turgenev's *Sportsman's Sketches*. There is, too, one other important (and quite surprising) influence upon Tarusa writing, namely that of Russian émigré literature. Many émigré writers are now well-known in Russia, and it is not without significance that two, Marina Tsvetaeva and Ivan Bunin, are represented in *Pages from Tarusa*.

You will look in vain, however, for direct Western influences: *Pages from Tarusa* is thoroughly, even exclusively, "Russian" in spirit. Some would explain this phenomenon (analogous more to the "native soil movement" in nineteenth-century Russian literature than to Slavophilism) as being the inevitable result of the long isolation of Russian writers from the West, but there are also more positive causes for their intense feeling — the heavy past they have all shared, the obligation they feel towards the future, the Tarusa region itself. They seem, as it were, to be looking back (and forward) to an idealized Rus, beautiful even in suffering, a Rus which includes all hues and colors except the gray of the Stalin years.

That is not to say, though, that they are seeking to deny or ignore the less pleasant aspects of the recent past. Far from it. Vladimir Kornilov's narrative poem, "The Driver," is, in particular, remarkably outspoken in its comments not only on the Stalin era, but also on problems which still exist today in the Soviet Union. Yet Kornilov's remarks form a natural element of his artistic structure and are not merely the pretext for a poem. Bulat Okudzhava's quiet and tightly constructed story translates war into intensely human terms in a prose that, seemingly against its will, has poetic force; and similarly, Lev Krivenko's poignant evocation of the Oka region after the war is an amazing achievement of prose craftsmanship in which past and present time and emotion impinge upon one moment of consciousness. In the Tarusa stories officials can be appealing characters, and heroes are often uncomfortably ambivalent types. We draw our confidence in the integrity of these stories from just such ambiguities.

New Russian poetry shares many of the traits which I have already mentioned in connection with prose. Although a great deal of "Western" poetry, often in free verse, is being published by young Soviet poets, the great majority of serious and talented artists belong to what I have chosen to call the "quiet school" of Russian poetry. In 1912 Mayakovsky proclaimed that he was about to cast Pushkin and all of classical Russian literature "overboard from the steamship of modernity." This task was finished for him by others, who, as an afterthought, heaved in Mayakovsky too. Now the classic poets are being pulled back on board. The models for the poets of the "quiet school" are the great masters of the last century: Pushkin, Lermontov, Tiutchev, Fet; and from our own times: Blok, Mandelstam, Akhmatova, Zabolotsky and Pasternak. The poets of the "quiet school" know what all good poets have always known — that content is form.

Evgeny Vinokurov's controlled but direct response to life, with its combination of serious elements and echoes of the more whimsical moods of Zabolotsky, will bring to mind for many readers the poetry of Robert Frost. It is quite conceivable that Vinokurov, nominated for the Lenin Prize in 1963, may emerge as a poet of major stature. Naum Korzhavin's poetry strives to achieve the "lightness and lucidity" that is characteristic of Pushkin, to whom many of his most outstanding poems are addressed. Korzhavin's neoclassicism has the force (and the beauty) which only a calm, gentle voice can attain. Andrei Dostal's impressionism recalls Fet and Blok and, perhaps even more, the émigré school of epigrammatic poetry of the thirties. His poems are dreams, as strange and as natural as Henri Rousseau's couch in the jungle. Boris Slutsky, whose poetry is valued very highly by many connoisseurs of Russian verse, possesses an extraordinary range of feeling and empathy. Slutsky's poetic voice, as the selections in this book well illustrate, leaps effortlessly from youthful exuberance to the dusk of old age. All these poets — and there are others too — make the outlook for Russian poetry bright indeed.

What judgment, finally, ought be made of the literary quality of *Pages from Tarusa?* Granted, there is little here which qualifies as "great" literature, but then I do not like to trade in superlatives. Certainly there *is* much here which is equal or superior in quality to, say, the *O. Henry Prize Stories* or the stories and poems which appear in some of our best literary quarterlies. All the factors essential to a creative climate are to be found in *Pages from Tarusa.* If Soviet literature still has a long way to go, let us realize how far it has come. Even the theater, weakest of the Soviet arts, may yet find a source of new life in the dramatic theories of Vsevolod Meyerhol'd, the brilliant director who is considered the "Stanislavsky of the modernist theater" and whose work, until its appearance in *Pages from Tarusa*, had long been banned in Russia for political as well as artistic reasons.

Pages from Tarusa commands literary respect and has unquestionably earned a place of importance in the history of Soviet literature — the question now is whether it will be a solitary monument or the signal for the beginning of a new era . . . The outcome is still far from clear, but the subsequent publications of the Tarusans and other "new wave" writers such as Andrei Voznesensky, Bella Akhmadulina, Ivan Stadniuk, Natalya Tarasenkova, Vladimir Tendryakov and Aleksandr Solzhenitsyn give cause for optimism.

ANDREW FIELD

Cambridge, Mass.

1963

A Note on the Translations

�֍ ✶ ✶ ✶

The stories in this anthology, although translated by various hands, have a uniform system of transliteration which is a slight modification of the Library of Congress system. The Russian soft sign, which is not pronounced but softens a preceding consonant or separates two letters, has been retained in all names and is designated by an apostrophe. It will aid those who do know some Russian without hindering readers who do not know the language. In the pronunciation of Russian names, the reader should bear in mind that "e" is always pronounced as in our word "*yet*" and that "i" is pronounced long as it is in Italian.

The poetry translations have been done from literal versions and metrical schemes supplied to the poets, in addition, of course, to oral readings. While there is a close proximity to the originals in all instances, the poets have taken certain liberties. The poems stand first as English poems in their own right, the only valid standard, it seems to me, by which to judge poetry translations.

The enthusiasm with which the translators and poets undertook their assignments and the skill with which they have completed their tasks have been gratifying. Special thanks are due to Peter Reddaway for his admirable prose rendering of Vladimir Kornilov's long poem and to Collyer Bowen for his translation of the seemingly untranslatable story by Marina Tsvetaeva. Also, I should like to thank my friend, Professor Michael Rywkin, who with his expert knowledge of contemporary Soviet slang provided invaluable assistance at many points. The manuscript was prepared by Mr. and Mrs. Richard D. Martin.

The present volume is somewhat shorter than the original Russian version; since the English translation is being presented as a literary anthology, many "sketches" of Tarusa life in the Russian edition were deleted. Also, the selections of six other Tarusa writers have not been included, an editorial decision which was especially hard in the cases of the fine poet David Samoilov and the writer Vladimir Maksimov (author of *A Man Survives*) who are not, however, represented by their best work in *Pages from Tarusa.*

A. F.

Contents

�֍ ✖ ✖ ✖

I

Prose

Once on a Humid Night

YURY TRIFONOV

❈ ❈ ❈ ❈

THE THREE of us go out into the street: Yakov, Achilov and I. We are waiting for a taxi which we called an hour ago. A deserted side street on the outskirts of Ashkhabad. One-storied little houses. Warm darkness. Widely spaced lights in the distance, beyond the trees. And the sky filled with stars.

As always happens in southern cities, a smell of toilets emanates from some unseen source.

We are a bit tight. We're speaking softly. Some man approaches us out of the darkness and says something unintelligible under his breath. He comes up and stops.

We look at him with surprise.

"What do you want?"

"Do you have an axe?" the man finally asks in a distinct voice. He is a small, dried-up, dark-faced man in a dark suit and worker's cap.

"Why do you need an axe?"

"There are two of us: one's a Russian, the other's a Spaniard. I'm the Spaniard," the man explains hastily, and for some reason takes out his wallet and pulls his passport out of it.

"You don't have to. We believe you. Well, go on, then."

"We're living in one room. He went out somewhere, locked the door, and now what am I supposed to do — spend the night in the street?"

The Spaniard is stammering in a nervous, soft voice, and in such a tone as though it were our fault that he has to spend the night in the street. He has round, bright eyes — this can be seen even in the darkness. Perhaps he's drunk. Perhaps he's no Spaniard at all. All of this is somehow absurd and unexpected.

"But still, why do you need the axe?" Achilov asks after a while.

"To break the door! Why an axe? I'll break door and get into the room!"

The Spaniard looks at us angrily, as though offended, and, when one added to that his frail figure, his eyes and small, dry mouth, there was something pitiful, childlike about him.

"Do you have an axe?" I ask Achilov.

"I don't know. I had one somewhere, without a handle . . ."

"Okay, give me without a handle!" the Spaniard says in the same broken Russian as Achilov.

Not hurrying, the stout Achilov goes into the house. A light goes on in one of the rooms. The rest of the windows and the rest of the houses on the street remain dark. It's after two in the morning.

"So you're a Spaniard?" Yakov asks.

"Yes, I'm a Spaniard." Again he goes for his wallet.

"All right, we believe you!"

"No, if you think I'm a thief or something . . ."

"Did you come when you were a child with those Spaniards who came in '38?"

"No, I wasn't a child. I came as an adult."

Even now he has the look of a teenager. How old was he when he came over? Twelve. He came from France in 1941.

"I work as a beterinarian in the Chapaev Kolkhoz, far away . . ."

"Did you study in Moscow?"

"Why Moscow? France I learn. Beterinary school."

He pronounces each phrase with offended bewilderment. Wanting to show off his erudition, Yakov starts a conversation about the Spanish Civil War. Finding out that our interlocutor is from Navarre, Yakov asserts that Navarro, Asturias and the North in general, were the most dependable regions of the Republic. The Spaniard suddenly becomes unusually animated. He speaks about the war as though it were only yesterday. He becomes excited. He curses Delladier and General Miakhu, is delighted with Barcelona and Madrid, and he stigmatizes Toledo.

My God, how long ago all this happened! Ah, magic, stirring names of childhood: Casa del Campo, General Walter, General Lukac . . . And what happened afterwards? Oh, afterwards! A whole life. Millions of lives. Shocks and hopes. Nineteen thirty-seven, the war, victory at a gigantic price, Stalin's death, and again, victories, shocks and hopes. But for the Spaniard an "afterwards" doesn't exist. He still raves about the scorched Sierra Nevada and curses Franco and gets excited. An angry little man, an eternal youth, an eternal Spaniard . . .

And how strange it is to hear his incensed speech. Perhaps he really is drunk — on this Ashkhabad street at night, where dogs are howling, and it smells of toilets, and there is still no taxi (the driver probably went home to have some tea), and the huge Asiatic sky filled with stars is equally indifferent both to General Walter and to General Miakhu and to all the Spaniards on earth!

"*Parlez-vous français?*" he asks Yakov intently.

Yakov shakes his head from side to side.

"Are there other Spaniards here?"

"No. I alone in Ashkhabad."

"Do you have a family?"

"I have a wife. She's in the Ukraine, in Kherson. And I'm alone here."

Why is he here while his wife is in the Ukraine? And why did he choose Ashkhabad? There are plenty of Spaniards — he could have lived in other cities and have been with his fellow country-men, talked to them about Casa del Campo and General Walter. I decided not to ask.

"My wife is Ukrainian," he says.

"But why aren't you living with her? You could have worked as a veterinary just as well in Kherson," Yakov says. "Or she could have joined you wherever you were."

"She could have?" he asks, smiling mysteriously. "No . . ."

"Why not?"

He again smiles ironically and shrugs his shoulders. He has a very mysterious air about him.

"Man does not live independently," he says quietly and a bit pompously and raises a finger. "And life itself knows what's best. Right?"

"Absolutely."

"There you have it then. And you shouldn't ask."

Achilov comes out of the house.

"There's no axe," he says. "We looked and looked. Can't find it anywhere. They're fixing our house."

The Spaniard sighs.

"Well, then . . . I'll spend the night in the street."

He doesn't go away, and we continue to stand there.

"Want a smoke?" I ask.

"No. I don't smoke. Thank you."

"You're a Spaniard?" Achilov asks, and he delicately pokes the little man with his finger.

"Yes, yes, I'm a Spaniard."

After some silence, Achilov says, "That's good."

Now we are silent again. The Spaniard still isn't leaving. We're waiting for the taxi. And finally it drives up. The Spaniard gets in with us, with Yakov and me; he also wants to go to the hotel. Doesn't want to spend the night in the street. Achilov says good night, and we take off. Even now, late at night, it's humid in the car.

"Warm night," I say.

"In Spain it's even hotter than here," the Spaniard says.

"Hotter?"

"Yes, much hotter."

"Yes, but not everywhere," says Yakov, wanting to show his erudition again. "In the mountains of Nevada it's probably . . ."

"Hotter," the Spaniard says firmly. "Always hotter."

translated by ROBERT SZULKIN

Pale-blue Tears

VLADIMIR KOBLIKOV

❈ ❈ ❈ ❈

"FERRY-Y-YMAN!"

"Y-yman!" mimicked the forest from the opposite bank.

Sergei grew tired of shouting.

At last a man came out of a hut and stood looking at the river. Sergei shouted louder: "Ferry-y-yman!" and waved his arm.

The man rowed with slow, energetic strokes, heading the boat into the current so he wouldn't be carried downstream.

Sergei sat down on a log to have a smoke. The log was soaked with water and had turned dark, and it was covered with a crust of ice which melted immediately. It was disgusting to sit there in the wet, but he did not feel like getting up. "To hell with these pants," Sergei decided.

The river was drowsy, cold, and uninviting — like a tired woman being pestered for some love. A rim of new and transparent ice had already formed along the banks; the dark, lead-colored water flowed slowly and lazily by; not a single fish splash; then suddenly — a boat. Intrusive, peace-disturbing splashes of oars . . .

An old man was working the oars. About three yards from the bank he started to back water and hold the boat in place, displaying no interest at all in Sergei, who had gotten up from the log. Then he unexpectedly shouted out, in a voice hoarse from a cold, "What are you hollering about?"

"Take me over to the other side."

"What did you forget over there?"

"I have to cross over, pop, real bad! . . . I'll pay you well."

"Take your money and go away. I'm a fisherman, not a ferryman . . . Go take the regular ferryboat." The fisherman started the boat off upstream. "It's not far from here; about three miles or more. Follow the shore. If you follow the shore, you'll get there."

Sergei angrily threw his rucksack on his back and set off for the regular ferry crossing.

"Hey, you!"

Sergei didn't turn around.

"Hey, you, snooty, wait up!"

Sergei stopped.

"What do you want?"

"What, what! By the time you get to the ferry there'll be no one to take you over. Get in!"

The old man was thin and dark. His whole face was covered with deep, fine wrinkles, and it wasn't just from age — the fisher-man was not that old yet — it was from the burning river winds and from the hot sun. A bright-colored city scarf was wound around the old man's scraggy neck, and he had a cap with ear flaps on his head.

"You from Tarusa?"

"No, from Moscow."

"Well, sure, there's as many vacationers here as there are carp in the Oka."

"I'm on business," said Sergei curtly. He huddled down into his coat.

"They're all on business here. What's your line?"

"I'm with a newspaper . . . Have you heard about Taranov-sky, the engineer?"

The old man did not reply.

"From the Voznesensky State Farm. I have to write about him."

Easily breaking through the crisp thin ice, the boat headed smoothly into the shore.

"Now where to?"

"I was just going to ask you how to get to the forestry station."

"You won't make it there today."

"I'll make it."

"Well, shit on you, then; get lost!"

Sergei no longer existed for him. The old man put the boat on lock and chain, took the oars over to some poles near a tree and went into a mud hut. Sergei felt like hitting the miserable old codger, but he knew that even if you beat the daylights out of people like that, it still wouldn't help any . . .

The soup consisted of smoked perch in a sour broth. Tikhon Petrovich and Sergei sat opposite one another on flat wooden sleeping benches made out of poles and covered with fresh straw. Between them was a small homemade table.

After supper Sergei wanted to go right to sleep, but this was impossible because the old man was yearning for someone to talk to. Tikhon Petrovich changed: his eyes became kinder, his stiffness disappeared and he softened up completely. The fisherman was reminiscent, then, of a doll from Obraztsov's puppet theater. His neck was thin and not at all tanned; his head seemed as though it were made out of a large wrinkled mushroom; and his hair stuck out like wisps of tow. Perhaps, being aware of the impression his outward appearance produced on other people, the old man had even grown to love life on the shore by himself.

Tikhon Petrovich had a lot of things he wanted to find out from the Muscovite, but the fisherman was a peasant with understanding and therefore, apparently, he began a conversation about Sergei's business.

"So, you've come to write about the engineer? Tell me, what did he do to warrant this?"

"Taranovsky? He's simply a very interesting person."

"Every person is interesting. Only some people wear it on the outside like a necklace, and others hide it from sight. What did he do, set a production record or something?"

"That's not it."

"Wait, he's one of those guys who burst out like a nightingale with their song of: 'With heart and soul I've given up the sweet life of Moscow.' I've seen them like that. Every year they come flocking around here. 'How wonderfully you live here! Fresh air, water' — in a word, a heavenly climate. But they eat Moscow grub. And I wouldn't even let 'em take one gulp of our sweet fresh air."

The old man got all worked up again, and now and then he gave a tug at his little beard of tow.

"You know, you end up with a hell of a mess. He grows up in some place like Veligozha or Levshin, gets his wings there and takes off for the city, and you just try to feed him then, the nut.

In the summer he comes a-running for a little fresh air, a mug like a sheat-fish's, and a belly . . . He comes up to me, parts his lips and says, like the master used to say, 'Petrovich, go catch a little fresh fish.' 'You'll eat shit, brother,' I tell 'em, 'not fish!' " The old man waved his hand. "To hell with them, they just get you worked up. Let's cook up some tea. Did you ever fix any marjoram? We'll have some right away. Go out and get some water from the river — the walk will do you good. And I'll stir up the coals; that'll make it warm, and it's good for sleep."

Outside it was dark and cold. The Oka was grumbling at its banks. The forest gave noisy, angry answer in return, and the trees creaked. Sergei hurried off to the river . . .

The marjoram tea was pleasing. Tikhon Petrovich was satisfied with it and promised to give him some to take with him. They put out the lantern, lay down and smoked — the old man had a package of cigarettes, and Sergei rolled his own. The smell of the straw was overpowered by that of wormwood.

"That's to keep the fleas away," the old man explained simply. And then he added pensively, "Someone should invent some such thing to get rid of all kinds of parasites. I wish they'd croak! Well, how come you haven't said anything about the engineer?"

"You don't give me a chance."

"Stubborn. Go on, let's hear about him."

"I'm not very good at telling. I write most of the time."

"So don't put in any fancy stuff; you just tell the gist of it."

"Well, the gist of it is this: a young fellow from Moscow finished the program at the Aviation Institute. He wanted to build airplanes, and they sent him off to repair tractors. And he got married."

"Got married, you say?"

"Very well, I think," said Sergei, taking a puff.

"So, go on with the rest."

"As for the rest . . . Workshops, like at an airport — everything in order. Invents new machines, mechanizes farms, plants gardens. He says: 'Without gardens you don't get into Communism . . .' "

"What are you telling me all that for?"

"What do you mean, what for?" said Sergei, trying to make out the old man's face in the darkness. "You asked me."

"Well, Yury Svyatoslavich and I are friends."

Sergei jumped up from the bench and banged his head painfully against the ceiling.

"What have you been stringing me along for?"

"Better be a little more careful jumping up like that. This isn't one of your Moscow mansions."

Sergei lay down and turned over to the wall. He decided not to talk any more to the old sneak.

But the latter said, "Sergei, my boy, don't be mad. I was just seeing if you might accidentally blurt out some lie about a good man. You know, it's as easy for you to fib as it is for me to down a glass of vodka . . ."

The old man occasionally sighed and muttered in his sleep. A raging wind from the river hurled itself against the mud hut. The hut creaked and groaned. It was pleasantly eerie. It seemed to Sergei that there were no towns or villages at that moment on the earth and that only three people remained in the world: he, the sleeping old man, and Marina, somewhere quite near by in a little house in the forest.

He had been searching for her a long time. And suddenly that day in Tarusa, on an advertising iconostasis of a local photographer, he saw her portrait.

"Her?" said the photographer trying to remember and understanding nothing. "Her? I think she's the wife of a forest ranger . . ."

Sergei awoke and called the old man. He lit the lantern. It was after four o'clock. Where had the fisherman gone?

Tikhon Petrovich returned in about ten minutes and brought in a skillet with fried fish in it.

"It's a fine morning out. I was afraid I'd oversleep. He who has many worries sleeps lightly. It snowed a bit. Soon I'll have to head for the village, till next spring." The fisherman sighed. Sergei felt sorry for the old man. Tikhon Petrovich sensed this and shouted, "What are you sprawling around for? Run to the river and wash out your eyes!"

Sergei got the brandy and poured some into the fisherman's mug.

"How come you aren't drinking?"

"Don't want to."

"You know best. Well, here's to life!"

The old man walked quickly, and Sergei was barely able to keep up with him. It was slippery. Several times he stumbled and fell, cursing each time.

The old man stopped and waited.

"Now you can find it yourself. Don't turn off the path."

They had a farewell smoke.

"When you come back — drop in. If you feel like it. I'll take you over."

"Thanks. I'll drop in. Maybe I won't be alone . . ."

As he was leaving the old man advised, "Knock at the first house. That's where your Marina Georgievna lives."

"Wait," said Sergei, detaining the fisherman. "How did you know I was looking for her?"

"What a secretive one you are!" said the old man, not even looking at Sergei. "She gave me your book to read. Your picture is hanging in their house . . . I was trying to think where I'd seen you. Last night I remembered. But your poems are so-so . . . crappy."

It was growing light. The small farm was lazily waking up. The dawn reddened the snow on the roofs and the columns of smoke which were rising high into the frosty sky. It was quiet . . .

There was no light in their house, but Sergei knocked eagerly on the door. Then again and again. An inner door creaked plaintively.

"Who's there? Who's there?" Marina asked again, slightly louder, as she came to the outside door.

"Me."

And again it was quiet.

But then the bolt clanked feverishly, and the door burst open . . . Sergei stepped into the hall. He found her in the darkness with his hands and pressed her to his lips.

"Enough, Sergei, enough," Marina pleaded. She grabbed hold of a shelf and knocked over a pail.

"Who's there?" came the sleepy voice of a man from the next room.

Marina was silent.

"Are you here? Why don't you say something? Who was knocking out there?"

"Sergei has come," answered Marina softly.

She went to her room. Sergei could hear her and her husband getting dressed. He felt like getting up and leaving this house and all its furnishings and objects. In his own Moscow apartment there was a table, three chairs and an ottoman, as it was before.

"Hello."

Sergei saw a man of his own build with a large forehead, glasses in thin frames, sun-bleached hair and a thin weather-beaten face. He was about five years older than Sergei, perhaps even more; it's hard to tell when a person is wearing glasses.

"Taranovsky, Anatoly Svyatoslavovich," the man said, and he put out his hand. "We're very glad that you've come to visit us forest dwellers."

"Taranovsky . . . Svyatoslavovich . . ." — Sergei sensed that the "forest dweller" was also nervous.

Marina came in, a gracious hostess — and that was it. But her dress was pretty!

Sergei remembered Marina's run-down shoes and the buttons on her coat that didn't match. "What in hell did you come here for?" he cursed himself. He saw his picture on the wall — from his book — and that didn't make him feel any easier.

They had breakfast. They drank homemade cordial and Sergei's brandy. Taranovsky struck up a conversation about literature and began praising Sergei's poetry.

"The poems are so-so . . . crappy," retorted Sergei.

"What do you mean — crappy?"

"Don't you know what crap is?"

"How did you find us?" interrupted Marina.

"Us," "we," "ours," "our place"?! Sergei wanted to pound his fist on "their" table, break "their" dishes to bits and leave the place. But for some reason he felt ashamed. Marina guessed his thoughts, just as before, and she blushed, but his double — the book portrait on the wall — looked sad and reproachful.

Sergei began unwillingly and reservedly to tell about his mission, about engineer Taranovsky.

It turned out that Yury was the younger brother of Anatoly Svyatoslavovich. The forester had "dragged" Yury over here from another region, helped him to "settle down" and get "set up" and to feel at home. They exchanged visits now with one another. Sergei took a sincere liking to Yury. Both his life and his house: the same things in the rooms as here. The same "Moscow" sofa-bed. But that was at Yury's. For Marina he had imagined everything different, everything simple and hard, as he had for himself. But even for himself he had still not done anything. The three chairs, table and ottoman had been offered to him by the neighbors when they had acquired an expensive bedroom set. Sergei, in a hurry to catch a train, had left them money and had asked them to transfer to his room whatever "extra" things would fit in, and to throw out whatever wouldn't go in. Marina had also been on a mission. So she had not even seen the "new" ottoman or the well-worn Viennese chairs. When Sergei had returned, they handed the key to the room over to him: there were only objects in it. Old things, new things — people are always leaving people, but they never leave things: things are resold or simply thrown out.

Sergei had not thrown his things out yet. But suddenly at that moment he felt like breaking them and throwing them out of all the windows and doors and burning them in a huge bonfire that would make the sky hot. Things, dumb idols, adulating slaves. People never leave things! . . .

"What are you so silent about?" asked Marina, looking tenderly and kindly at Sergei. But he was thinking about the time they walked along the deserted Arbat, under heavy, sticky snow. It lay like a white hat on Marina's bare head, like a white collar on her shoulders and like a white muff on her sleeves in which she was warming her once frostbitten red hands. Sergei saw this scene in his mind's eye and almost believed that all that white — the hat, the collar and the muff — had been given to Marina by him and that it would be that way always. But Marina shook herself — and the snow fell away. "What are you so silent about?" she had asked then, and Sergei had asked her to "Read something that isn't published yet." Perhaps it was a coincidence, but Marina asked now in just the same way as he had then: "Read something that isn't published yet."

This request always caught Sergei unawares, now — more so than ever. In the best of poems there is a great deal that is personal, "about yourself." And why should he speak "about himself" there, to Taranovsky and even to Marina? Nothing "casual" occurred to him, but suddenly he began to speak unexpectedly for himself. He did not read or remember anything he had prepared ahead of time. He simply spoke, looking over their heads, and it was easy to speak — he had to hold back his words.

They were verses about things people don't leave, about people who live among these silent slaves and gradually lose control over them and become themselves slaves and also silent. And the things then begin to speak, no, to dictate! And people wear themselves out dragging them along and pampering them. People are chained to them, and for people there no longer exist the huge round earth, the wind, an autumn night in a cabin which becomes a bonfire toward morning, which warms your hands and boils water for tea . . .

Sergei grew silent; his supply of words was exhausted.

"And what comes next?"

"I don't know yet what comes next . . ."

"Nevertheless they are good! And you said they were 'crappy,' " said Anatoly Svyatoslavovich as he got up from the table. "I have to go to work now, Sergei. See you at dinner."

Taranovsky dressed for outside and silently nodded a friendly smile in parting. In his quilted coat and cap he looked taller and younger to Sergei . . .

All three of them lay down in different rooms. All three of them were not asleep. All three of them were disturbed. No one knew what would happen the next morning.

In Marina's verses about happiness Sergei had read that day:

> *Happiness is simply being happy,*
> *Happiness is living and not longing . . .*

He remembered an old conversation: flint is a burning stone. You must not rub two flintstones together. If you rub them together sparks will fly.

"Look at how much you've written without me," said Marina,

both joyfully and with bitterness the day before. Sergei remembered several lines from her poem about "simple feminine happiness." He repeated them aloud and cursed.

Marina got up from her bed. Sergei listened while Marina went
into Taranovsky's room.

"Simple feminine happiness," Sergei repeated once more. An
animallike jealousy clawed at his heart . . .

Soon he again heard footsteps. Marina came to the door and
softly asked, "Are you asleep?"

Sergei did not reply.

As dawn was breaking he got up, dressed by the light of the
lantern and left.

Sergei headed for Tikhon Petrovich's. He walked slowly, having difficulty getting used to the darkness. And again it seemed to
him that there were no towns or villages on earth and that there
were only the silent darkness and two people: he and the old man
who was waiting for him in his mud hut.

When it had become completely light outside, Sergei no longer
doubted that he had lost his way. He should have reached the Oka
sometime ago, but there was nothing but forest and more forest
around him and a number of various paths. Which one should he
choose? He selected the widest one and went on. To his left Sergei
heard a whistle. He turned and walked more quickly. The light
snow squeaked under foot. A woodpecker was hammering away
at a resonant tree, and a jay cried. In a small clearing Sergei saw
many dark spots. He went up to them — they were mushrooms.
Someone had forgotten to pick them, and now they were sticking
up out of the snow — black, wrinkled and of no use to anyone.

"That's the way it is with people once in a while," Sergei
thought. "They aren't noticed until they are no longer of any use
to anyone. Perhaps she was afraid of that too."

In the resinous freshness of the forest Sergei smelled smoke. The
smell became stronger and stronger until he came upon several
enormous bonfires. Dry branches and pine needles crackled in roaring flames which were throwing out myriads of sparks. The bonfires were being tended by women in scorched padded jackets and
canvas gloves. They all looked like one another with their ker-

chiefs pulled down low and with their poppy-red noses and cheeks.

The women surrounded Sergei, and they all began telling him at once how to get to the fisherman's hut which was not more than a mile and a half away.

Not far from the bonfires men were cutting down trees. They fell to the ground with a hollow, rebellious groan.

"You don't even feel badly about the forest," Sergei said, scolding the women.

"What's there to feel bad about?" said the women, not understanding. "It's ours, isn't it?"

Sergei sighed and left without even saying goodbye to them.

And right after him came: "Hey! Come here, you soft-hearted bum, let's have a roll in the snow!"

All around there were stumps, stumps with yellow tops where they had been cut. The trees lay on the ground, but they were no longer trees, just trimmed logs. And not far from Sergei stood several graceful pine trees which had not been cut down yet. They were looking at the sun and pale-blue tears were running down their bark . . .

On the hill Sergei stopped to have a look from above at the Oka and its banks with their forests which here and there still preserved their autumn gilt. The launch was on its way from Tarusa, but there was almost no one on board. The autumn had chased people back to the cities.

After seeing the old man, he had to go to Tarusa, call Yury Taranovsky, say goodbye to him, straighten out a few points — and then to Moscow. *Finis.*

"In the summer I'll come here and go fishing with the old man and gather marjoram," Sergei decided and imagined the many different flowers that were there during the summer.

"Flowers. Flowers . . . Flowers," Sergei said and grew thoughtful. "I don't have anyone to give flowers to . . ."

> *Roses are red and violets are blue,*
> *But there's no one for me to give flowers to.*
> *There's no one here for me to blame*
> *For what I did that merits fame.*
> *Today a woman was returned*
> *To someone . . . whom she her husband termed.*

To what husband? He just couldn't find the right epithet. He took out his notebook, wrote it down, and set out for the river. The river seemed to Sergei still wider, and the current quicker that day. He walked towards the hut along a path close by the water, and he felt its icy freshness. The sun no longer warmed the Oka; its warmth was no longer even sufficient to melt the snow which had covered the icy edges along the bank of the river. And the river itself licked away at the snow with its waves. The fisherman's boat was not at the shore. "He must have gone a-fishing," Sergei thought. He would have to wait. A desire arose in him to lie on the bench for a while; he even smelled the wormwood, and so he hurried up the path . . .

He stood for a long time before the door which was nailed up with boards; then he threw his rucksack over his shoulder and set out for the regular ferry crossing.

translated by COLLYER BOWEN

Three from a Town

BORIS BALTER

I

THE WINDOWPANE reflected the shimmering blue sea and floating white clouds. A wide band of sunlight stretched from the window to the door. A writing table and the sunlight separated us from Alyosha Pereverzev, secretary of the local branch of the Komsomol. When the wind jiggled the open casement of the window, the sun slithered along the floor and rested on the corner of the table, and on our legs which were bent almost double from sitting on a low, imitation leather sofa with broken springs. After first hearing what the military commissar had to say, we were now listening to Alyosha.

We knew Alyosha well: two years ago he had finished our school. We – we were Vit'ka Anikin, Sashka Krieger and myself. Pavel Baulin was also sitting on the sofa – he was a sailor from the harbor and about three years older than us.

Alyosha was an experienced speaker. He could deliver a speech on any occasion. For example, we remembered very well his speech about the harmfulness of gophers. He delivered it in the ninth grade at a time when the whole school was preparing to set out on a campaign against them. He opened our eyes to the parasitic life of the gopher, which is a treacherous enemy of newly started collective farms and the Soviet state.

Alyosha was bent forward over the table with his elbows resting on its green fabric covering.

"Did you understand what the military commissar said?" he asked. Like every good speaker, Alyosha assumed the worst; he did not trust our ability of comprehension. And perhaps the dry, laconic words of the commissar seemed unconvincing to him. The commissar was sitting in the cool shadow with his elbow on the edge of the table, and he was intently surveying the toes of his boots.

"It is a question of the great honor," continued Alyosha, "the tremendous trust which the Party and the Komsomol are prepared to bestow upon you — you, a bunch of kids who still haven't passed your final high school exams." Alyosha peered attentively into our faces and tried to guess what was taking place in our hearts. This did not necessitate any special perspicacity; we were trying our best to appear serious, but it was evident that our best was not good enough to hold back our self-satisfied smiles and cover up the excited shine in our eyes.

It was simplest of all with Sashka; he did not have to pretend. Since the day he was born no one had ever known Sashka to be serious, and his protruding eyes were always shining. Sashka was sitting to the left of me with his aquiline nose and sharp chin thrust forward.

With Vit'ka things were different. He poked me in the side with his elbow. I turned around. He was sitting between Baulin and me and had accidentally poked me: I understood this from the expression on his face. Vit'ka was looking at Alyosha and smiling with an open mouth. This was because of his naïveté. Vit'ka was a very naïve boy. No matter how much Sashka worked on him, the results were nil.

"You are standing on the threshold of a great life," said Alyosha, as if he himself had long ago crossed this threshold. "The Komsomol organization of the city is proposing that you begin your own independent life where it will be of the greatest service to the work of the party. We are not planning to export revolution. But beyond our borders our enemies are dreaming about the restoration of the old order of things in our country. They are preparing to attack us. And so you will lead the armies of the greatest worker-peasant state in the world.

"More and more the army is calling for young men with a high school education. The old command personnel, who are skilled only in military affairs, can no longer fully satisfy the spiritual needs of the soldiers."

THREE FROM A TOWN *Boris Balter* ❧ 21

At this point in Alyosha's speech we glanced at the commissar and felt our superiority over this elderly major with his wrinkled, coarse face, high cheekbones and thick forehead which protruded over his eyes. Gold chevrons glittered on the left sleeve of his pressed uniform and on his right sleeve the gold shimmered dimly in the shadow.

"Yes, comrades, modern technical equipment demands all-around knowledge from the soldiers and commanders," thundered the voice of Alyosha showing no mercy. "The Komsomol was first in the constructions of the Stalin five-year plan. The Komsomol must be first in the formation of armed forces. That is why we decided to turn to you — the best of the best — with an appeal to enter military schools. Just think, in three years you will be lieutenants . . ." Alyosha paused.

Just think! He was asking us to do something which we were completely incapable of doing at that moment. The excited pounding of our hearts drowned out our thoughts. An hour ago, when we entered this large, minutely familiar room, each one of us had plans for the future which had been worked out together with our parents. I, for example, was planning to become a mining engineer because the husband of my elder sister was a mining engineer. Sashka Krieger was supposed to go to medical school because his father was a doctor. Vit'ka Anikin wanted to become a teacher. And with Vit'ka's patience and kindness, he couldn't have picked a better profession. We didn't know anything about Pavel Baulin's plans. We were scarcely acquainted with this broad-shouldered fellow in bell-bottomed trousers and striped vest. We knew him only as a local celebrity: Pavel was boxing champ of the Crimea.

"Now you know why we invited you here. Now you may have a word," said Alyosha in his ordinary, non-oratorical voice. He sat down on an antique chair with a high, carved back. The chair was such an old one that it should have been thrown out long ago. I think that Alyosha had not done it because of its back; there was not another chair with such a back in the whole town.

"Upstairs your applications are in order," announced Alyosha rather casually, as he pointed his thumb at the ceiling. We understood what he meant by "upstairs" since right above us was the office of Kolesnikov, first secretary of the local branch of the party.

Alyosha turned to the commissar and asked, "Are declarations necessary right away?"

Before answering the commissar looked at us.

"Agreement is important. They can write their declarations after their exams," he said.

We refrained from looking at each other so as not to betray our inner bliss. We knew that military service had become a profession. There had been a lot written about it in the newspapers when the military personnel ranks were introduced. But we had not even dreamed that this could have any sort of effect on us. Like all boys, we had the highest opinion of ourselves and our abilities. We were vain and impudent. And suddenly it turned out that we had a right to be so. We were called "the best of the best," and the party and the state needed us.

I often say "we" because Vit'ka, Sashka and I were at once very different from and very similiar to one another.

The military commissar talked a while with Alyosha, and I didn't hear what they said. Never before had I had to make such an important decision.

We knew a little about army life. There was a naval airport beyond the town on the barren coast of the bay. On the Kai-Burunsky spit there was some sort of an anti-aircraft unit situated in long caserns made out of porous yellow limestone which were similar to wooden barracks. During June a squadron came from Sevastopol for open maneuvers. It came unexpectedly: in the morning, out at sea opposite the beaches, stood ships which had not been there the day before. During the whole month the reverberations of cannon shots which sounded like distant thunder could be heard at sea. On Sundays the town was filled with the white uniforms of the sailors, and it gave them the best of everything it had.

In our school there were two groups of the Civic Guard — a rifle club and a sailing club. We were proud of our success: the clubs helped to strengthen our manly consciousness. But we regarded military activities as a fascinating game.

The father of my Inka, a girl from our school, was a navy flyer. He would disappear for whole days out at the airport, and everyone at home lived in constant waitfulness for him. He was a simple and cheerful fellow, but the danger of his profession created a halo of unusualness around him. I often used to visit Inka at home. Her father behaved towards me with derisive benevolence and he used to call me "the prospective bridegroom." He loved his profession, constantly talked about it, and when he learned that I was planning to become a geologist, said, "Well, I guess geologists are people too. Their work is almost like a pilot's — you don't get rich from it," and thereupon he told about how he once had had to search by plane for a geological party lost in the taiga. Now he would have something to say . . . And what would Mama, my sisters and Sergei say? Most of all, though, I was thinking about Inka and her father. Of course, it really was not a question of "thinking," but rather, their faces simply appeared more frequently in my mind.

"We're waiting," said Alyosha. "Decide."

We remained silent, ready to agree and vaguely realizing how serious the demands to be made upon us were, how our entire future would change after the short word "yes," and how much uneasiness would enter into our lives.

"Let's assume I say 'yes.' But what about when I come home and my father and mother say 'no'?" said Sashka. He began to speak while sitting, but after a glance at the commissar he stood up and blocked out the sun.

"Krieger, you're already eighteen years old. Remember that members of the Komsomol went to the front at your age. Remind your parents of that," said Alyosha.

There was no point in mentioning this to Sashka's parents for they had never been members of the Komsomol and had never gone to any war whatsoever. Alyosha knew this just as well as Sashka, and for this reason he added: "What sort of Komsomol member are you if you can't convince your parents?"

"I say 'yes,'" said Sashka. "But we will have to convince my parents together." Sashka sat down as if he had bent in half, and the band of sunlight came to rest on his knees.

From the tone of Sashka's voice I understood that he still had strong doubts about his parents' agreement. I also had my doubts — not about my mother but about Sashka's parents. I was sure of my mother. Therefore, when Alyosha looked at me, I said: "I agree."

"Of course," said Alyosha, bending down to the commissar.

"This is Belov, Nadezhda Aleksandrovna's son." The commissar nodded his head and looked at me.

"It's your turn, Anikin," said Alyosha.

Vit'ka blushed and drops of perspiration appeared on his forehead.

"I also agree," said Vit'ka.

"How much do they pay a lieutenant?" asked Pavel Baulin. He had a slightly hoarse, bass voice and a heavy drawl. Pavel sat leaning on the back of the sofa with his hefty arm lying freely on the armrest. This was the relaxed position, with his legs thrust forward, in which he usually rested in his corner of the boxing ring.

Alyosha shrugged his shoulders and slightly parted his hands above the table — a gesture which was sufficiently frank. However Pavel was not looking at Alyosha but at the commissar.

Before answering the commissar rose.

"In the army pay is calculated according to one's post, not by rank," he said. "After the termination of your schooling you will be assigned posts as platoon commanders . . ."

"That doesn't matter. What pay do platoon commanders get?" asked Baulin.

"Six hundred twenty-five rubles," answered the commissar. "And it's not authorized to receive more than your seniors."

"That'll do!" said Pavel looking at Alyosha. "Sign me up; I'm willing."

"The agenda of the day, as they say, is finished," said Alyosha, and he got up. We also stood up. "Bring your application to the office as soon as your exams are over. By the way, I'm also going to military school . . ."

And so our skilled agitator Alyosha saved his announcement to the end. He expected we would be happy, and we really were glad. We had grown accustomed to Alyosha, and we were certain we would not fail with him along.

II

THE health resort season began at the end of May in our town. By that time the bathing beaches were dry after the winter storms and the yellow sand shown like gold in the sun. Our beaches were even called "golden." It was an accepted belief that our beaches were the second-best in the world. First place belonged to some beach in Italy on the Adriatic coast. Where and when the contest took place which determined these choices, no one knew, but I had no doubt but what the judges had cheated, for it was my belief that our beach was the best in the world.

In winter and summer the town looked different, and its winter life was not like its summer life.

During the winter, cold northeasters tore through the streets and chased the occupants into the houses. The town seemed died-out, and the angered roar of the sea could be heard in its remotest corners. In the entire town there was only one movie theater operating, and it gave only three showings — the last one ended at ten o'clock in the evening. We spent all the days and evenings at school and at the house of the Pioneers; in our own homes we were infrequent guests.

The whole town was divided into three parts: the New Section, the Old Section, and the Dunes. Our school was in the New Section, and the health resort with its beaches, sanatoriums and *kursaal* was also in the New Section. The health resort guests were very amazed when they discovered that there was a Dunes section in our town. For some reason they imagined that only Odessa had a Dunes. Nonsense. Odessa is not the only place where the sea sifts the sands and piles up offshore sand dunes. And this is what settlements built up on these dunes are called in all the southern towns.

Vit'ka lived in the Dunes, whereas Sashka and I lived in the New Section. Sashka and Vit'ka went around with Katya and Zhenya, girls from our class. I went with Inka Ilina; she was two years younger than us. And although we all lived in different parts of the town, this did not interfere with our spending time together every day after school. We weren't looking for solitude; we felt freer and more at ease together.

On Sundays, when the weather was good, we used to go to the health resort. The vacant beaches seemed unusually broad. A restaurant was built out over the water on black, metal piles. It stood there without its windows and doors, which had been removed together with the footbridge so that they wouldn't be damaged by the storms. Birds sat on the terrace railings and on the roof. The bright green sea with its white-crested waves was hostile and cold. From time to time the birds would cry, and in their cries could be heard longing and despair.

We wandered through the naked, frozen parks, and the sanatorium buildings with their windows boarded up shone white between the trees. We were unable to stand the quietness and desertedness of vacant places very long. We would start shouting and singing. Sashka Krieger would run up the long stretch of broad stone steps and turning around to us recite:

> *I wander*
> > *and if I look outside, ah!*
> *Flowers*
> > *and the wide blue sky.*
> *And for your nose there's*
> > > *magnolia,*
> *And for your eyes wistaria.*

He recited, of course, other verses as well, but for some reason these were the ones I remembered. Undoubtedly it was because the blue sky was above us and the sun was shining, but it was cold and there were no flowers.

On the front steps of the Sacco-Vanzetti Sanatorium we often arranged improvised concerts. Katya danced and Zhenya sang. It was our opinion that she differed from professional singers only in that she was not afraid of catching cold in her throat. We all possessed some sort of talent. My Inka was the only untalented one. But she was not aggravated by this. In any case she never got into a bad mood over it. The teachers nicknamed Inka "windmill." But we went along with her excessive gregariousness and her disposition to laugh at anything.

We were all excellent students. The exception again was Inka. A grade of "excellent" in her notebook was a rarity for her, and Inka would tell all her friends and acquaintances about it. On the other hand she carefully hid the check marks even from us. But we still found out and excluded Inka from all of our recreational activities. Neither eloquence nor solemn promises that it would never happen again were of any avail. We showed no mercy. Each one of us was preparing to become an important person in life. We never spoke

about it, but it was taken for granted. Vit'ka was assigned to help
Inka. It was a difficult test of his pedagogical abilities. I took upon
myself the voluntary role of consultant. To be sure, Vit'ka had no
need of my help, but I simply was unable to go for long without
seeing Inka.

We did not avoid our other contemporaries. Each one of us had
friends outside our group. But the six of us were inseparable.

In the fall and spring the students in the upper grades went out
to the collective farms. We had some good workshops in our
school. Two yachts built with our own hands were being used for
trips to Sevastopol and Yalta. The whole year round our hands
were never free of calluses, which were yellow and hard like
porous limestone.

In May the acacia bloomed. It bloomed a long time, strewing
the town with white petals. The blossoming of the acacia coincided with the beginning of the health resort season. Announce-
ments that "the Maynaki has opened," "the Dulbert opened," "the
Clara Tsetkin is open" traveled from mouth to mouth like important events. These sanatoriums were always the first to open. The
first vacationers appeared on Coastal Boulevard. The streets of the
town became more crowded each day. The best rooms were rented
out to the arriving guests. They became sole masters of the town.
The face of the town changed; it became noisy, gaudy and gay.
Stores, pavilions, restaurants opened. Celebrities from the capital
appeared in the *kursaal*. They arrived dazzlingly bright, got everybody excited, and disappeared. Slogans were hung in the establish-
ments of the town urging everyone to create all the conditions
necessary for a healthful rest for the working people. And these
conditions were created.

But the grown-ups for some reason did not like the resort guests.
It was probably because they were dependent upon them and in
contrast to them their own lives seemed uninteresting and dull. But
we behaved indifferently to the guests, although this indifference
was only external. For us they did not exist as separate entities, as
human individuals. Our interest and curiosity were aroused by
the entire heterogeneous, colorful mass of them: women who, it
seemed, were concerned about appearing on the streets in a maxi-
mum state of undress and men who spent all the days at beer cellars

and stands. We met them all on the streets and in the trolley cars. They filled up the beaches. Old and young, thin and fat, beautiful and homely, they devoured the sun with an equal degree of voracity. We saw them in the *kursaal* — all dressed up, clean, smelling good, somehow particularly fresh and condescendingly friendly. People look that way when they are free of daily cares. Among them there were famous engineers, scientists, servicemen and everyday workers. All of them blended in our eyes into one whole — the "resort guests." And it never even entered our heads that in the towns from whence they came they were ordinary people with the same everyday problems that everyone has.

They lived among us and did not notice us. They were completely uninterested in what others were thinking and saying about them. But the town saw all of their weaknesses, and therefore our fathers and mothers considered themselves better than they. But at the same time the recklessly free life of the resort guests laid its impression on the local way of life.

On Market Street, not far from Sashka's house, was the workshop of the producers' cooperative called "The Metal Worker." There you could have primus stoves, oil stoves or bicycles repaired, or get pots soldered and tinned. All this work was done by one man. He undoubtedly had a first and last name, but among ourselves we called him simply the "Tin Man." He lived in the workshop so as not to have to pay rent on an apartment, and he always wore the same overalls with big patches. In the workshop, among the smells of kerosene and rusty iron, there was an especially sharp odor of fish: the Tin Man always ate fish because it was cheap. A joiner's bench served as his bed and a heap of rags took the place of bedding which he put away during the day on a shelf fixed near the ceiling.

When the resort season began the Tin Man washed his hands in an alkaline solution, locked up the workshop and took the most expensive room in the Dulbert Hotel, which was the best hotel in town. In a white flannel suit and foreign shoes woven from fine leather the Tin Man was completely changed. He did not reappear at his workshop until autumn, and he spent all the days on the beach. In the evenings one could meet him in the *kursaal*, and, after the concert, on the Poplavka boardwalk or in the Dulbert restau-

rant in the company of beautiful women and carefree men. When
he met someone he introduced himself as a captain on a long voy-
age temporarily stopping over on shore. And the women were
thrilled when he squeezed their waists in his rough hands while
dancing. At the end of the resort season the Tin Man would return
to his workshop.

But once he came back to it in the middle of the summer. This
happened after a certain incident which set the whole town talking.

A famous ballerina arrived for guest performances after a tour
abroad. She danced on three different occasions on an open platform in the *kursaal*. And on all three of these occasions we saw the
Tin Man sitting in the same seat in the first row. Every evening
when the ballerina was performing her last number, an usherette
appeared in the aisle in front of the stage with a basket of light blue
roses, the color of a morning sky. These rare roses were cultivated
by a gardener in the Dunes, and in order to give them their unusual color he injected something into their roots. When the ballerina came out to the front of the stage for a curtain call the
usherette placed the flowers at her feet. The Tin Man would rise
and walk up the aisle; he was tall, elegant and had an immutable
calmness about him. At the last concert I saw his eyes. Usually
they were pale, but this time they sparkled with cold brightness as
if they had taken on the color of the roses. He passed us by as if he
were a blind man. I poked Vit'ka with my elbow, and Vit'ka stared
at me. I made a circular motion with my finger in front of my forehead, and then Vit'ka understood that it was not me he should
look at. The usherette was walking next to the Tin Man, and she
said maliciously, "You're thinking of paying? This is the third
basket I've lugged . . ."

"Later, later," answered the Tin Man. But the usherette continued to walk along beside him. We knew about her scandalous
character very well, and we set out to follow them so as not to
miss anything. But we met with complete disappointment: no
scandal took place. At the exit the Tin Man took a bill out of the
side pocket of his jacket and crushing it in his fist he thrust it into
the usherette's hand.

That evening the Tin Man did not leave the concert alone, and

the next day he disappeared from the town together with the ballerina.

After a month the Tin Man returned . . .

Vit'ka and I were waiting for Sashka at the corner of Market
Street. Sashka was late. None of us were ever late. We were stand-
ing and cursing him out with every word we could find. At last
Sashka appeared and informed us from a distance:

"I've got news . . ."

"To hell with your news. Why are you late?" asked Vit'ka.

"Come on now, did you ever see the likes of it? I come running
to tell him a bit of news and all he can do is swear. He doesn't even
know what he's swearing at but he's swearing anyway."

"Sashka, don't babble," I said. "Why are you late?"

"I'll tell you why: the Tin Man has returned."

"Really?" asked Vit'ka.

"It's first-hand news. I have it from a most authoritative source."

We didn't believe Sashka. His bits of news were always "first-
hand" and from "the most authoritative sources." This time the
authoritative source was Sashka's mother.

"Shall we see if it's true?" I asked Vit'ka.

"I've already done it," said Sashka.

"Just the same, we'll go and verify it now," I said.

The workshop was just around the corner. We went toward it
and looked in the door. The Tin Man was standing behind his
workbench in his overalls. He was accepting a piece of work from
an elderly woman and was dickering over it at great length with
her.

"Well, what do you have to say now?" asked Sashka. "Have
you seen it?"

Sashka pulled a newspaper out of his pocket. In the chronicle
section it said that after a short interruption the ballerina had re-
sumed her professional tour through the cities along the coast of
the Caucasus.

We forgave Sashka for being late. The Tin Man was our personal enemy. Why? — we didn't know. He had never done anything bad to us, and we had never even said so much as a word to
him. But nevertheless he was our enemy; we felt this and despised
the Tin Man for his double life.

Vit'ka was especially vehement in his dislike for the Tin Man.
There were no open collisions between them, but the Tin Man undoubtedly sensed our animosity towards him. Whenever we met
him with some woman, Vit'ka could never help saying, "Look at
the parasites. You can't get a stove fixed any place in town, but
they're walking around . . ."

Not once did the self-appointed captain give himself away with
either a glance or a movement of his head. We had a strong desire
to follow him up and expose him. We even dreamed about it. But,
frankly speaking, we were afraid of the Tin Man's impenetrable
eyes and his huge hands. Probably for that reason we disliked him
even more.

Last summer we often saw the Tin Man on the beach with a
young and very beautiful woman. Later on we accidentally came
across her in the town, alone, as she was coming out of a dime
store. Vit'ka stepped toward her and blocked her way.

"The man with whom you spend time at the beach is betraying
you," said Vit'ka, and he blushed terribly because the woman was
looking at him with her green eyes and smiling.

"How is he betraying me?" she asked.

"He isn't what he pretends to be . . ."

"My dear boy, for a woman that is not the worst form of deceit.
I know he's no captain, but what business is that of mine?"

Vit'ka returned to us red and fuming. The woman was looking
at us and laughing.

"Saving the drowning is something for the drowning themselves
to do," said Sashka loudly, and we walked away, proud and misunderstood. The woman laughed and her laughter pursued us for
at least two blocks . . .

We, of course, did not suspect that the recklessly gay life of the
health resort had been having its effect upon us, too, since the time
we were children. I, for example, wandered around town in bathing trunks until I was thirteen, and in this primeval costume I felt
as free and unconstrained on the town streets as the natives in
Africa apparently feel. I continued in this fashion until a young
lady called attention to me one time. I was having a soft drink, and
she was walking along with a man. They also stopped at the stand
for something to drink. Out of the corner of my eye I caught their

reflection in the show window. The lady nodded at me to her companion and said, "Take a look at that boy — a real live Apollo . . ."

I was sufficiently knowledgeable in mythology to be able to understand this flattering comparison. For a moment I looked at my own reflection as something not belonging to me, and suddenly I saw the woman's eyes reflected in the windowpane. She smiled. I was sorry to leave my drink unfinished, and so I drank it up, but no longer with any satisfaction. I did not look at the window again, but nevertheless I knew that the woman was still staring at me. I put the glass down on the counter and ran. I ran all the way home, and that familiar distance seemed to me unusually long. I tried not to look at the passersby for I was embarrassed by my nakedness.

At home we did not have a large mirror. I surveyed myself in sections with a hand mirror: first my legs, then my stomach, chest . . . Up until then I had not noticed my body; I simply had not thought about it. It served me well during games and that was completely sufficient. Now there arose in me a burning interest in it which made me feel ashamed. I didn't go out of the house again that day. I sat at the window and waited for Mother. And as soon as she entered the room I said, "I'm not going to run around in a bathing suit anymore."

"What happened?"

"Nothing. But I'm not going to wear a bathing suit anymore."

"I'm sorry, but you will have to anyway."

Mother was not malicious. It was simply difficult for the two of us to live on her salary. My categoric announcement caught her unawares. Her maternal pride prevented her from admitting that she could not give her son what he actually needed. At dinner I usually told Mother about all my daily activities and adventures. But that evening I was silent. I could have told what had happened to me to my father or to Sergei, my elder sister's husband. But my father had been dead a long time, and Sergei and my sisters were working in the far North.

In the morning I waited until Mother left and then I got a pair of trousers and a velveteen jacket out of the chest of drawers. I had worn them to school during the winter. The trousers turned out to be hopelessly short and they were badly worn at the knees.

I got a pair of scissors and unstitched the cuffs. After this operation
the length of the trousers fit me perfectly. To be sure there was a
fringe showing at the bottom, and the color of the trousers under
the cuffs was considerably darker, but this did not disturb me very
much. The situation with my shoes was worse: they had dried up
and I couldn't get them on my feet at all. In a drawer containing
old foot gear I found Sergei's summer shoes. The tops were almost
whole, but the soles were worn right through. In addition to this
they were too wide for me. But that was all insignificant. The
important thing was that my nakedness was securely covered by
trousers, which were originally black and now had a dirty gray
look to them, by a brown jacket and by wide-toed shoes in which
my feet rattled around as in a pair of rubbers. I appeared on the
streets for the first time that morning in this getup and I wore it
in ninety-degree heat until my sisters sent me a new linen suit and
some sandals.

The life of the resort town with its unmasked intimacy, which
the tourists did not even try to hide, awakened our interest in girls
early. In the eighth grade Sashka and Vit'ka made friends with
Katya and Zhenya. And last year I finally turned my attention to
Inka. Actually I had noticed Inka as soon as she entered our school
(they had come from the Far East), but in the beginning she liked
me more than I liked her. Katya used to bring me notes from Inka
which I read over and over again, but I didn't answer them. I was
preserving my independence. It was sufficient for me that Sashka
and Vit'ka had lost theirs. But when Inka invited me to a birthday
party, I went. This was, of course, a mistake, because from that
evening on I was no longer able to pretend.

The end of our school work coincided with the opening of the
health resort season. We poured forth into the vacation turmoil of
the town and became so immersed in it that we forgot who we
were. In the morning, first the beach, then the *kursaal*, and after
the concert a bath in the black, thermal water above which spray
flashed like little, cold, white lights. But the keenest satisfaction for
us was playing volleyball in one of the sanatoriums. The gym in-
structors of the sanatoriums were well-acquainted with the skill of
our school team, of which Sashka was captain, and in order to
accommodate their guests they willingly invited us to play. It pleased

us that every game was announced on the billboard in front of the dining hall entrance. Many guests gathered to look at us six sun-tanned boys pulling up "dead" balls in unbelievable throws and falls. Our girl friends, of course, were among the spectators and emphatically ignored them: our girls knew how to share with us in a manner befitting the occasion both our glory and the bitter-ness of defeat.

And that, in short, is all there is to tell by way of introduction about us and our town.

III

UPON leaving the Komsomol building Vit'ka and Sashka went to the beach where Katya and Zhenya were waiting for them. I had to pick up Inka at school since she was taking an exam.

She, of course, was not at school. Some boys were playing volley-ball on a court in the corner of the large schoolyard. I went up to a girl from Inka's class who was standing at the edge of the court looking at the game and asked her, "Have you seen Inka?"

"Yes, I have," she said and didn't even turn her head my way.

"When?"

"Well, a half-hour ago, or an hour — I don't remember . . ."

"Where did she go?"

"She went to the Komsomol office."

With Inka it's always like this — you agree to meet her at one place, and she gets carried away to another. I got irritated.

"Why didn't you tell me so in the beginning?"

"Well, why didn't you ask me in the beginning?"

The boys on the left were playing better. The ball struck the ground untouched on the right side of the court. The girl turned sharply to me.

"What are you pestering me for?" she asked. "I suppose I don't have anything better to do than keep an eye on Inka."

So, what could a person find out from this girl, burdened down as she was with so many duties?

"Don't get upset, they'll lose just the same," I said and went towards the gates. I needed to see Inka so badly. I just had to tell her why I was called into the Komsomol office. But there was no point in going back there. She undoubtedly had left long ago.

I stood for a while on the street. The velvety black shadows of the acacias were sharply outlined against the sun-whitened pavement. The low wall of the harbor stretched along on the other side. Beyond the sloping edge of the shore the sea glistened motionlessly, and the tarred sides of motor launches equipped with sails showed black on the yellow sand.

Still not knowing where to go, I set off down the street. Inka caught up with me at the corner, and, breathing hard, she blurted out:

"I have a real story for you . . . I ran so hard and so fast. I covered the whole town." She didn't have to convince me of that: it was simply impossible to imagine her quietly walking down the street when she was looking for me. "Everybody's at the beach. Zhenya made a scene with Vit'ka. She's afraid that they'll send him to a town where there's no conservatory."

Inka was in a hurry to say everything before she was interrupted.

"Just think," she said, "Papa and you — you're both in the service. Papa will surely get promoted to captain. They've recommended him for major, but he says that he'll get a captain's promotion . . ."

There was only one way to stop the torrent of Inka's words: "Where have you just come from?"

"From school."

"And how did you get into the school? Over the fence?"

"Well, I couldn't run around the whole block. Look here. I peeked over the fence and saw Raika. She is furious because Yurka is losing. Raika said you had just gone out to the street."

Some teachers had just come out of the gates, and so we turned the corner to avoid meeting them. I was walking somewhat ahead. Inka did not even try to catch up with me. She could see very clearly that I was angry.

"Why didn't you wait for me at school?"

"I waited. You know how long I waited. I waited so long that I simply couldn't wait anymore."

When I spoke I had to turn my head in order to see Inka. Every time I did this I met her look.

I've never seen molten gold, but I'm sure that it has the same color as Inka's eyes. I have seen eyes like Inka's on red-haired dogs.

Inka also had red hair — she was all red, from her luxuriant hair and the large freckles around her nose to the golden down on her legs.

It was simply impossible to be angry with Inka for long. I slowed down and Inka then walked beside me as if she had not noticed a thing.

Now it was my turn to speak. No one could listen to me the way Inka could. I told her everything that was on my mind. If she understood me then it meant that everything I said had been carefully thought out to the end. Whenever she stopped listening I found contradictions in what I was saying, and I would be silent and unable to relax until I had resolved them. It was Inka to whom I was indebted for the iron logic which received such praise from my teachers.

"I simply didn't realize I could enter the armed services," I said. "There's no comparison between a geologist and a soldier. The job of a commanding officer comprises many different professions. First of all, that of a teacher: a commanding officer has to instruct his subordinates. Secondly, that of an engineer: there's so much technical equipment in the army now. Third, he must know history very well. Who knows, perhaps the battle at Cannes will help to win a decisive victory for Communism. Or perhaps not at Cannes at all but at Verdun or, say, the military reforms of Makedonsky will suggest a reorganization of the army . . ."

I was talking as though I had spent my whole life dreaming about the military profession and had studied all of its peculiarities down to the last detail. Not long before this I had pointed out the advantages of the geological profession in just the same way. But what significance did that have? The main thing for me to do was to convince Inka and myself that there was nothing strange in my decision to change the course of my future. Most of all I was afraid of appearing light-headed in Inka's estimation. Everything I said occurred to me as we were walking along the way from the Komsomol building to the school. It came to me because I had already read all of it in the newspapers, and I had heard it from the commanding officer and from Alyosha Pereverzev. But these thoughts had already become my own; I had succumbed to their influence, and they had begun to control my actions.

"The program at the military school lasts three years in all, right?" asked Inka.

"Yes . . ."

"That means that, not in five years, but in three years you will be completely, completely independent?"

"Of course . . ."

"You know, Volodya, I have no morals . . . I asked Mama when I could marry you, and she said that until you became independent it's even immoral to think about it."

Inka stole a side glance at me from underneath her eyelashes: you see, she simply had to know what sort of an impression her words had produced on me.

I broke out into a cold sweat, and I understood why Inka's father had called me a "prospective bridegroom." I frowned, and this always made Inka anxious.

"Well, what did I say now, what did I say?" she repeated quickly. "Am I to blame for being bored when you're not around? In three years you'll be a lieutenant. You'll only be twenty-one and already a lieutenant! You'll be living in Sevastopol or Kronstadt, or perhaps in Vladivostok . . . And I'll come to you. No, better you come for me . . . No, better I'll go, and you can meet me at the station with flowers."

"Romanticism!" I said carelessly, trying as hard as I could to maintain the ominous wrinkles in my eyebrows, but they betrayed me and kept smoothing out.

We were walking down Main Street. It was already too late to go to the beach. The street was hidden in the heavy shade of the acacias, and here and there, where the sun broke through the shadow, blinding white spots stood out on the walls of the houses. The narrow sidewalk was filled with people. They seemed to be just wandering about, and, when they went into a store, it seemed as if they were simply doing it out of curiosity. They were just as uninterested in us as we were in them.

Afterwards we sat for a while on Coastal Boulevard. Our bench was located right at the edge of the shore. The sea swelled and fell away down below at the base of the inclined wall, at times noiselessly creeping up on it and at times striking it. And the blows were like caressing love pats. Brown bunches of last year's seaweed, cigarette butts and pieces of paper were floating in the water. They rose and fell and remained in the same place. The horizon was covered with a whitish shroud, which was broken up with slanting streaks: a rainstorm was moving in from the sea, but the sun still shone its usual self above the town.

I remembered that I still had not heard about Inka's main event of the day.

"How was your exam?" I asked.

Inka waved her hand.

"I took it . . ."

We knew from experience that one of the essay themes always given on exams in the eighth grade was "Evgeny Onegin — the superfluous man." For pedagogical reasons we advised Inka to select this very theme. Vit'ka spent the whole of the previous evening coaching Inka on it. One would simply have to be a dunce not to be able to get at least a "B" after that. But it was possible to expect anything from Inka.

"Inka, tell me truthfully, how would you like to live? Well, what would you really like to do if you could do anything?"

"You won't get angry again? Actually, I would like to do just nothing. Well, of course I would do something, but only things that are fun. I wish that it was always summer, and that it was warm, and that I was the most beautiful girl in the world, and that things were fun . . . And, of course, I wish that you could always be with me and that the three years were already by and that we didn't have to part . . ." Inka looked at me and burst out laughing. But her eyes said: I know what you are going to say now.

"Your program is not very definite," I said. "But I understand, and, I suppose, I even like it. It's not bad at all when things are fun. But if everyone decides to live like that, then who's going to work?"

"Well, I am studying," said Inka. "Today I took an exam and in two days I'll take one in math. But you asked what I 'really' wanted to do and so I just told you."

Inka raised her outstretched legs and pressed her feet firmly together. She knew how to display everything beautiful about her. She was wearing flats so as to emphasize the natural curve of her instep, and to show off her teeth she always kept her mouth slightly open, even when she was not laughing. She was sixteen, but she always told anyone who didn't know her that she was eighteen. That was my Inka, and all the same I still loved her very much. I looked at Inka's legs, already slightly tanned. Her white silk sock tightly enveloped her ankles. Inka's legs were full and strong. I always liked them. She lowered them, but I still kept looking at them.

"Don't stare that way," said Inka quietly.

I don't know how I was looking. But I do know that I wanted to kiss Inka's legs, and that was something I had never before wanted to do.

"You said that it was all romanticism," said Inka. "But what do you think? How do you think things will be?"

What answer could I give Inka? Happiness always prevents me from seeing life as it is. It seemed to me that the only thing waiting for me was happiness, happiness of the unknown and the unexperienced. It seemed that real life was only just now beginning beyond a certain imaginary point. It always seems that way at eighteen, and at forty it turns out that the real joys were experienced right then and that the greatest of them all was the joy of expectation . . .

"Okay, Inka," I said. "I'll work for both you and me. You have to finish school, though. And then you will simply be my wife, like your mother . . ."

"But how would you like it to be really: simply or not simply?"

"No, Inka, deep down inside I'd like it not to be just simply."

Some resort guests were sitting on the next bench. A man was unwrapping expensive candies and feeding them to a woman. She opened her mouth, and he put a piece of candy in. The woman bit down on the candy with her teeth leaving half of it on the outside, and parting her lips she turned to the man. He carefully moved his mouth toward her lips and bit off the candy.

"Do you smell the sea and the acacia?" said the woman.

"Do they please you?" asked Inka.

"No."

"But you were just now looking at my legs the same way he does," said Inka.

I blushed.

"Was it unpleasant for you?"

"I don't know . . ." I was a bit taken aback and a bit embarrassed. But if it hadn't been for that I certainly would have said it was pleasant.

The rain made a noise as it approached over the water. The first drops rustled through the leaves of the trees leaving wet spots on the sand. People ran under the trees and the awnings over the shop windows. Our neighbors also left. Inka and I remained on the deserted boulevard.

<h2 style="text-align:center">IV</h2>

I RAN home. My wet shirt had dried a little and no longer stuck to my body. But I still continued to run . . . Why? I wish someone would tell me.

Mother was not at home and one could not expect her to be, as she did not get home before eight o'clock. I went into the empty-sounding apartment, walked through the kitchen and the spacious hallway — the light in it came from above, through a narrow window above the front door — and entered my room. I opened the windows, but the streets at that hour were still empty and quiet.

Why our apartment looked empty I still can't understand. We did not have that little furniture. For example, in my room there was a narrow bed, a kitchen table and a den sofa. The leatherette covering on the last was all cracked, but it was completely intact. We even had a buffet — a cumbersome one with multi-colored glass panes in the doors, and Mother had a mahogany dressing table in her room. I don't remember Mother ever sitting at it, but it was there. And still, the apartment seemed empty. Even the air in it seemed somehow unalive, cold and hollow-sounding.

I stood in the middle of the room. There is nothing worse than when everything inside of you is rushing, and there is no place to rush to. I went out to the kitchen. A mountain of dishes was piled up in an enamel basin: Mother did not wash dishes until there was not a single clean plate left in the buffet. I think that there were still some plates left in the buffet, but I heated some water and washed all the dishes. Then I swept the rooms. This was actually my job to do, but I usually performed it badly. I eased my conscience with the thought that Mother was also not very careful with her household chores. She would cook everything at once for the next three days, and when the soup turned bad she would say: "That won't do at all. I break my back cooking, and you won't eat."

It's interesting how a person can eat a spoiled dinner. I tried it once, and then I did not eat anything for three days; I just drank tea with dry toast. People said that even then I got off easily. I don't know. As far as I'm concerned it wasn't very easy at all.

I carried out the trash and the slops. I even wanted to clean the stove, but it was covered with such a thick layer of grease and soot that just to touch it was revolting. I touched it but did not begin to clean it — I just wiped it off with a newspaper. Instead of the stove, I got busy with the mailbox: I fixed a hinge and put on the little door. It's amazing the number of things one can do when one has to kill time. But still it dragged on slowly.

I returned to my room.

On the other side of the street the panes of open casements glittered. I sat at the open window straddling the chair. The windowsills were low. The wet street looked into the room. It smelled of acacia and earth. I remembered the words of the woman: "Do you smell the sea and the acacia?"

It's strange, but before that I had not noticed the smells of our town. It was probably because I had long ago grown used to them. But in the meantime the town was simply drenched with smells: in the spring it smelled of acacia and lilac; in the summer, stocks and tobacco. And there was always the smell of the sea. Now I was sure that I would recognize our town out of a thousand towns just by its smell.

It would have been better if I had not remembered the woman's words. As soon as I remembered them I immediately began to think about Inka. And everything inside of me started rushing somewhere again. I wanted to recall what we had talked about. But nothing would come; everything got mixed up and jumped from one thing to the next. I understood that something had happened on Coastal Boulevard, and that we could no longer return to our former relationship. But I didn't want to return to it, either. I wanted to find out as soon as possible what would happen next.

But this could be answered only by time. I did not have to do anything. All I had to do was simply wait . . .

Now I know that waiting is not the worst thing in life. But at that time I was bursting to get along — it did not matter where to, just so as not to remain alone in the empty apartment.

I was barely able to remain sitting on the chair. My hands sorted out the figures of a chess set, which were heaped into a pile on the windowsill, onto the chess board. I did not remember how the thought came to me of working out the game between Alyokhin and Capablanca. But as soon as the weight of the lead figures was in my hands I felt better right away.

I considered Capablanca my teacher. Personally I liked Alyokhin better, but he was a White émigré. This sort of thing happened to me in life; I would like a person, for example, whom I knew I should not like, and I would try to convince myself that he was not worthy of my consideration. Sometimes I succeeded, but more often I did not.

The end of the game was familiar to me . . . I played it out twice and Capablanca lost. This did not bother me, but I set myself the task of finding the mistake of the ex-champion and proving to myself that Alyokhin's victory was accidental.

I tried to find the next move without looking at the book. In the beginning my brain, as though separated from the rest of me, felt out the possibilities hidden in the arrangement of the dead figures. For me they were not dead, for suddenly a moment of enlightenment would come when I somehow entered into the train of someone else's thoughts and easily followed them, unraveling the clever interlacements of mutually hostile schemes. But that evening this moment did not come. I looked more at the street than at the board. Drops of rain were suspended in the grass growing between the cobblestones of the street. The late afternoon sun was reflected in puddles of rainwater which had collected in the depressions of the brick sidewalk. It was getting near the time when the resort guests returned to the *kursaal* or walked along Coastal Boulevard after their rest at the beach. Today they came later than usual, for the rain had interrupted things. When they passed by my window I saw them from head to toe. And even before they appeared beneath the window I heard their voices and the clopping of their heels. They passed by, and only the width of the windowsill separated them from me. Their voices resounded with a hollow sound in the room.

That evening I sensed for the first time the lifeless emptiness of our apartment. It had surrounded me since my childhood, but I had not noticed it. I had had no time to notice it. I rarely had remained alone by myself and I had never given a thought to the life of our family, which consisted of me, Mother and my sisters. I had never thought about why, no matter when I came, the mothers of my friends would always sit me down at the table and feed me. I ate at their places always with great enjoyment and did not notice that in offering me tasty things they were feeling sorry for me, and undoubtedly they personally criticized Mother and our disordered life.

And our life really was disordered. Only then I did not understand this. I was proud of Mother and her fame in our town. I was proud of the fact that she had joined the Party even before the Revolution, had been in the tsarist prison and had even spent time in exile. As far as I could remember she had always worked a lot. In our town she was president of the medical sanitation workers' union. For this work she received a salary. But she still had many other public duties. For several years in a row she had been elected member of the local branch of the Party and deputy of the town council. And two years ago she set up the House of Sanitation Education, or San-Ed House. There was no possible way of including it in the estimate of the town budget, and the San-Ed House had no wage fund. No one wanted to run it without pay. Therefore Mother was temporarily running it.

For as long as I can remember Mother always wore a jacket of soft brown kidskin and a cap to match with a wide round visor. Her short curly hair could be seen from under the cap. I wore out Mother's jacket when I was in the eighth grade, but she never parted with her cap. It had long since faded and was covered with wrinkles, and only in front, under the strap, had it retained its former color. Mother's hair was turning gray and her face was covered with the same sort of wrinkles as were on the cap.

I loved to look at a certain photograph. It was kept in an old cardboard folder among the papers. A young woman in an old-fashioned dress with a flounce around the hem was sitting on a chair. The narrow toes of her white slippers were peeking out from underneath the flounce. I never grew tired of looking at her hands, which were amazingly slender and soft. She was sitting very comfortably, at ease, and her eyes looked at me with amazement and gaiety. This woman was also my mother. But I had never known her this way. Behind her chair stood three men in a row. One of them — with a mustache and a high forehead — was my father, who at that time was a medical student at the University of Petersburg. It was immediately apparent that he was in love with Mother. He had bent his head down to the side and was looking into her face, forgetting that he was being photographed. And it was somehow strange to know that this man who was completely unknown to me was my father, that he and Mother and my sisters had lived together, and I did not know anything about that life of theirs.

My father died when I was a year old. He was never mentioned in my presence. And for some reason I was hesitant to ask about him. I just guessed that Mother had disagreed with Father and that my sisters still condemned her for it. Afterwards Mother had a second husband. We were not living in the Crimea then. I remembered him, but very dimly. He disappeared somehow, unnoticeably, and I could not remember when it took place. But there were some unpleasantnesses connected with his disappearance about which Mother also never spoke.

My sisters had been living independently for quite some time. They were working in the polar region and came to visit us on their vacation once every three years. The elder one, Nina, was married. She got married while we were still living together.

I had grown fond of Sergei before he became Nina's husband, and I was very much afraid that for some reason he would not marry her. They met on the beach. I usually did not go to the beach with my sisters, but that day I was with them. We were in the water together, and I thought at first that Sergei liked my other sister, Lena. I took an immediate liking to Sergei. When he was eighteen he was already commanding a squadron and for the battle at Orenburg he was awarded the Order of the Red Banner. Afterwards he attended trade school, finished the Industrial Academy and went to the polar region to build a new city. All of this, of course, I found out later, but that day we simply fooled around. For me Sergei was the hero of books I had read. And who I was to him I didn't know. Later I guessed, but I was not offended. I just never thought that Sergei and Nina would get married so quickly. It was different with Lena. With her I would not have been surprised. But Nina was the serious one in our family and, in my opinion, not pretty.

I accidentally found out that they were married.

On the way home from the beach Sergei sort of announced that his time at the sanatorium was up.

"I shall have to move to your place," he said.

Nina exchanged glances with Lena, and Lena said to me, "Volodya, dear, run buy some ice cream."

She thought she could fool me! I, of course, stayed. Then Nina said, "Nonsense. Mother will chase both of us out of the house."

"No, she won't," answered Sergei.

After that I myself offered to go and get ice cream, and I left. What they talked about while I was gone I don't know.

In the evening Sergei arrived at our house with a suitcase. Up until then Mother had not once laid eyes on him. As soon as Sergei entered the room, my sisters ran out into the yard. They took me with them, but then they told me to go quietly back into the hallway and listen. I did more than eavesdrop. I could see Mother through a crack in the door which was not quite closed. She was sitting at the table and smiling. Whenever Mother smiled that way it was very difficult to come to terms with her. Sergei I could not see. I only heard the way the springs in the sofa creaked.

"Nadezhda Aleksandrovna, you misunderstand me. I haven't come to rent a room," said Sergei. "Of course, I should have come earlier. It didn't work out. Nina wouldn't let me. I don't understand why they are so afraid of you."

"Nina? Afraid of me? . . ." I saw red spots appear on Mother's face. "Are you drunk?" she asked. "Who gave you the right to come here to my home?"

"I had a little drink," said Sergei. "Is it noticeable? Generally I don't drink. But here's the situation. I've never had to ask for a girl's hand before. How it's done I don't know. I'll just say it simply to you: let me marry Nina."

"Clear out right now," said Mother.

But Sergei had no intention of leaving, and he did right. I knew Mother; she herself did not want him to leave. She was looking across the table and quickly smoothing out the tablecloth with the palm of her hand. The sofa springs creaked louder.

"Let's say I don't have any place to go," said Sergei. "My sanatorium pass is up, and I still have two more months vacation. And then, why should I leave my wife? And there is no point in your separating from your daughter before it's necessary. As it is, she'll be living so far away from you . . ."

I really don't recall how I got into the room. I stood with my back to Sergei and looked at Mother. She slowly rose from the chair, so slowly that I had time to suppose: "Now Mother is really going to throw him out."

"Seryozha! Go away immediately . . ." shouted Nina, but for some reason everyone was looking at me. I didn't notice my sisters come into the room. Mother went around the table. Her deeply sunken black eyes were shining and her lips were smiling. She passed the hot palm of her hand over my hair and forehead and went to her room.

Sergei remained with us. I offered him my bed to sleep in, but Nina fixed him a bed on the floor.

Sergei lived at our place two months. Then he, Nina and Lena left for the polar region. Mother made peace with Sergei just before their departure.

Since then Sergei and my sisters have spent their vacation with us twice.

Sergei was ten years older than Nina, but, according to Mother, he behaved like a kid. Perhaps. Personally I didn't see anything wrong with it.

On the day of their arrival, while my sisters were scrubbing and sweeping their quarters, Seryozha set off for the beach. He disregarded the shade. And it is not very difficult to imagine the results; a boiled lobster in comparison to him looked pale. In the evening Seryozha was lying in shorts on the washed floor, and my sister was smearing sour cream on him. The next day, with blisters on his shoulders, he again set out for the beach. Mother called this idiocy and lack of discipline. But Seryozha said, "You're just prejudiced. I've come here to get properly warmed up. And I'll get warmed up if it kills me!"

Among our group Seryozha was liked by everyone. He was the same sort as us. But Inka especially liked Seryozha — probably because he was also a redhead. We spent every day together. We taught him how to work a sail, and he didn't become offended if one of us shouted at him. Nina considered herself too grown up for our company. All the worse for her. Seryozha told her so straight out. But Lena went with us. I simply couldn't understand why Seryozha had not married her.

There was a great deal I didn't understand. For example, I saw that Mother was somewhat afraid of Seryozha. Why, I did not know. She preached to him just as she did to the rest of us, but with him she never insisted on her own way. And Seryozha, on the other hand, played the part of the obedient son-in-law, but when he talked with Mother it seemed as though he was trying to provoke her.

The last time Seryozha and my sisters came to visit us was during the summer when Mother opened the San-Ed House. I suspected that Mother was in a hurry to open it before their arrival. Mother and her San-Ed House were written up in the town and district newspapers. When we all gathered together for supper, it was the main topic of conversation. Seryozha was the only one who had nothing to say about it. The San-Ed House did not interest him — this was immediately apparent. Once when Nina said: "It would be nice to go and see it," Sergei right then and there got the idea of making an overnight excursion to Turtle Island. That time we did not go to the island, but we did not go to see the San-Ed House either.

Mother could not hold back.

"Sergei Nikolaevich," she said. "Really, is there nothing in our town besides amusements which interests you?"

"I'm at a health resort, Nadezhda Aleksandrovna. Resting doesn't come easily either."

Mother was offended. Everyone noticed it. When she went to bed, Nina said, "Okay, Mr. Health-Resorter, whether you like it or not, tomorrow we're going to have a look at the San-Ed House."

The following day we were planning to take a yacht to Turtle

Island. Seryozha was also planning to come. He looked at my sister with sad eyes.

"Never mind, never mind, you'll get over it," she said.

"I guess I'll have to," answered Seryozha.

I would not have been able to do it, but Seryozha never argued with Nina if she seriously wanted him to do something. For this I liked him even more.

In the morning we went to sea without Seryozha.

In the evening I asked him, "Did you like the San-Ed House?"

We were alone on the porch where he had gone out to have a smoke before going to bed. He did not hasten to reply.

"Did you like the House?"

"It was all right; lots of photographs. The pictures are very pretty — they're colored. Is the sand good on the island? We'll have to go there once more together."

From the glowing end of his cigarette Seryozha's face seemed red.

"You talk to me like you talk to Mother."

"That's your imagination."

"What did you say to Mother about the House?"

"Just what I told you."

"And then you say 'my imagination.' Why have you been teasing Mother all this time?"

"You're a strange one, Volodya. You know she's my mother-in-law. Perhaps the Chinese do things differently, but in Russia since the beginning of time mothers-in-law and sons-in-law have gotten along together like cats and dogs."

Seryozha threw his cigarette butt away and got up.

"No, wait," I said.

"It's time to get some sleep, lad . . ."

Relations between Seryozha and Mother were completely ruined. I felt that they became worse than they were when he and Nina got married. Mother hardly spoke to Seryozha. And if they happened to exchange a word or two about something at the table, I immediately pricked my ears up. I was afraid they would get into an argument, and then I would have to choose which side I was on. And this was something I myself didn't know.

Seryozha and my sisters stayed with us until August. As before,

we did not all get together until suppertime. And the short time
we spent sitting at the table seemed painfully long to me.

Once Lena was telling about how Seryozha got out of doing a
job offered to him by their Party Secretary in the new polar town.
Who asked her to tell this I don't know. Lena was always the one
who felt the need of something, more so than the others. She
wanted Mother to understand how much Seryozha was respected
at work. But Mother understood everything the other way around.
In front of her on the table was a glass half-full of tea. She had
stopped drinking and was listening attentively. Mother put her
hand over her eyes, and this alarmed me more than anything, for
from her eyes I could always predict her frame of mind.

"This I didn't even expect from you," said Mother and pushed
her glass aside.

"What can you do, Nadezhda Aleksandrovna? I'm a geologist.
And I like my work."

"Okay. But the Party felt the necessity of using you in different
work. What right did you have to refuse?"

"The fellows from the district branch made a mistake. They
selected another engineer for secretary of the municipal branch. I
studied with him at the Industrial Academy. He's not a very good
engineer. On the other hand, he's an organizer the likes of which
you can't find anywhere. Under his direction they accomplished
more in a year than you could get done in five years."

"I don't doubt that the Communists found a worthy replacement
for you," said Mother. She got up from the table. Her eyes were
shining, and her lips were smiling. There is nothing worse than
when Mother puts on such a face. Mother wanted to say something else, but she looked at me instead and then went to her room.

I followed Seryozha out onto the porch. He was smoking.

"I displeased her again, and you say . . ." said Seryozha. I was
not so much struck by his words as by his voice, which was tired
and gloomy. I sat down next to him, and he placed his hand on my
shoulder.

"You don't like Mother. Why?" I asked.

"Is there any reason to discuss it?"

"There is. After all, I'm her son."

"You're right. I suppose there is a reason. It's not right to say that I don't like her, Volodya. But you, Nina and Lena — you're like my own kind of people, and she isn't. And there's nothing anyone can do about it."

"Probably Mother feels the same way."

"Probably . . ."

"It's too bad. You're both members of the Party. You've both struggled for the Soviet state."

"That's different, Volodya. We'll still be in it together. Only I can't change, and Nadezhda Aleksandrovna can't change. That's the way things are in life, my friend, so don't get upset."

Seryozha squeezed my shoulder firmly in his hand. I leaned back against his chest and was silent.

That he and Mother were two different people I could see without his telling me. This did not prevent me from loving them both, but for some reason it prevented them from loving each other. I could have asked Seryozha why, but I didn't. I guessed that he wouldn't have been able to answer me anyway.

From our place Seryozha and my sisters went to Moscow, from there to Leningrad, and from there they were planning to go to Orenburg to visit Seryozha's family.

The day before their departure they went off to town for provisions and promised to return in an hour. I waited two hours. Of course, it would have been no trouble at all for me to go and hunt them up. But what for? I purposely went to the wild parts of the beach so as not to meet up with them.

I came running home towards suppertime. Everyone was already sitting at the table and eating in silence. Things had never been so wistful at our place as on that evening.

Mother went off to her room. My sisters continued to sit at the messy table and kept endlessly repeating that they wanted to go to bed, but they didn't go. When I was smaller, and they had something to discuss with Mother, they used to chase me off to bed by force. They were about to try it then. I looked at them angrily, and then I got the idea that the best way of finding out what they wanted to talk to Mother about was to go to bed myself.

They put the light out in the room. My sisters walked about listening to my breathing, and their white dresses showed up in the darkness.

"I don't think that he's asleep," said Nina in a whisper. "You can't hear his breathing at all."

"On the contrary," answered Lena. "When he sleeps he breathes very quietly."

They were in no hurry to leave my bed. That was all right; my lungs were sizeable enough. Then Nina quietly called Sergei. They went into Mother's room and closed the door. Now really! Even with the door closed I heard everything perfectly. All I had to do was lie on my back.

"Mother, let Volodya come with us." This was said by Nina.

"Very good," said Mother. "I was beginning to think that you had become completely callous. Volodya can go, but he has to be back home a week before school starts."

"Mother, we would like for Volodya to come all the way with us, to live with us . . ."

"You've gone crazy. No, you've gone completely crazy."

"Mother, listen. It will be better for Volodya at our place. What does he get to see here? Where we live, they're building a new city, a huge center, and there are so many interesting and different people working there."

"I am sure that this magnificent idea belongs to Sergei Nikolaevich."

"You're mistaken, Nadezhda Aleksandrovna. It's not mine, but Lena's. It's true, I've been thinking about it for a long time, but I didn't dare speak out first. I thought about it a long time ago. The boy will have to choose his path in life, but what does he know about life."

"He's already chosen what he wants to do, and not without your help. He has decided to become a geologist. I have given my consent. What more do you want? Besides the big things there are also the little things in life. Someone has to do them. They are not any the less necessary, and you have to give them everything you've got. You're thinking of the big things — and I too. But let my son learn to understand and respect the people who, day by day, year in and year out, perform the unnoticed dirty work . . . and perform it as though it was of top national importance."

"And you can perform useless nonsense in a big way too," said Sergei. "It's not a question of importance but of usefulness . . .

Perhaps it's true that I drummed it into his head to become a geologist. Let him get to know some other people now. The more you know, the easier it is to choose what suits you best."

"Mother, you're still smarting from a personal affront. That's not right." This was said by Lena. While she was silent everyone talked quietly. An amazing being Lena, all she had to do was to say a couple of words and immediately a storm would break loose. I no longer had to strain my ears — I heard everything as if they were talking right beside my bed.

"Affront? What affront?" asked Mother. "Surely you don't think I could be offended because the San-Ed House seems a useless undertaking to someone?"

"Mother, don't pretend." This was also said by Lena.

"Very well, my dear daughters, go to bed. I am tired."

"Mother, you're wrong. You just can't think only about yourself and take only yourself into account," said Nina. "You don't want to live with us — that's your business. But Volodya should go. He's a growing boy, and he should eat well and on time."

"Oh, how touching," said Mother. "I raised, dressed, fed, and brought you up. But I'm no longer good enough for Volodya. Let's stop this conversation. Volodya needs me, and I need Volodya . . ."

"We don't need any irony. You understand perfectly what Nina is talking about. Remember Father." This again was said by Lena.

Seryozha came into my room. A narrow beam of light penetrated through the crack in the door which was not quite closed. It cut off the window where he was standing. I didn't see him, but I heard the rustle of a box of matches in his hand.

"Well, so what," said Mother, and through the opening in the door I could hear her breathing. "What am I supposed to remember? His drunken scenes of jealousy? Well, say it. What am I supposed to remember?"

"You can remember whatever is of any use to you."

"Stop it, Lena," said Nina. "Mother, you're not right either. Father was a very talented and soft person. Is it possible to blame him because he loved you so much? He loved all of us, but you most of all. He gave up the clinic and his friends, renounced his future, took Lena and me and followed you into exile. And what happened there? After all, he had to bear the burden of everything. He had to work for our living, look after us, and continually guard you from danger. You musn't blame him because he couldn't hold out and began to drink. He was too soft for the struggle, but he was always a good and true comrade to you, and a father to us. But you have often forgotten about him. We've gotten used to it, though. We don't have to talk about Father right now."

"No, we do. I was a bad mother. I forgot my children, my husband, and myself. You can punish me for it. But first answer me: for what purpose did I do all that?"

Seryozha walked along the streak of light and firmly closed the door. In Mother's room everyone grew quiet. I held my breath so as to be able to hear better. But from not breathing for a long time my ears began to ring.

"Volod'ka, are you asleep?" asked Seryozha.

"I am," I answered angrily. "They've dreamed things up for me, too. I'm not leaving Mother to go anywhere."

V

I THOUGHT it would be good to write to Seryozha and my sisters about the change in my future. But I didn't want to get up, and so I continued to sit straddling the chair near the open window. My shirt and pants were still damp, and I felt chilled, but still I sat.

The last rays of the sun went down and the air in the street turned gray with the twilight. But the sky was still blue above the roofs of the houses; the squares on the chess board faded away into one solid dark spot, and it was no longer possible to distinguish the color of the chessmen. And I didn't try. I was listening to the footsteps of the now infrequent passersby. A woman began to sing:

> *Weary, the sun*
> *took tender parting from the sea.*

Her voice came closer. She went by one of the wide-open windows, and the words of the song rushed into the room. Then they took on a muffled effect as she passed by the neighboring portion of the wall.

"*At that hour you confessed*," she sang.

A man was walking along with the woman and had his arm around her shoulders. They were happy together and were not hurrying anywhere. The woman looked at me and said in a singing voice: *"For want of love . . ."* I felt uncomfortable from her stare, and, from the happy shine in her eyes, I knew that she didn't believe the words of the song.

In the room a light went on behind my back.

"How was your examination?" asked Mother. I hadn't heard her come in.

"Excellent . . ."

"Was it hard?"

"Not very."

Mother put down her bundles on the table and went out to the kitchen.

"Well, look at that, he's washed all the dishes. You're simply a dear, and you've earned a luxurious supper," said Mother in the kitchen. "I'll fix you an omelet with sausage."

Mother began to sing. This happened very seldom. The last time she sang was a year ago when we received a telegram that Nina had given birth to a baby girl and that they had named her Nadya in honor of Mother.

I went around the table and stood opposite the open door into the hallway.

> *Wistfully wails the autumn wind,*
> *The circling leaves are now turned pale,*

sang Mother as she shook the grate in the stove. She had a Gypsy voice, slightly throaty with a tremolo. Whenever Mother sang it was very easy to imagine her a young woman, as in the photograph.

"Mother, the Komsomol wants me to go to military school," I said loudly.

I looked into the dark hallway and listened. In the kitchen the stove was making a lot of noise. Mother had stopped singing. She passed by me on her way into the room and sat down on the sofa. Had she heard me or not?

Mother took off her shoes, her black shoes with the lining, with low heels. She wore size seven, the same size as Nina, but Mother's feet seemed considerably longer than Nina's.

"You said something?" asked Mother.

"Today I was called down to the Komsomol office. The town has to send the four best Komsomol members to military school."

"No, Volodya, that's impossible. I can't allow it. Your sisters would never forgive me."

"You're not the one sending me to the school."

"That doesn't mean a thing. They won't be willing to acknowledge the difference. Tomorrow I shall have a talk with Pereverzev."

Mother spoke with a certain lack of certainty.

"I guess I'll go and lie down," she said.

She walked to her room in her socks which were canary-yellow with blue borders.

"Mother, you promised me an omelet with sausage," I said. My heart was pounding so hard that it resounded in my ears.

"Fix it yourself, son. I'm quite tired . . ."

Never had I seen her so at a loss, and suddenly I got the suspicion that it wasn't a question of my sisters. For some reason Mother did not want me to enter military school. This frightened me. To talk Mother into something if she did not want to do it was a difficult thing. Everything fell through. I imagined how I would look at Inka the next day, and yet this did not prevent me from thinking about the omelet with sausage.

I went to the kitchen, spread some grease around on the bottom of a frying pan, and, when it got hot, I put in thick round slices of sausage. I watched them fry and scolded myself for my light-headedness. Then I cracked three eggs into the pan, thought a moment and added two more. While I was frying and eating the omelet, I suffered from the idea that I probably wasn't suited for anything serious.

A light was burning in Mother's room. I went to the door and stood on the threshold. Mother was sitting on her bed. Her feet in those ridiculously colored socks did not touch the floor. She was leaning with her back against the wall, and her lips were firmly pressed together, the upper one covering the lower one. This made the wrinkles around her mouth and on her chin seem more noticeable. Could anybody possibly have loved Mother like I love my

Inka? I became ashamed, and I am ashamed to this day that I could think such a thing. Mother was forty-five years old. To my way of thinking that wasn't just a few years. But I know that grown-ups at this age are not yet considered to be old.

"Mother," I said. "For the first time in my life I am of real use to the Komsomol. Do I actually have to refuse? Would you refuse?"

Mother gave me a look as though she saw me for the first time. "Volodya, have you ever shaved?"

All right, suppose I haven't shaved yet. That was very evident from the silky tassels of hair on my cheeks and from the dark-colored fuzz on my upper lip. But what connection did that have to what I was talking about?

"You've grown up a bit," said Mother. "It's hard to recognize you, you've gotten so tall this past year."

Of course Mother hadn't had any other opportunity for looking me over. I began to be provoked.

"You're not going to see Pereverzev tomorrow," I said.

"All right, I won't go . . . I can't go. But you must understand — this is very serious. Much more serious than you think. I hope that you understand what's going on in the world." Mother's sunken eyes shone in their black sockets.

"Of course, I understand," I said. The fortunes of the world at that moment disturbed me least of all. I gave a kick at the void behind me, turned and waltzed around the room on tiptoe in a dance. From a detached viewpoint, this probably did not seem very serious. But I was not thinking about how I looked from a detached viewpoint.

I fixed my bed, and, when I had closed the windows and turned out the light, Mother asked, "Haven't you gone to bed yet? Bring me today's papers . . ."

Afterwards I lay there and just looked at the ceiling, feeling glad about my victory over Mother which was won with such unexpected ease. It would be interesting to know, I thought, what was going on at that moment at Sashka's and at Vit'ka's. Sashka's mother, of course, would be crying, and her eyelids already would be red and swollen. But her tears are by no means a sign of submission to fate: her tears are a frightful weapon against Sashka and his father. Sashka's mother not only cries — she screams, too, summoning the gods and all her relatives as witnesses to her ruined life.

Vit'ka's father doesn't scream and, understandably, doesn't cry. But this probably does not make things any easier for Vit'ka. His father didn't learn to read till he was grown up; he considered teachers the most important people on earth, and he lived in the hope of seeing his son a teacher.

Every Saturday Vit'ka's father arrived at school dressed in his best suit. The soles of his shoes thundered down the corridor as he went to the teachers' room. There he talked with the teachers at length and in detail. And Vit'ka, according to an established procedure, was obliged to stand in the corridor at the door, just in case the reports of the teachers demanded immediate punishment. But the reports on Vit'ka were always the very best. We suspected that his father simply could not refuse himself the pleasure of listening to his son being praised. He left the school with a satisfied, stern look, threatened Vit'ka with a finger eaten away by the salt and said, "Look to!"

It was difficult even to imagine how Vit'ka's father received the news of the possible change in Vit'ka's life. And perhaps things even turned out more simply for Vit'ka and Sashka than I imagined. I had thought that Mother would be proud of the trust shown me. With parents it's always that way. You never know ahead of time how things will turn out. Only the following day could clear up everything. But there was a whole night to wait out yet. I knew from experience that if I fell asleep the time would pass easily and quickly. But, as my luck would have it, I couldn't get to sleep. On the boulevard I had been unable to tell Inka what I imagined our future would be like. But right now I could have done it. When I was alone and was not afraid of appearing naïve, I could picture anything at all to myself, and just as interestingly as in books.

People were again appearing on the street, which meant that the concert was over. John Danker, the king of the Hawaiian guitar, was performing in the *kursaal*. We had not seen him yet. We had given many famous artists the once-over, but so far we had missed seeing any kings.

VI

THE next morning I was awakened by Vit'ka. There was no need to question him about his conversation with his father: the skin over his right cheekbone still retained the first lavender tints of an oncoming black eye.

I pulled on a pair of mouse-gray cotton pants with a wide light gray stripe in them which resembled a cheviot. I tried not to look at Vit'ka's face. The left half of the face was Vit'ka's — thin, with a broad prominent cheekbone, but the right side was not his: it was puffed up, with a swollen and ominously shining eye.

"Is it noticeable?" asked Vit'ka.

The naïve guy, hoping that such a black eye was not noticeable!

"Quite," I said and went to wash up.

Vit'ka smiled guiltily and passed the ends of his fingers over the bruise. He stood close behind me and said, "Mother did me in. I trusted her, but she let me down."

He thought I would ask him about it. Why should I? If he wanted to, he would tell me himself. It was much more important to figure out how to convince his father. I wiped myself dry and began to think, but Vit'ka said, "You understand: first I told everything to Mother so that she could prepare Father. Mother was okay; she heard me out. She fixed dinner for me. Then she asked me to water the garden, and she left. I thought that she had gone to the neighbors. I was watering the garden when I saw Father coming from the gate. Mother was trying to run on ahead, but he blocked her way with his arm. He came up to me and asked, 'Is it true?' I said, 'Yes, it is.' Then he lit in to me . . ."

"He didn't do too bad."

"Mother let me down . . ."

"I already heard. You'll get over it."

We returned to my room. Mother had already gone. There was a note on the table. She wrote that she had gone to the market and that I should wait until she returned and made breakfast.

"You see what mothers are like?" I asked. But I didn't wait for her.

We finished yesterday's sausage and swallowed it down with

cold tea. The sugar wouldn't melt in it, and so we scraped it out of the glasses with spoons.

"Father promised to go down to the Komsomol office and give Pereverzev a going over . . ." said Vit'ka.

I choked. Vit'ka's father didn't cast idle words to the wind. It was a sure thing that Alyosha Pereverzev's hide was as good as gone.

"Great," I said. "There's a scandal taking place at the Komsomol office, and I sit listening to a touching story about how your mother let you down."

"There's no scandal yet. They're loading today at the saltworks. Father's going down there after work."

"Alyosha should be warned."

On the back of Mother's note I wrote that I was going to study. I had long since stopped confiding my activities to her if they did not demand her immediate participation. Things were easier that way both for her and for me. For example, it was easy to imagine how she would have reacted if I had been so naïve as to tell her about yesterday's conversation with Inka. And as far as I was concerned, my relations with Inka and a lot of other things I did, which I did not tell Mother about, did not interfere with anyone or anything, and I concealed them with a calm conscience. Undoubtedly this showed Seryozha's influence on me, but at that time I did not realize it.

We rarely used the front door, but in order not to meet up with Mother, we went out the front.

"Maybe we should wait for your mother," said Vit'ka.

"What for?"

"To ask her advice."

"There's no need to ask her advice, Vit'ka."

"Why not?"

"You know that she'll make a fuss . . . It's better if we try to convince your father ourselves."

Vit'ka walked on the inner side of the sidewalk, hiding his black eye in the shadow of the houses. It was early in the morning and fortunately for Vit'ka we met almost no one. We passed the early morning beach-goers, mothers with their children. The women were carrying tightly packed net bags, the weight of which kept their arms pulled down straight as they walked along. Three years before then, the comedian Vladimir Khenkin had visited our town and called these nets "maybes," because at that time everybody was carrying one around in a pocket, briefcase or lady's handbag in hope that somewhere something would be given out. Even my mother never parted from her "maybe." I was convinced that Khenkin thought up this name in our town and that the resort guests had spread it over the whole country.

A heavyset woman was walking in front of us. She was taking short quick steps. The net which she was carrying in her hand was almost dragging on the sidewalk. And, looking at this net filled with bundles, I simply couldn't believe that there was a time when I used to drink tea without sugar, and Mother would try to slip me her portion of bread unnoticed.

Behind the woman walked her son, a thin, long-legged boy in red shorts. For some reason fat mothers most often have thin children. The woman was in a great hurry. There are such women; they're always in a hurry. Probably they are afraid of missing something. I was sure that the woman in front of us didn't have anything else in mind except a comfortable spot under an awning which someone else might get. And the boy wasn't hurrying anywhere, and I understood him very well. He was giving everything a good look, his pace became slow and guarded, and for a fraction of a second he completely stopped. He knew what only children know, that the most interesting things happen unexpectedly and that the main thing is not to miss out. The woman now and then looked around and called her son. Sweat was pouring down her round face with its triple chin. The boy caught up to her by running, but then something again attracted his attention.

The boy looked around and saw Vit'ka. His feet continued to move forward, but his eyes were fixed, observing Vit'ka's shiner. At last the boy found what he had been looking for so long.

"Mama," he shouted and ran.

The woman turned around and gave us a suspicious, guarded look, but of course she did not see what her son had seen. He was walking now and holding onto a loop of the "maybe" just in case.

"The kid has decided you're a pirate," I said. "He hasn't thought about where you got your shiner."

Vit'ka smiled and turned his head away slightly. But the boy was still looking at Vit'ka and making faces at him.

Many people who didn't know Vit'ka took him for a rough, none-too-clever fellow. Actually, our stocky, square-faced, strong-chinned Vit'ka had the most tender and easily vulnerable feelings. Of the three of us, he was the most polite and unselfishly trusting. The attention of the boy embarrassed him.

"I thought that Mother would help me, but she did me in," said Vit'ka. "You always know what's going to happen. But I never seem to know. I stumble around like a blind kitten. I want things to turn out good, but they always turn out bad."

"Never mind. Live a little, and you'll learn. The main thing is to know how to apply the dialectical method in a real situation."

We turned the corner and almost bumped into the boy. He was standing and waiting for us, ready to take to his heels and already disturbed because we hadn't appeared yet. The boy squealed and ran to catch up with his mother. This time he pretended to be frightened. He ran, jumping on one foot, looking around and laughing.

The street sloped downhill towards a small square. The streetcar tracks glistened in the sun. Some people were crowded near a stop waiting for the streetcar. A yardman of Tartar descent, whom we knew, was sprinkling the pavement with a hose. From time to time he raised the hose and the stream of water tore noisily into the thick foliage of the trees, and sparkling drops of water fell from the wet branches. The yardman smiled and sent a tight stream of water under our feet. We jumped high, and he laughed and began to wash away the partially dried dirt left on the cobblestone pavement after the last rain.

We went up to Sashka's house on the corner of Market and Stalin Streets. Sashka lived on the second floor above a pharmacy.

"You go by yourself," said Vit'ka, and he immediately became absorbed in reading the signs on a billboard.

At the streetcar stop the resort guests were standing close to one another in several rows. From the steps of Sashka's house I saw the little boy for the last time. He had lost sight of us and was turning his head in all directions, while his mother was bent over forward dragging him along by the hand. I waved to him and began climbing the steps.

VII

THE door slammed as if it had been caught in a cross draft. Sashka didn't even look around. I stopped several steps from the landing. Sashka stared at me from above with startled eyes.

"It's a nightmare!" he said and pressed his hands to his head.

There was such shouting going on in Sashka's apartment that you could hear it out on the stairs.

"Sonya, how old are you?" Sashka's father was asking. Judging from the sound of his voice, he was standing right by the door.

"What's the matter with you, have you gone crazy? You don't know how old I am?" Sashka's mother shouted from the room.

"Okay, so I know how old you are. Only I don't know when you'll understand what sort of times we're living in. The country needs your son — that's both his and our good fortune."

"Good fortune for my enemies," shouted Sashka's mother. "Let that bandit and his Party Mama have such good fortune . . ."

The "bandit," of course, was me, and the "Party Mama" was my mother.

"What a nightmare!" said Sashka again. He nudged me in the back. "She's gone completely crazy. This nightmare has been going on since yesterday evening."

I didn't hurry going downstairs.

"You can tell your mother," I said, "that she doesn't need to think of treating me anymore to sweet-and-sour roast. And don't ever expect me to come see you again."

"Well I like that! What have I done?"

It smelled of the pharmacy on the stairs. Sashka sniffed his hands and said, "Last night Father woke me up three times. He was unable to give Mother valerian drops himself. I had to watch her suffer. Valerian drops make me sick to my stomach."

"All right, Sashka. If you must know, my mother didn't agree right away either. As for Vit'ka, you'll see immediately for yourself."

We went out onto the front steps, but we didn't see Vit'ka. He was standing behind the billboard and talking to the Tartar yard-man.

"Ah, Vit'ka, Vit'ka," the yardman was saying, "why have you been fighting?"

"But I tell you, I haven't been fighting. I bumped against the side of a boat."

Vit'ka had probably repeated this version several times, because his voice was hopelessly worn-out.

"You bumped yourself very accurately, right on the mark," said the yardman and laughed. "Since you didn't have a fight, then you must have been hit. Why did you get hit? Because of the girls?"

Vit'ka was standing on the pavement. The yardman was wind-ing up the hose.

"You're in one piece, but your friend's all busted up," he said as we approached, and his white teeth gleamed with moisture. He threw the hose over his shoulder and left, saying loudly, "The friend's all busted up, but you're in one piece . . ."

Sashka was studying Vit'ka's black eye with exaggerated atten-tion.

"There's war in the Crimea. The Crimea's smoldering . . ."

"Mother did me in. I trusted her, but she did me in . . ."

Vit'ka's tender feelings had been shaken up by his mother's treachery more than anything else. And who wouldn't get shaken up by it? We loved our parents and liked to see in them allies and helpers. It upset us when our parents didn't understand us. But we didn't think about the fact that we upset our parents. And it wasn't because we were mean or inattentive sons. We simply acted the same way our parents did when they were our age. In this eternal struggle between fathers and children, the children are probably right even in those situations when they are wrong.

We stood in the shadow of the billboard.

"That's enough lamenting," I said. "We are grown up enough. Nothing will change because your parents are against it. They can't seriously interfere with our entering the school. Do you understand — we're already adults."

I said what had dawned on us since the day before. And perhaps even earlier. Everyone reaches a time (and it's probably different for everybody) when he suddenly feels himself grown up. It's unimportant that after this there still remains in him a lot that is childish. The feeling of maturity, once it has been acknowledged, will gradually become stronger. Standing on the pavement near the billboard, we felt ourselves grown up.

I saw on the faces of my friends that what I had said had pleased them. But Sashka would not have been Sashka if he had not added, "I like optimists. He didn't get a black eye. He didn't get awakened three times last night. In general everything's fine with him; he's going to school with his mom's permission."

"Nonsense! Vit'ka, do you remember the woman with the boy?" I asked. "The one who was hurrying to get to the beach? She had a goal — to grab a place under an awning. Except for a place under an awning, she didn't have anything else in mind. So there, Sashka is like this woman. Our goal is the school. But as far as I'm concerned, the road to the goal is also interesting. We won't want to forget it."

I was not sure that Sashka and Vit'ka had properly appreciated the depth of my thoughts.

"I wouldn't mind recalling it right now," said Sashka.

But Vit'ka couldn't forget his black eye for a second, and therefore was studying a notice again. His intense interest in this attracted Sashka's attention. On the notice there was a figure of a man in a dress coat. His wavy hair was separated by a deep part. Huge red letters announced that the name of this man was John Danker. And those who didn't know who he was were informed slightly below this that he was the "king of the Hawaiian guitar."

"I disagree," said Sashka. "The real name of this king is Peisahovich, and before they put a crown on him he was a salesclerk in Kiev at Madame Fischer's."

"How do you know about Madame Fischer?" asked Vit'ka. Naïve fellow: most of all he was impressed by the details. This prevented him from seeing that Sashka was lying.

"Well, well," said Sashka. "Haven't you heard about Madame Fischer? Don't you know she has a dress shop on Kreshchatik Street? And don't you know that there is a Kreshchatik Street in Kiev?"

"Sashka, cut it," I said. But it was impossible to stop Sashka once he began to unwind.

"Collars with Madame Fischer's trademark on them are known

throughout the whole world. Only a dope like you doesn't know anything about them."

Vit'ka looked at Sashka and smiled distrustfully. Vit'ka was confused by the collars. As if it were more difficult to think of the business about the collars than it was about Madame Fischer herself.

A postman crossed the street. Sashka looked at his bag as if he were spellbound.

"You see?" said Sashka slapping me on the shoulder. Of course I saw, but the postman's bag didn't say anything to me.

"We've had a good Komsomol organizer for two years," said Sashka. "I can imagine how our parents will look when they get the newspapers tomorrow morning, and we'll be written up in them. For Vit'ka's father I can't say anything. But my mother won't be able to stand it. Vit'ka, can you imagine what it will be like with your father?"

Vit'ka had not imagined anything yet. Sashka was always coming up with a million ideas. But then it would turn out that out of a hundred — one would be worthy of attention. Vit'ka looked at me. I immediately understood that Sashka's idea about the newspaper was a good one, but I didn't want to show it right away.

"We can try it," I said. "Let's go see Pereverzev."

We walked across the pavement to Stalin Street. The streetcar stop was almost vacant. The mothers with their children were already at the beach. And those who had come to our town to enjoy themselves were still sleeping. Their day ended shortly before dawn when the restaurants closed, the sand on the beaches cooled off and the sea turned warmer than the cold air. And their new day began when the stifling heat of the houses warmed by the sun raised them out of bed.

The sun was already burning down on us, but it wasn't hot yet. We walked along in the warm, moist shadow of the street. The sidewalks had been washed down, and the small puddles of water on them glistened like bits of glass.

We again felt grown up, and we walked along unhurriedly, although we had the urge to run. When we arrived at the Komsomol building, the clock in Alyosha's office was striking nine. Alyosha himself had just arrived and was sorting papers on his desk.

"Greetings, professors," he said.

Pavel Baulin had nicknamed us "professors." What he wanted to emphasize by this nickname we didn't know and didn't ask. The direct meaning of the word suited us completely, and the intonation with which it was pronounced could be ignored. Pavel himself had had difficulty in finishing the first seven grades. He tried to study at the physical education technical school but gave it up. He explained it by saying he couldn't live without the sea.

"Your recommendations were confirmed last evening here at the office," said Alyosha, and he moved our personal documents to the edge of the table.

"Alyosha, Vit'ka's father is coming to see you this evening," I said.

"What for?"

"To give you a going over . . ."

Alyosha lifted the strands of his long straight hair from his forehead, and they fell back of their own accord into two equally divided halves on his head.

"Babies," he said. "Where is Anikin?"

I called Alyosha over to the window. Vit'ka was standing on the other side of the street, and, of course, he was still facing the notice of the same John Danker. These notices were posted up all over town, and I am sure that Vit'ka committed the picture of the king of the Hawaiian guitar to memory that day for the rest of his life.

"Vit'ka," I shouted. He turned around. "Just look," I said to Alyosha. "You're a fine one with big words."

"Anikin! Come here," called Alyosha.

Vit'ka shook his head and turned back to the notice.

"He won't come," I said. "Let's decide ourselves what to do."

"Ye-ess," said Alyosha and returned to the table. "The situation . . . The main thing is that it's already been confirmed at the office and Kolesnikov approved . . . But what does Viktor think? What sort of a mood is he in?"

"He feels the same as he did before. He won't change his mind for the time being."

"Then everything is all right," said Alyosha and lifted up his hair with both hands. "Let old man Anikin come. I'll have a talk with him in Kolesnikov's office."

"Wait, Alyosha. You don't know Vit'ka's father. Why bring on a scene? Sashka, present your proposal."

Sashka was sitting on the sofa and attentively studying the end of his own nose. I couldn't remember a single instance when it had been necessary to drag him by the tongue. This was the first time it had happened to him.

"Do you hear?" I said. "Present your proposal."

"Alyosha, you know us," said Sashka. "We're modest guys; we're not looking for fame. But if Mother reads tomorrow morning in the newspaper that her son is the best of the best and that the army can't get along without him, she'll calm down. Well, not completely. But it will be possible to live in our house again. That's my mother. But Vit'ka's father . . ."

Alyosha didn't need any details. He was very bright and understood everything. As soon as he heard the word "newspaper" he began to walk about the room and was now standing by the door.

"Gentlemen, professors," he said, not letting Sashka finish what he was saying. "You may consider the article printed. Wait . . . I'm going upstairs."

"Hold it," I said. "We don't have time to wait. We are going to see Vit'ka's father. Anyway, leave the building by five o'clock. Just in case . . ."

It was hot in the street. I couldn't remember there ever being such heat at the end of May. To think in the sun was scarcely pleasant. My head was buzzing, and the morning had just begun.

"Everything's all right," said Sashka. "Alyosha will find a way. I always said that Alyosha had a head on his shoulders."

"Vit'ka," I said. "You come with us as far as Zhenya's. Tell the girls that we've been held up. Then come to the saltworks. Don't let your father catch sight of you until we call you. Understand?"

"I'm not going to see the girls," said Vit'ka.

"Nonsense. Black eyes don't go away in one day. I suppose you aren't going to take your exam tomorrow either?"

VIII

VIT'KA got off the streetcar near Zhenya's house, and Sashka and I went on to the last stop in the Old Section. People were sitting and standing in the narrow shadow cast by a low, windowless wall.

They picked up their sacks and baskets from the ground and went to the streetcar. They seemed unreal and weightless to me. They passed by me and I watched them in a sort of strange forgetfulness. How did I get here? Why was I here? The final exam was on the next day. We should have been sitting in Zhenya's garden long ago. Around the table, which was fastened to the ground, it was cool. There was a delicate smell of sun-warmed lilac there. When a breeze touched the pages of a book, they rustled. Their rustling mixed with the whispering of the leaves. The voice of the person reading at the time was audible only to us, it could not fill the whole area.

Days were always just days. Up to that minute I had always felt that way. But right then my faith in the stability of time was strongly shaken, no more than twenty-four hours separated the previous day from this day, and everything which existed for us until the summons to the Komsomol office had become distant past.

Beyond the last stop was the beginning of the Dunes. On the broad streets without pavement or sidewalks the small houses looked still smaller.

"What are you standing there for? Let's walk along the shore," said Sashka. He imagined that I was standing on the streetcar circle and thinking about which way to get to the saltworks.

The streetcar departed, and the glare of the tracks was added to the glare of the sun.

"Let's go," I said.

We walked down to the shore along a narrow path which extended between olive bushes. A wide strip of barren beach stretched all the way down to the saltworks. The morning tide had cast fresh seaweed far up onto the sand. It had dried out and turned white. Two fishermen were repairing a scow on the shore. The echo of their axe blows was louder than the blows themselves. Tar was boiling in a black pail over a bonfire, and the flame under the pail seemed transparent in the sunlight.

We took off our shoes and stuck them in our pants pockets. The hot, coarse sand felt pleasant as it pricked the soles of our feet. From the time we had stopped running around the town barefoot our feet had become amazingly sensitive. We walked along the wet sand which was so tightly packed that no footprints remained on it.

Warm water, splashing over the sand, washed over our feet.

"Sashka, did you get it all? The main point is to complain to Anikin about the unreasonableness of your parents," I said.

"I'll do no such thing," answered Sashka. He had become obstinate while we were still in the streetcar, and it was awkward to argue with him there. Now that we were alone, however, I could say everything I thought about him.

"Ass," I said. "Either you do what you're told or go home."

"Lay off!" said Sashka.

It was very hot. Sashka walked behind me and fumed. That was fine with me — his mood didn't bother me in the least. We took off our shirts. Our moist skin was refreshed by the air. But we didn't feel it long. By the middle of the summer when our skin was covered with a dark tan it became thoroughly immune to the sun. But for the time being we were quite sensitive to the burning heat. We stuck our shirts under our belts and rolled our pants' legs up above the knee. This is the way we looked when we passed under the wooden arch into the area of the saltworks.

The salt was obtained from the seawater. The water was pumped into rectangular basins, which for some reason were called cards. After the water had poured from one basin to another and had evaporated, the salt was scooped out with shovels. Basin-cards stretched along the shore for about three miles. In our town the saltworks was the only industrial undertaking of national importance. Our salt, which was blindingly white and fine like powder, carried the highest quality mark of table salt.

There was still a long walk ahead of us through the grounds and past the docks where launches were waiting. Somewhere beyond the mounds of salt a brass band was playing the "Cracowienne." The brassy sounds, weakened by the heat, grew stronger and then almost died out again.

"Coming through . . . !"

I pulled the languishing Sashka off to the side. A fat old geezer was rolling a wheelbarrow past. He looked at us with round, angry eyes. His dirty-gray shorts had slipped down under his round belly. His arms were set wide apart. He was leaning forward with his chest on the handlebar, and he took short quick steps with his bare feet, kicking them out to the side as he went along. The wheel of the cart thudded along on the run-board, and it seemed as though the old man was straining his utmost to keep it from jumping off into the sand.

Workmen with wheelbarrows were running all over the shore from the mounds to the docks. So as not to disturb anyone we walked along the narrow edge of a basin. The white salt on the bottom was covered with a transparent film of water, and our images with outstretched arms for keeping our balance were reflected in it. The nearer we came to the center of the saltworks, the better we could hear the band. We caught sight of Vit'ka's father as he was returning from the dock with an empty wheelbarrow. But before we saw him Sashka pointed out a placard to me. On a square piece of plywood opposite the fourth dock was written: "To the STAKHANOVITE CREW of Pyotr Andreevich Anikin — HONOR!"

Vit'ka's father's crew was the first *Stakhanovite* work crew in our town. This event took place not too long ago, and we remembered all the details very well. Vit'ka's father and his crew-mates set a leg-breaking loading record at the saltworks just a few days after the newspapers announced the heroic labor feat of a Donbas miner. Up until then, in every crew it took one to load the wheelbarrows with a shovel and five to cart them away to the launch. While the wheelbarrow was being loaded, the carrier just stood there, and while the wheelbarrow was being carted away, the shovel man just "tanned." On the day of the record in Vit'ka's father's crew every man had two wheelbarrows: while one was being dumped, the other was being loaded.

The town newspaper carried on a discussion as to whether or not such work could be considered *Stakhanovite*. The results were summed up in a meeting at the local Party office. Some pointed out that *Stakhanovite* activity meant a high degree of mechanization and not muscular labor. Others said that it would be a political mistake not to support the initiative of the workers. The best to speak out at the meeting was my mother. She said that *Stakhanovite* work is not only mechanization, but also good organization of the productive processes. After that the majority of the members of the committee decided to recognize Vit'ka's father's crew as being worthy of high standing.

But even before that we acknowledged the crew as being *Sta-khanovite*. Formalities interested us least of all. The most important thing was that in our town, too, a movement had begun that swept the entire country. And it was begun by none other than Vit'ka's father.

Now all the crews at the saltworks were working according to Anikin's method. When the launches came for salt a "*Stakhanovite* shift" was announced at the saltworks. On such days they kept score in the competition. Then the works grew quiet. New water was pumped into the newly cleaned cards for evaporation, and the salt was thrown out into mounds for drying.

On loading days music and flags flying on the docks gave the saltworks a festive look.

Vit'ka's father was pushing an empty wheelbarrow. He glanced at us. His eyes were just like Vit'ka's — light blue, only the blue color of his was colder.

"Hello, Uncle Petya," we shouted in unison, but our greeting had no effect on Vit'ka's father. His canvas pants rustled past us. He was running at a trot to the music, and his broad back shook. Heavyset, middle-aged men run like that.

"Did he say hello?" asked Sashka.

"I don't think he did . . ."

"Great . . ."

"And you thought he'd see us and start smiling," I said. "Come on!"

We caught up with Uncle Petya just as he was starting off with a loaded wheelbarrow.

"Uncle Petya, where's Vit'ka?" I asked.

Uncle Petya leaned on the handles and placed the wheel on the run-board. Then he gave the wheelbarrow a shove and set out at a short, quick pace. Very polite of him. But if he thought he could frighten us, he was mistaken; we weren't frightened by silence.

"Let's sit a while," I said.

We sat down on the edge of an evaporating basin. Sashka fidgeted around getting settled down more comfortably.

"Are you certain that we won't be leaving here with black eyes?"

I was not completely certain, but I was counting on Mother's

authority and on the respect with which Uncle Petya behaved towards her. We sat on the edge of the basin and watched. A thin,
sinewy character with a round, cropped, gray head was bent over
loading empty wheelbarrows with a large scoop-shovel. Every once
in a while workmen would bring up empties and take away full
ones. When the shovel man raised his head we saw his bushy gray
eyebrows and his horseshoe-shaped mustache. His mustache and
eyebrows seemed glued onto his sunburned face. His long thin arms
moved as if they were on hinges. But the most amazing thing was
that this middle-aged character was not sweating at all.

Uncle Petya came running up and turned his empty wheelbarrow over with a jerk. He had already returned several times from
the dock, but he continued as before to pay no attention to us. We
were not offended: a contest was a contest.

"Mikheich," he said to the man with the mustache. "Zaitsev is
gaining . . ."

"Why shouldn't he gain. It's not even a hundred yards to his
dock, while to ours it's a good two hundred."

"We'll have to give each man a third wheelbarrow."

"Sure, why not. We can do that. While they're standing they
don't have to be fed. Only there's no one to load them. I'm getting
behind with these as it is is."

Uncle Petya turned toward us. He didn't even turn, but just
nodded his head in our direction. But this was sufficient for us.
When Prince Andrei thought, "This is my Toulon," he probably
felt the same way as we did. We were already standing with scoop-
shovels (there were a lot of them scattered about the basin) and
looking at Uncle Petya.

"Get the third wheelbarrows. We'll help," I said.

Uncle Petya looked at Mikheich.

"We can give it a try," said the latter. "Zaitsev will raise a stink."

"Let him. The boys aren't strangers; they're friends of my
Vit'ka. Next time we'll take on a seventh man for the crew."

Uncle Petya wheeled out a load. He didn't give us a look, just
tossed over his shoulder: "Put your shoes on."

We stood sideways to the mound of salt. In one swoop you had
to take a shovelful and with a turn of the body and arms empty the
salt into the wheelbarrow. As long as the former number of wheel-

barrows remained there was nothing for Mikheich to do. He wasn't
bored. He sat down on the top of the mound, began to smoke and
shared his impressions of the loading with the workmen as they
came running up.

"That Zaitsev, ha, does Zaitsev's belly shake. He's been running
behind a wheelbarrow for ten years, but seems his belly has gotten
still bigger . . ."

When Uncle Petya brought the empty wheelbarrows stacked
one on top of the other, Mikheich slid down from the mound.

"Anikin, we're going to make it. Remember my words," he said.
"Zaitsev won't get wind of it in time. We'll make it . . ."

"Let him sniff," said Uncle Petya.

The workmen looked at us with curiosity. This didn't bother
us. This wasn't the first time we had had shovels in our hands. The
main thing when you work with a shovel is not to tense your
stomach. We knew how to support the weight below the stomach
and relax the muscles in time. The band increased its tempo and
stopped. Only the scraping of iron against the salt could be heard.

At the docks a man in a linen suit was shouting out the results
of the loading through a loudspeaker. When we took up the
shovels, Zaitsev's gang was ahead of Uncle Petya's by half a ton.
The results of the loading were reported every hour. But we didn't
hear the next result because the band was playing again — this time
a *hopak*. Uncle Petya came running up — he was running both
ways now.

"We're even," he said.

Mikheich answered, "Hey everybody? Zaitsev will lay caviar
now . . ."

How Zaitsev was going to lay caviar didn't interest us. We were
working. On the end of Sashka's nose hung a cloudy drop of sweat.
I saw it fall myself. But when I again looked at Sashka's face there
was another such drop hanging from his nose again.

"Sashka, stop diluting the salt. They didn't evaporate it just for
that."

"Simple Simon, how can I dilute it when it's salt that's pouring
off of me?"

"Never mind, you're not eating dumplings."

"Suppose, when I eat dumplings, I also sweat . . ."

I saw that I wouldn't be able to get Sashka angry. Too bad. When you're angry it's easier to work. The sunlight and the glare from the salt cut into our eyes. Salt settled on our backs and shoulders, and it penetrated through the cloth tops of our shoes. You could rub your shoulders and back with the palm of your hand and relieve the itch at least for a while. But it was impossible to stop the itch on our feet. However we didn't let the shovels out of our hands.

Something happened on the shore. We heard a faint "hurrah!" which was muffled by the distance . . . A red flag shot up on the mast of the launch our crew was loading.

"Knock off!" said Mikheich, and he set his skinny rear end down on the salt.

I hadn't noticed where the familiar old guy in shorts and a straw hat with a torn brim had come from. He stood and looked at us for some time.

"Aha!" he said and ran towards the shore. His fat legs did not bend at the knees, and his elbows were pressed into his sides as he ran.

A crowd had already gathered at the shore. Men were running to the dock from various parts of the saltworks. They tossed Uncle Petya up and down and caught up with the rest of his crew by the shore.

"I think I'll have a ride, too," said Mikheich. He threw away his cigar and stood up. His pants seemed empty on him. He ran toward the crowd and shouted, "Boys, here I am."

The band hurried to the dock. The drummer was the last one to come running up. Only his head and feet were visible behind his huge drum.

"Volod'ka!"

I looked around. There, above a mound of salt, Vit'ka's face stood out in full splendor with a diagonal bandage across it.

"How are things going?"

"So far they aren't. Wait," I answered.

Sashka and I sat modestly on the edge of the basin and watched the shore, intoxicated with the deeds of our own hands. Everyone was getting tossed in the air. Anyone who got caught got tossed. The band played a flourish. The launch left the dock on its own motor power, and two sailors hoisted a sail on the bow. These pot-bellied little boats traveled along the coast down to Feodosia. There the salt was unloaded in an hour's time from their holds into rail-road cars. We knew that towards the end of the five-year plan a mechanized dock would be built at our saltworks, too. We knew everything about the future of our town.

Uncle Petya came up. With him was a man in a linen suit and the fat old guy in shorts and a straw hat.

"Where's the right? Where?" he shouted. His voice turned out to be unexpectedly high-pitched with an incredible vibration.

"Look, Zaitsev, the main thing isn't the boys," said the man in the linen suit. "They've set a new *pace*. You understand, a new pace . . ."

Zaitsev fell about two steps behind and stopped, as if getting ready to butt someone.

"Pa-ace!!! I'll outpace you, Anikin. Just remember! . . . I'll put all seven of them to loading. If that's not enough, I'll make the women haul. I'll outstrip you!"

Zaitsev turned and started off at his awkward little trot. He probably couldn't walk calmly anymore.

"Interesting. Does he run home too?" said Sashka.

"Thanks, Anikin, for your initiative. And thanks to you, too, boys."

"Why thank us, Gavrila Spiridonovich? We're not so much working for you as for our country."

"In the name of our country, I also thank you."

"Well, since you have such rights, then thank them," said Uncle Petya.

The man in the linen suit laughed. He left, and Uncle Petya turned the wheelbarrow upside down and began unloading rad-ishes, onions, eggs and smoked sardelle from a satchel.

"Rather a lot for one person," said Sashka in a whisper.

"Shut up," I said, also in a whisper.

The workmen of Uncle Petya's crew were also eating. Almost all of them had brought some new wine with them. It bubbled and foamed in the cut-glass tumblers. After pouring the glasses full the workmen raised them and said, "To your health, Anikin."

"Drink up, boys," answered Uncle Petya.

He did not drink wine himself, but we knew that he did not consider drinking a vice.

We sat quietly with our hands between our knees and watched. Uncle Petya took up a handful of salt from the mound and tossed it between the things he had laid out to eat. Now he was also watching us. It was very difficult to return his gaze, but we did.

"Please come to the table, your honors," said Uncle Petya.

I felt that we should not accept the invitation immediately. Sashka thought otherwise. I didn't have time to blink before he had already sat down by the wheelbarrow. There wasn't anything else to do except sit down, too.

"Why aren't you studying for the exam?" asked Uncle Petya.

"Vit'ka's disappeared somewhere. We've been looking for him half the day," I answered.

"You're looking for him here? They say some king has appeared in town. Plays the balalaika, or something."

"The Hawaiian guitar," corrected Sashka.

"What's this Hawaiian thing? Never heard of it."

"We haven't either. We're planning to go."

"It comes out to a ten spot you've earned so far. And for your help I'll add a five of my own. Is that enough, huh?"

"We didn't do it for money, Uncle Petya, we just did it . . ." I said.

"You don't just do it even under Communism," answered Uncle Petya. He cracked the shell off an egg, salted it and bit off half of it.

Sashka was gobbling down smoked sardelle as if he had come there just for that. I poked him. Sashka turned to me with his mouth open, put a sardelle in it and commenced chewing. I thought his jaws would never stop moving. But finally he swallowed the thing and said, "Uncle Petya, I'm not anti-Semitic. But tell me, why do the parents in Jewish families interfere in the lives of their children?"

"Why are you asking me that?"

"Why not? It's a nightmare. I don't know, did Vit'ka tell you about the school? I told my parents. I told my dad and mom that we were the best of the best. There are no others like us, and there can't be. That's just why the Komsomol is sending us to the school. And so? My highly respected father grabs a strap and my loving mother holds me by the arms . . . It's a nightmare!"

"So your old man couldn't manage alone?" Uncle Petya salted part of a radish.

"What difference does it make whether he could or not? It's simply a disgrace to the whole town," I said.

"So that's it. You came to lecture me . . ."

Uncle Petya lurched backwards so as to get a good look at both of us at once. Sashka put his sardelle down and wiped his hands on his pants.

"Why so violent?"

Naïve question. Uncle Petya ignored it, of course.

"Don't tell me stories about the Jews. Understand?" said Uncle Petya raising a fist at Sashka. His clenched fingers were white from the salt and covered with deep cracks. "I don't need a strap. And no one's going to hold you by the arms."

Uncle Petya understood everything. In our situation the best thing to do was to be silent. But to do that one had to have at least one ounce of common sense. Sashka didn't have it. Instead of keeping quiet, he shouted, "When things are bad for you, when your own parents are poisoning your life, where can you go? To the father of a friend, to a leading man — a *Stakhanovite*."

There was nothing to be done about it; it was hereditary. But perhaps Sashka was shouting from fear? I had no time to decide. Uncle Petya slowly got up, the palms of his hands resting on his knees. Sashka didn't notice anything. Probably, still from fear.

"And if this person doesn't understand you? If he supports not you, but your old-fashioned parents, what can you do then? What?" shouted out Sashka, and at that moment he was very much like his mother.

Uncle Petya slowly sat down. Sashka reacted to everything after the manner of a giraffe. He didn't move away until Uncle Petya was already sitting again.

"Anikin, what are they agitating you about?" asked one of the workmen.

Uncle Petya did not answer.

"In one hour they changed everything all around. And did they ask the parents?" he said. From the lowered corners of his mouth and his heavy arms drooping listlessly on his knees he seemed crushed. But I was mistaken. Uncle Petya had no intention of giving in.

"I began at the wrong end. That's for sure," he said. "I should have started with Pereverzev: he's the one who's stirring up the water. Where's it taking you? You went to school. Ten grades — that's more than most get. And who ever went with a full high-school education to become an officer? Only fools. I got through school after the service. All I can do is be thankful. I learned to read in the army, and I'll be grateful to those who taught me till the end of my days. But there were others: for example, the platoon commander. Two bars he wore — nowadays that would make him a lieutenant. He served well, and he got decorations. But other than his name he couldn't write a thing. He was demobilized for illiteracy. What was the sense of it? What did he fight for? Just to go and twiddle his thumbs somewhere? He went to Moscow to see Voroshilov, and they reinstated him. He tried going to night school, but gave it up. Our teacher tried to talk to him; he was a good man, but it didn't help. 'I ain't edjucated,' he says, 'but I've punched around them that is. And if need be I'll punch 'em some more.' Now this guy is commanding a regiment. No wonder he didn't want to leave the army. But what's pushing you?"

"The time has come to replace the uneducated officers with educated ones. Technical equipment . . ." I said.

"I've heard. So this officer will just let you come and replace him. What does Nadezhda Aleksandrovna say?"

"Mother understands. She says we should be proud of the trust shown us."

"That's her business. She reads the newspapers. But don't go turning my Vit'ka's head. Call him here. There's no point in his hiding from his father."

Sashka and I exchanged glances.

"That's enough hide and seek for now," shouted Uncle Petya.

"Vit'ka!" I called.

Vit'ka moved sideways out from behind the mound. While he was approaching, we were silent. Vit'ka stopped two steps away and looked at his father with a wary eye. Uncle Petya took another string of sardelle and some more eggs out of his satchel.

"What sort of a newfangled idea is this — running out of the house without your lunch?" he asked.

Vit'ka turned away and was silent. His eyes filled with moisture, and I simply couldn't look at him.

"What are you turning away for? Are you sore? You can get sore over what your own father does?"

"I'm not sore at you."

"Well, your mother's not to blame at all. She can't go against my will. Sit down and eat before your friends here clean up everything."

Uncle Petya waited for Vit'ka to sit down with us. "Used a whole kilometer of bandage, no less," he said.

Vit'ka immediately raised his hands and began searching for the knot.

"Leave it!" said Uncle Petya in a loud voice.

Vit'ka ate, we were silent. Mikheich came up and asked, "Shall we start the water going, or quit for the day?"

"This is no time to quit. Look at the way the sun's roasting," said Uncle Petya and got up. The workmen quickly did up their food satchels and bundles. "Wait for me at the first card. And you, go home and study. Come tomorrow, and I'll give you your money," said Uncle Petya to us.

"Well, we had a talk with him. Now let Pereverzev talk to him," said Sashka when Uncle Petya had left.

"Let's wait till tomorrow. The article will appear and everything can change."

"Nothing will change." This was said by Vit'ka.

We were already walking along the shore past the docks. The brass band again played a flourish. This time it was in honor of Zaitsev's crew. He himself was being tossed. He flew up in the air still retaining the serious expression on his face. His white heels glistened on his sunburned legs. Uncle Petya was standing just a short distance away together with the man in the linen suit.

"So long," I said in parting.

"Till tomorrow," said Sashka significantly.

Vit'ka was silent, and, as we were leaving, the man turned to Uncle Petya and said, "They're regular eagles!"

"But with pin feathers on their chests," answered Uncle Petya. He could have left that unsaid, at least.

We walked under the arch. A woman in a blue smock was standing on a ladder taking down the slogans. The salt and the sun caused the red material to disintegrate quickly, and therefore the slogans were taken down after the loading was done.

"Vit'ka, how come you haven't hanged yourself yet?" asked Sashka.

"Why should I hang myself?"

"With a father like that, you could hang yourself five times and drown yourself twice."

"Your mom isn't any better."

"My mom is a different story. She came from a petty bourgeois milieu. With her it's excusable: her psychology is old-fashioned."

I was walking between Vit'ka and Sashka. Vit'ka remained quiet, but this was not the best means of putting off Sashka.

"In your position I would publicly renounce such a father," said Sashka. "Write the newspaper a detailed letter . . ." Sashka didn't have time to finish, for Vit'ka lunged at him behind my back and threw him to the sand.

"Psycho, neurasthenic!" roared Sashka, but Vit'ka stood over him and panted. Then Vit'ka also sat down on the sand and said, "I'm not going anyplace with you."

"You've had your fun now," I said and sat down next to Vit'ka. Now all three of us were sitting. I wanted to say that everything would turn out all right one way or the other, that everything in life works itself out. But just in time I saw how completely out of place my philosophy was and didn't say anything. I saw that things were easier for me than for them. I didn't have to fight for my right to go to the school. I think that for the first time, on those wild beaches by the sea which sparkled all the way out to the edge of the horizon — for the first time I understood that, with all the disorder in my life, I was still living very easily and freely.

"Let's take a swim," I said, and began to undress.

IX

THE table top had formulas written all over it, and it was covered with sketches of little devils. Zhenya's father had tried to rub them

off, but then he gave up. It was easier to plane the boards down
than to break us of the habit of writing on them. Zhenya's mother
was cleverer; she covered the table with an oilcloth, and, when we
came to the garden to study, she took it off. We weren't offended.
On the contrary, if Zhenya's mother forgot to take off the oilcloth,
then one of us reminded her.

I was sitting in a wicker chair with a hole in the back. I always
sat in that chair. For three years no one had tried to usurp my
place. And to be honest about it, I'm the one who poked a hole
in the back. I loved to lean backwards and rock on the back legs.

In school we hadn't been able to finish the project on the new
constitution, but we had been warned that there would be questions about it on the exams. Therefore, while we were at the saltworks, Zhenya and Katya had worked everything through and
now Katya was retelling in her own words about the peculiarities
of the new constitution. She was trying very hard, but I wasn't
listening. Rather, I was listening, but poorly. Inka was bothering
me. I would never admit this to anyone, but I was keeping an eye
on her.

Inka was sitting behind a lilac bush. I saw her head bent over a
book and her legs pressed close together. When we studied, we
sat Inka down separately so she wouldn't bother us. Of course it
was boring for Inka, but what could you do? Whenever she
couldn't stand it any longer she came over and sat down with us.
She always found a pretext for this. But today she hadn't moved
from her place, not even when we arrived from the saltworks.

I looked at Inka's knees and thought that someday I would absolutely have to touch them with my hand. But even without that
I could see that her knees were soft and warm. The hem of her
light blue dress with black polka dots was so tightly stretched over
Inka's legs that it was simply amazing that the material didn't split.
Many were the times I had seen Inka at the beach with no dress
on at all, just a swimming suit, and nothing happened. But yesterday on Coastal Boulevard everything had changed. I thought that
it would pass. But as soon as I caught sight of Inka again, I saw
that nothing had passed. Since the day before my power over Inka
had been seriously shaken. But, on the other hand, her power over
me had immeasurably grown. Inka felt this also. She always sensed

things before I did. Inka was pretending to be absorbed in her reading. Her elbows were resting on her knees, and she had put her fingers into her hair. The shadow of the leaves fell on her, and wherever the sun struck her hair it shone like bronze.

Behind the lilac bush was a bench embedded into the ground. In order for Inka to be as visible as she was she undoubtedly had had to move down to the very edge of the bench. I imagined how uncomfortable it must have been for her to sit there. But she was sitting. When I looked at her I saw an eye sparkle between her fingers.

"Our constitution will be the most democratic," said Katya, and asked: "Why?" She had a habit of asking herself questions. "Because all the citizens of our country, who have reached the age of eighteen, will be able to elect and be elected. There will no longer be disenfranchised people in our country."

Katya was a very thorough girl. Any other girl so thorough would have bored you to death. But with her it didn't matter, and it would never have entered anybody's head to call Katya boring. Katya's gray eyes were always shining, and there were dimples in her cheeks from her constant smiling. In those days all the girls were envious of Katya's dimples, but three years previous to that they had teased her, calling her a "bun."

"So, a priest or a NEP-man can get into the government? I don't agree," pronounced Vit'ka. He was lying on a wooden cot with a pillow under his head. Zhenya had made him lie down as soon as we arrived from the saltworks. He felt awkward, but he stayed there. It was useless to oppose Zhenya — this we knew well. Vit'ka felt especially out of place when Zhenya's mother came out onto the patio and looked at us. Vit'ka blushed and smiled stupidly.

Katya was silent. She so liked to explain things, she was so happy, but now, if you please! Katya was simply at a loss over Vit'ka's question. She always got lost when someone sidetracked her from her train of thought. Katya looked at Sashka. And whom else could she look at? Sashka would immediately come to her rescue in such instances. And so it was this time.

"We know, he doesn't agree," said Sashka. "He doesn't like the part about the priest."

"And you like it?"

"I don't like it either . . . Theoretically he can be elected, but in actuality — who's going to vote for him? Not you, I hope."

"There, you see? Everything is so simple," said Katya. She didn't like it at all when there was any argument.

"You understand, Vit'ka," said Zhenya. "In order for you to be elected, someone has to put forth your candidacy. Who, for example, is going to nominate the Tin Man? And the Tin Man isn't even disenfranchised. Get it?"

I never thought that Zhenya could talk so lovingly to Vit'ka. She always treated him like her own personal, movable property and, in addition, she shouted at him. Zhenya was ill-tempered in general. To understand this all one had to do was look at her thin lips. Zhenya had an elongated face with velvety, almost powdery skin and eyes as black as the night. When my sisters saw Zhenya for the first time, they said that in time she would become a beauty. I don't know. Enough time had passed. As far as I could tell, even Katya was prettier than Zhenya, to say nothing about Inka. We had told Zhenya that she was ill-tempered, but she didn't agree.

"I simply have a strong character," she answered.

She felt that a strong character was necessary for her in order to become a singer. Nonsense! Strength of character hasn't got anything to do with it. The main thing is the voice. And Zhenya had a voice. No one had any doubts about this.

Zhenya was leaning over Vit'ka and talking with him as though none of us were around. What she wanted to express by this is a mystery.

> From bread that's black and a wife who's true
> We've caught the greensickness, so what's there to do,

said Sashka.

"It's none of your business!" answered Zhenya.

"But I still don't agree," said Vit'ka. "Since you can't vote in practice, there's no point in writing about it in the constitution."

That's what condescension will lead to. At any other time Vit'ka wouldn't have dared even to lift a finger against Zhenya.

"No, you just think a bit," said Katya. "Volodya, why are you silent?"

She couldn't manage without me. And as luck would have it I just at that moment had turned to take a look at Inka. And although by then I was looking at Katya, I didn't understand what was going on. Sashka laughed. He was sitting to the left of me, looking me in the face and laughing.

"Socrates said, 'Never have I seen such a blank expression on a face,'" said Sashka.

"You weren't alive then . . ."

"Done?" asked Zhenya.

"We won't be able to review anything." This, of course, was said by Katya.

"As concerns what's serious, let's talk seriously," I said. "It's perfectly clear, like two times two is four. Socialism means complete freedom for all. Everyone receives equal rights to build a Communist society . . ."

"It will be interesting to see how the priests go about their building of Communism."

With Vit'ka it's always like that. You would think that he had to deal with the priests every day. In our whole town there was only one priest, in the Greek church. And even he walked about the streets like everyone else. He wore an ordinary suit, and he even wore a hat to hide his hair — in summer a straw hat and in winter a felt hat.

"The priests are a different group!" I said. "The church in our country is separate from the state. How is it possible to elect a priest to fill a government position?"

"Okay, to hell with the priests. But can the Tin Man be elected?"

"Listen, Vit'ka," I said. "What's your opinion, is it possible to elect your father to the Supreme Soviet?"

"He wouldn't agree to it . . ."

"What do you mean he wouldn't agree?"

"He'd say he hasn't enough education."

"Nonsense! Every scrubwoman should know how to run the government. Your father can't be elected for another reason. Only the most conscientious will be elected to fill government posts."

"Now you're going too far. My father and the Tin Man . . ."

I would sooner have swallowed my tongue than compare Vit'ka's father to the Tin Man.

"Don't interrupt," I said. I had everything so well worked out in my head, and then Vit'ka messed it all up. "I took your father as an example so you would understand, they won't elect just anyone. Everyone will have the same right to elect and be elected. But only those will be elected who have earned the confidence of the people."

"Are there any questions?" asked Sashka. "Logic! I always said that Volod'ka had a head on his shoulders."

Great discovery! Our history teacher way back in the eighth grade said that I had extra-fine perception and understood our era. Of course, she only said this for my mother's benefit. Nonsense! Mother had nothing to do with it. I simply understood everything very well myself.

I glanced around. Inka was looking at me. She smiled and bent down over her book.

"People like the Tin Man should be drowned in the sea and not granted rights," said Vit'ka.

First the priest, now the Tin Man. But I saw from Vit'ka's face that he was just saying that in order to say something. No one likes to admit defeat.

"There's no need to drown him. He'll die of his own accord," I said.

"Well, that's good. Now they've finished," said Katya. "Let's go on some more. Some more about you boys. Our constitution will be the most democratic, also, because those in military service will also take part in the voting. In the capitalistic countries the army does not participate in elections. There the army has nothing to do with politics," said Katya, as if she were reading. Even if she looked at any of us, she still didn't see anyone. This was apparent from her eyes. Katya had an amazing memory. Once she got carried away, she could recite whole pages one after another. Only she couldn't be interrupted from her train of thought.

I looked at Sashka out of the corner of my eye. He was sitting with his eyes closed. His eyes were unusual: they protruded and had short lashes. Even when he was sleeping, his eyes didn't close all the way. From the side it seemed as though he were spying on someone. Sashka was pretending to doze. But I saw right through his game. He had not forgiven me for Socrates and undoubtedly was preparing some sharp comment, just waiting for me to look at

Inka. He needn't take me for a fool. I had absolutely no intention of looking at her. Why should I? I imagined Inka to myself and thought that she was also thinking about me.

Zhenya's neighbor was watering the garden behind the fence. The water was splashing and the woman was monotonously shouting, "Shurka, don't touch the faucet . . ."

Shurka had not yet touched the faucet, and the woman was just shouting, for the sake of prevention. I knew this troublesome kid; once the woman started shouting, it meant that he had turned up some place close by.

Sashka opened first one eye, then the other. But he wasn't looking at me. Sashka's nose turned toward the terrace of Zhenya's house. His nose was also unusual. It was large and thin and could turn like the rudder of a boat. When we were smaller that's what we used to call Sashka's nose — a rudder. Sashka would be offended. After a while we left his nose in peace.

"Fritters!" said Sashka. "We're going to have fritters today."

No matter how I tried I couldn't smell anything other than the lilacs and the moist earth. But Sashka did . . .

"Again you've interrupted," said Katya.

"Go on, go on," said Sashka, looking at me with his protruding eyes. We understood each other very well.

"Go on, go on," I said to him.

Sashka smiled out of the corners of his mouth and again half closed his eyes. He imagined I wouldn't be able to hold out and that sooner or later I would glance around at Inka. I wanted to find out what he had thought up, but it wasn't worth the risk. Now I also smelled the faint odor of cooking olive oil. One could become envious of Sashka's sense of smell. The whole thing was that Sashka was very fond of eating. Between classes he didn't leave the room. He would unhurriedly sniff the girls' school bags to determine what they had brought for lunch. He was fussy about this. He never took some of everything, but was selective about it, and then he would not take all of that, but just half. However, when someone snitched a whole lunch from one of the girls, Sashka was more indignant about it than anyone else.

Sashka's friendship with Katya also began in connection with lunches. Sashka was very fond of French rolls with butter and

liver sausage. As soon as Katya noticed this, Sashka began to find
a separate package for himself in her school bag every day. One
had to be a hardened egoist in order not to appreciate Katya's good
nature. Sashka appreciated it. But there was one thing we did not
understand: where did everything go that Sashka gobbled down?
He was half a head taller than Vit'ka and me. But he was so thin
that going to the beach with him was simply embarrassing. Vit'ka
explained it as having to do with a low coefficient of healthful
activity. Vit'ka was seldom successful with his witticisms and
therefore often repeated the good ones. Sashka fumed. But inasmuch as he didn't give any other explanation, Vit'ka's remained in
force.

The neighbor's Shurka at last got to the faucet. The splashing of
the water ceased on the other side of the fence, and the woman
shouted in a piercing voice, "Shurka, I'll rip your ears off!"

X

ZHENYA's father came in through the gate. But I had caught sight
of his uniform cap over the picket fence beforehand. Zhenya's
father had an amazing way of walking. First he would jerk his heel
up, then the toe of his shoe, and he did this with such intensity that
from the side it seemed as if he were practically jumping. His cap
bobbed up and down the same way above the fence.

Zhenya's father was carried several steps beyond the gate by the
sheer inertia of his entrance, and then he stopped.

Our relations with Zhenya's father were very complex. He
worked as an agent of the housing bureau. In the morning, before
the train arrived, he went to the station, ran along the platform
and shouted:

"Best rooms in town! Suit any taste and any pocketbook!"

Of course he wasn't the only one . . . there were about ten
other agents running around there too. But Zhenya's father was
more agile than the others. He had his addresses written down in a
fat little notebook. *He* rented out the rooms, but *we* found the
addresses for him. We also ran. We wandered unselfishly about the
whole town and found out where comfortable rooms were being
let. On especially successful days Zhenya's father gave us money
for ice cream.

At noon the agents met at Popandopoulo's wine shop. At the bar they looked like bosom friends who had gotten together for a drink. But we saw them not only at Popandopoulo's — we met them during "work" at the train station, and therefore we knew that friends they were not. With our help Zhenya's father earned more than the rest. He often treated the other agents, and they somehow remained at peace with him. On the other hand they despised us. But we didn't care a damn about that. If you look at it from the nation's point of view, then what difference does it make which agent rents how many rooms? The main thing was to provide the resort guests with living quarters. We looked at it from the nation's point of view, and therefore our consciences were at ease.

When we were smaller, we got along well with Zhenya's father. But from the moment he guessed about Zhenya's friendship with Vit'ka, everything changed. Vit'ka, in his opinion, was insufficiently cultured. In the past Zhenya's father had been a comic actor. In general, failures are difficult people. But actors or writers who are failures are simply unbearable. Zhenya's father didn't say anything directly against Vit'ka — he was afraid of Zhenya. But we saw clearly that he could not stand him. As soon as we understood this we immediately ceased helping Zhenya's father. Vit'ka attempted, secretly from us, to find addresses for him, but we would not put up with such groveling. Zhenya's father was vexed with all of us. That was his affair! We understood that children are one thing and that parents are another. This had been well demonstrated by Pavlik Morozov.

Zhenya's father stood on the path and watched. Under his high cap with its wide top of paper covert cloth his narrow face, which was entirely covered with heavy, deep wrinkles, seemed quite small. How he was able to shave was a mystery. He looked each one of us over in turn, and then he stared at Vit'ka. Vit'ka put his feet down off the cot, but Zhenya held him by the shoulders and would not let him get up. She turned full around toward her father and shielded Vit'ka with her back. It was like the scene from *The Inspector General* where everyone freezes to the spot! Katya was the only one not to notice anything. She was sitting with her back to the gate and saying, "The Supreme Soviet of the U.S.S.R. is divided into two chambers: the Soviet of Unions and the Soviet of Nationalities . . ."

She didn't catch sight of Zhenya's father until he was already on the patio.

"We haven't finished yet," said Katya.

"We know everything," Sashka assured her.

It was true: we knew the draft of the constitution very well. But it was a rule with us to review before every examination. Usually we studied until six o'clock in the evening and got through everything. After six o'clock none of us had the right even to mention exams. Everyone looked at me.

"This has been quite a day," I said. "An all-round parents' demonstration."

Zhenya got up and ran into the house.

"Fine attitude some fathers have taken, they don't even say hello," said Sashka.

"Shut up," said Vit'ka, who was now sitting on the cot with his head turned toward the house. Vit'ka couldn't stand it when anybody offended Zhenya. When that happened he became really dangerous. In the house everything was quiet. Only once we heard Zhenya say, "You have no right!"

We roughly guessed what sort of conversation was taking place in the house. But we were persons with finesse, and the highest manifestation of finesse was not to notice what did not concern us.

I placed my hands on the arms of the chair and raised myself up. As I walked over to Inka she looked at me and smiled. I also smiled — at what I don't know. Inside I felt as if I had never yet spoken with Inka. The same thing had happened to me when I answered her note and then went to her birthday party. But even then it was not the same. To be sure, I was smiling then for some unknown reason, also. But at that time I was excited in a different way.

Inka sat back on the bench. I glanced at the open schoolbook on her knees. When we arrived from the saltworks it was open at the very same page — I remembered it well.

"It's the wind," said Inka. "The breeze turned the pages back."

Water was splashing in the neighbor's garden again, and Shurka was howling at the fence.

"There's a breeze in your bonnet," I said. I didn't want to scold Inka, and I said that out of habit.

"True, true. Do you know how much I read? This much." Inka didn't know how to lie at all. She turned the pages very quickly, then covered them with her hand and laughed.

"I still have a whole day tomorrow," she said. "You yourself said what a day this has been."

Shurka was no longer howling; he was probably listening.

Inka stood up and her book slipped along her legs onto the ground. She didn't even think of picking it up. Inka looked at me and smiled. In my opinion, she knew what she was smiling about. She put her hands behind her neck and stretched. I squatted down on my haunches and felt the warmth from her legs on my face. I didn't hurry in picking up the book. But I couldn't just sit on my haunches forever. Even so, I don't know how long I sat that way. At such moments you never know how much time has gone by.

I looked around. Zhenya's mother was carrying a dish full of golden fritters. Sashka hurriedly took all the books off the table and without looking shoved them at Katya. Sashka, like Caesar, could do several things simultaneously. But he could not look at both the fritters and me at the same time. Sashka was looking at the fritters . . . and I got up.

"Thank you," said Inka quietly, but she didn't take the book from me. Inka turned and went to the table. I followed her and, like a stupid fool, carried the book with me.

"Where shall I sit?" Inka asked, and ran to the patio.

"Aunt Vera, may I get a chair?" she shouted. Inka felt at home everywhere.

XI

"Eat as many as you want, now," said Aunt Vera. "He had some difficulties at work" — she smoothed the oilcloth with her puffy hand — "but you go ahead and eat. Don't pay any attention . . ."

"We're eating, Aunt Vera, don't worry," said Sashka.

"It's nothing to worry about — anything can happen at work," Vit'ka said.

"Well, that's good. Is the jam sweet enough?

"Of course, Aunt Vera. The fritters are very delicious. They just melt in your mouth," said Katya.

The fritters really did "melt." Our hands reached out to the dish from all sides. Sashka was licking off the jam as it ran from his fritter, and he was chomping disgustingly.

"Sashka, stop chomping," I said.

"I've been chomping all my life. Since I was born."

Zhenya was sitting between Vit'ka and her mother. She put her elbow on the oilcloth, placed her cheek on the palm of her hand and stared off into space. When Zhenya was like that, it was better not to bother her. Aunt Vera knew that as well as we did. But the majority of mothers are apparently built that way, they can't leave their children alone.

"Dear, why aren't you eating? Come on, have a fritter. Look, here's a nice crispy one."

"Will the happy day ever come when I can finally go away?" asked Zhenya in a tragic voice. "Please understand, I'm not a little girl. You understand, I'm not a little girl!" Zhenya actually screamed.

I can't stand it when there's a storm in a glass of water. It was necessary to interfere, but I could not think of anything to say. For some reason I suddenly became dumb. And it was all because Inka had found my hand under the table and was quietly playing with my fingers. Even I did not notice her do it. She had put her hands under the table, and, to prevent anyone from noticing, she leaned forward onto the edge of the table. She didn't look at me. I didn't look at her either.

"Small children — tiny sorrow. Big children — big sorrow," said Sashka and dispatched the rest of a fritter into his mouth.

"The truth," said Aunt Vera.

"You can't imagine how clever my grandmother is," said Sashka. "When my mom does something wrong, Grandma always says, 'small children — tiny sorrow.' But my mom doesn't listen. And here I have to listen to my mom, but she doesn't. Where's the logic of that?"

"Oh, you!" Aunt Vera swung her hand at Sashka and laughed.

Sashka scratched the back of his head with his greasy fingers and stared at the empty dish.

"Aunt Vera," he said. "Zhenya won't eat her fritter anyway. Give it to me . . ."

"Here, eat it," said Aunt Vera as she got up from the table. With her bulk this was not simple to do, because the bench, as well as the table, was embedded in the ground. When Aunt Vera had reached the patio I said, "Sashka, you're a genius."

Sashka nodded his head. He couldn't give a verbal answer because he was chewing the fritter.

"Don't be upset," said Vit'ka. He was holding Zhenya by the hand in plain sight. "We're the ones at fault since we stopped helping your father. It's surely not easy for a man his age to run all over town the way he does."

"You don't know what he said to me in the house, do you? You don't know, so be quiet."

"He said . . . Well, what of it, what he said. At least he didn't hit you."

"What he said wasn't enough. He did hit me . . ."

Sashka finished the fritter and asked, "I wonder if Pereverzev is still alive?"

"I'll go," said Vit'ka.

"You'll go nowhere alone. We'll all go with you."

"Of course, we'll go with you," said Sashka. "And don't look at me that way. Do you think I'm a fritter or something . . . ?"

XII

WE were waiting for Zhenya in the street. Vit'ka had opened the gate and was looking down the path.

The poplar trees in Zhenya's street were unlike any others in the whole town. When they bloomed the whole street became covered with down. The layer of down muffled the footsteps of passersby. At night it seemed as if there was snow lying on the street. And when the wind blew it turned into a real blizzard. In itself the street looked very beautiful, but to live on it while the poplars were in bloom was not very pleasant.

From all indications the evening would be warm. Not one leaf was moving on the poplars, and there was no sound coming from the sea. And we were separated there from the sea only by the row of houses on the next street. The trees were enveloped in shadow below, but the sun still shone on the tops of them. We were standing in the shadow, but we could still feel the warmth of the sun.

"Tomorrow at this time we shall be completely free," said Katya. "Only I'm sorry to leave school."

"You can stay for another year," advised Sashka.

"You're crazy."

"Boy, what consistency! She's sorry to leave school, but she doesn't want to stay on for another year. What difference does it make to you? We selected just the institute for you."

Sashka was exaggerating: *we* didn't select the institute for Katya, *he* did. For a long time Katya didn't know where she would go on to school. But then she met Sashka, and it just came about of its own accord that she also would go to medical school. With Katya's memory there was no problem in memorizing the names of three thousand bones and several hundred muscles. If that was all there was to it then Katya could become a doctor in a week. Sashka said, "With Katya's memory and my erudition I shall be a professor in five years, and she'll be my assistant." Katya was not offended. I suspected that in general she was unable to take offense at anything. Such fortunate people do exist.

"There's nothing to it, really," said Katya. "Everything has turned out very well. My sister says that there are volunteer doctors in the service. During a war one of you definitely will be wounded, and I shall cure you."

Katya's sister worked as a waitress in the floating restaurant, and previously she had worked in a dining room for airmen. She, of course, knew whether there were volunteer doctors in the service or not.

"Did you ever see such brains?" asked Sashka. "But her heart? Did you ever see such a heart? We haven't even passed our last exams yet, and she's already dreaming about when one of us gets wounded."

"That's if there's a war," said Katya.

Inka, with her hands behind her back, was surveying the poplars. She threw her head back and stood with one leg crossing the other. Whenever Inka looked at something attentively it meant that the conversation interested her a great deal, but that she didn't want to admit it.

"She's coming," said Vit'ka, and he walked away from the gate.

Zhenya came out. We set off up the street. We usually walked with the girls in front and us about two steps behind them. But this did not disturb our conversation.

"Now tell us actually; what did you agree on with Uncle Petya?" asked Zhenya.

"Volodya, what did we agree on?"

"We already told you: nothing. He told us not to turn Vit'ka's head."

"We heard that . . . He's not planning to hit Vit'ka anymore, is he?"

"I advise you to ask Uncle Petya himself about that. At least he wanted to hit me. Volodya will back me up. If I hadn't stopped him with a glance, I would have been assured of a black eye. I looked him straight in the eye, and he saw that it was dangerous to strike me."

I dropped back a bit and observed Sashka's pants from the rear. Sashka became uneasy.

"What is it?" he asked, trying to see what was on the back of his pants.

"No, there's nothing," I said. "I was just looking to see if there were any holes. You crawled away so quickly that there might be some there."

"Nonsense. You don't need to worry about my pants."

"That's enough," said Zhenya. "It's impossible to talk seriously with you."

"These serious people should be drowned in the sea," answered Sashka. "What can I say about someone else's old man? I can't even vouch for my own."

"He won't fight anymore," said Vit'ka. "He wouldn't have hit me. Mother did me in."

"And he's going to see Pereverzev?" asked Zhenya.

"He's probably already there. It would be better if he hit me once more."

"Enough," I said. "Alyosha has been warned. He's no fool, and he's left the office long ago. And tomorrow the article will appear, and everything will be all right. Let's go see Alyosha on the way, and we'll find out everything."

"What article?" asked Zhenya.

My tongue had come unhinged. I don't even know myself how that had slipped out. And Zhenya had pricked up her ears, and even her eyes had grown narrow.

"What article?" she asked again.

Perhaps I could have wormed my way out of it, if Sashka hadn't crawled in too.

"Curious, which one of us is the biggest babbler?" he said.

There was nothing to do but tell about the article. And we had wanted it to be a surprise for everyone.

Zhenya lived on the outskirts of the Old Section, two blocks from the Dunes. I envied Vit'ka because Zhenya's house was on his way home, and I had to walk Inka across almost the whole town. During the summer this was even pleasant. It was something else during the winter, when the northeasters were blowing. While Inka was with me it was still bearable, but walking home alone I was always angry, as if Inka were responsible for the fact that the Airmen's Center was located at the health resort.

Inka walked along the edge of the sidewalk. She glanced back, then jumped and tore a leaf off a poplar tree. Then she glanced back again. She gave me a quick look as though I had offended her somehow. Suddenly it occurred to me that she would soon be walking home alone and that, in general, she would be alone for two whole years. I looked at Inka and simply could not believe that I could be angry at her for living so far away from me. I caught up with her and said quietly, "Three years — that's not five . . ."

Inka listened with her head down.

"Of course," she said.

We came upon a vacant stretch of sand. The asphalt had ended, and the twilight of the street was replaced by sunlight scattered high in the air.

"Look, it's almost as if it were still day," said Katya.

The rails of the streetcar circle glistened with crimson reflections. In town the tracks were level with the streets, but here they lay on open ties with wormwood growing between them. For the third time that day I was walking across this vacant stretch of sand which separated the Old Section from the Dunes.

We turned into a wide street. During the day it was empty except for the sun, short shadows, and chickens. There was a line of people standing near a fountain, waiting for water. The water was carted away in barrels on handcarts, with the wheels sinking deeply into the sand. Every now and then acquaintances would strike up a conversation with Vit'ka. They were intrigued by his bandaged eye. Zhenya stood and waited while they talked to him. Inka walked on ahead and peered into the yards. Outdoor cooking fires were burning on the other side of the low fences, and there was the smell of smoke and fried fish in the air. Before, I had never paid any attention to Inka's way of walking. She pointed her toes straight ahead, and her shoes left narrow footprints in the sand.

We arrived at Alyosha's house. His sister was scrubbing the patio. The girls in the Dunes were famous for their beauty and dashing spirit, but Nyura even stood out among them. She was no older than we were, but she had already managed to go through one marriage with a sailor and return home again. Alyosha did not have a high opinion of his sister. And I suppose he knew better — he was her brother.

"Has Alyosha come home yet?" asked Vit'ka.

Nyura straightened up and dropped the hem of her skirt which she had tucked up above her knees.

"Just so you won't go blind," she said, and laughed. She apparently was dying to have a chat.

"What do you want Alyosha for?" she asked.

"We need to see him . . ."

"Maybe so, but he's not here. He hasn't come home yet. Why do you need him?"

Sashka put his hands on the fence and asked, "Do you have any iodine?"

"Iodine? Yes . . . What do you want iodine for?" Nyura looked at Vit'ka's face and smiled, and her eyes, which were changeable like the color of the sea, squinted suspiciously.

"So you have iodine; but how about eye wash?"

"Eye wash? What for?"

"No eye wash? Then I advise you to buy some. You can get it

at a pharmacy," said Sashka and returned to us . . . we were standing on the corner waiting for him.

We turned off into a narrow lane with disturbed feelings.

"That's a happy story: Alyosha hasn't come back yet," said Sashka.

No one answered him. We came out into Vit'ka's street. The houses on it stood in a single row. The street extended out toward the sea but ended in a cluster of steep sand dunes. The sea glistened in the distance, but down below near the shore the early rays of twilight were growing cold over the wild stretch of beach. The closer we came to Vit'ka's house the more agitated Vit'ka was. He was walking ahead, and every now and then he glanced back, angry that we were lagging behind. I had fallen behind because of Inka. She was gazing at the sea, and I could see the sad oval of her cheek. I know that an oval can be neither happy nor sad, but that's the way it seemed to me. I was sure that Inka was thinking of other things besides Vit'ka's father, but I could not understand why she was sad.

Vit'ka's house was the last one on the street. It had been built two years before, and, while it was under construction, Vit'ka and his parents lived at first in town in a private apartment and, later, in a temporary building which had been thrown together overnight. We helped build the house. We mixed all the clay which went into the plastering with our feet. During the day Katya and Zhenya came — Inka was not with us yet. We went down to the sea and bathed and then Aunt Nastya — Vit'ka's mother — fed us dinner which she prepared on a fireplace made out of sandstone. The dinner smelled of smoke and seemed very tasty to us. Then Vit'ka's father came home from work with his fellow crewmen. He looked over everything we had done and said, "Fine, boys. You're not eating your bread for nothing." Satisfied, we went into town, and Uncle Petya and his crew worked on the house till midnight. The street at that time was quite narrow. During the last three years the sea has washed up sand dunes during storms, and now the street is wider.

Aunt Nastya was standing in the open gate. She was watching Vit'ka and buttoning and unbuttoning a button on her cotton jacket. Aunt Nastya was quite young, and it was hard to believe that Vit'ka was her son.

"Is Father home?" asked Vit'ka.

"He went out. He came home from work, changed into clean clothes and went out again." Aunt Nastya was staring at Vit'ka's face, and she seemed not to notice us at all. That was a bad sign. We walked over to the edge of the street, but we could still hear everything.

"Please forgive me, son. I didn't want to. I'm sorry for your father, and I'm sorry for you. You two have got me coming and going. Does your eye hurt? Does it pain you?" Aunt Nastya looked up into Vit'ka's face and with agile fingers rearranged the bandage which had slipped down over his cheek.

"You can bet it hurts. But what of it, haven't I had shiners before?" answered Vit'ka. He glanced at us out of the corner of his eye and almost backed away from his mother's hands. We pretended to be admiring the sea. The water was a display of colors: lilac, crimson, and violet — all in various shades and hues. The colors were stretched across the water in separate streaks, and in the distance the sea was aflame with the glow of the no longer visible sun.

Sashka turned around and brushed against my shoulder.

"Here comes Uncle Petya," he said.

Uncle Petya was walking down the middle of the street in a black suit made out of coarse material. He used to arrive in this suit at school on Saturdays. He passed through the gate right between his wife and son without glancing at them. Aunt Nastya and Vit'ka followed him. At the steps Uncle Petya stopped and stretched out his left hand. Aunt Nastya hurried up to him, and he lowered his hand onto her shoulder. They walked up the steps to the small covered patio in this manner and then entered the house. And as Uncle Petya was mounting the steps, the dry boards creaked under his feet. Before going into the house Uncle Petya stopped and said loudly, "Remember, Nastya, three men will say, 'You are drunk — lie down and sleep, although you haven't had a sniff of wine.'" Uncle Petya was presumably speaking to Aunt Nastya, but we understood whom he had in mind. We went up to the fence.

"Aunt Nastya is not like a mother at all," said Katya. Katya often spoke out of place. We were used to it, and didn't pay any attention to what she said.

Vit'ka came out onto the patio and said, "I'm staying home."

"What happened?" asked Zhenya.

Vit'ka came down the steps and over to the fence.

"I don't know myself . . ."

"Did he say anything?" asked Sashka.

"On the patio he said something about a drunk. He asked for some supper and hasn't said anything else."

"That was an aphorism," said Sashka.

"All right, but go now. Zhenya, don't be offended, but I can't see you home right now."

"Of course — am I stupid? Come and see me tomorrow when you get up. You get up at six, so come at six . . ."

"Your father won't make a scene?"

"Nonsense. Just let him try . . ."

We never paid any attention to her father's frame of mind and were completely uninterested in what he thought about us. Nor did the shouts of Sashka's mother affect me. But here, before Uncle Petya, I felt guilty of something. There was no use repeating to myself that we were in no way to blame for anything with regard to Uncle Petya — inside I still felt badly, as if I had committed some crime. I could tell from Sashka's face that he wasn't himself either.

Vit'ka stood at the fence until we turned the corner.

"It's infuriating. He's taking his last exam tomorrow, and they're getting him all upset," said Zhenya.

"You often become infuriated. You were also shouting at Vit'ka yesterday on the beach because of school," said Sashka.

"Nonsense. I wasn't shouting at all. I simply said that they might send him to a town where there's no conservatory."

"Right. Just where are they sending you? To what town? To what school? We really don't even know anything," said Katya.

"They don't know, but we do! No one has even told us anything about it," said Sashka.

"Let's go see Alyosha," I said when we came out onto the wide street.

Some boys were trying to fly a kite — an unrewarding task on such a calm day. A boy in a torn shirt was shouting in a piercing voice, "Hold it higher, higher!" He stopped in order to shout louder, and, in his excitement, he raised first one leg then the other. His playmate in the next block was holding the kite over his head, and he also was shouting, "Well, you pull it. My arms are worn-out . . ."

While watching the boys I began to feel easier inside. Even now, whenever I come across young boys, it makes life happier to live. Some well-fed cats were sitting on the fences, and, without blinking their green eyes, they were staring out to sea where the small black dots of fishing boats were visible. The girls from the Dunes were walking toward the streetcar circle. They always went to town alone. The kids from the Dunes gave them a bad time, and they pestered their boy friends even more, but the girls from the Dunes were not the sort one could frighten.

We met Nyura on the corner. She was walking barefoot in a stylish crepe de chine dress and was carrying her patent leather slippers in her hand.

"Your chief arrived. Go quickly before he leaves," she said.

Alyosha probably saw us from the window because he was already standing on the porch, barefoot and without a shirt, when we came up to the house. He tossed his hair back and said, "Everything is all right, professors. Don't miss tomorrow's paper."

Alyosha clearly wished to get rid of us. We knew his tricks very well. The newspaper interested us at the moment least of all. I went through the gate up to the patio, and Sashka remained with the girls on the sidewalk.

"All right is all right. Tell me what your conversation with Vit'ka's father was like," I said and sat down on one of the patio steps.

Alyosha tried to pass it off in jest.

"You're demanding an account? There are still two months before the conference takes place. Be patient," he said.

"What was your conversation like with Vit'ka's father?"

"Persistent, aren't you. It was very ordinary. Kolesnikov explained to Anikin that one should not sail against the waves during a storm or else one would be capsized."

"We asked you not to make a scene out of it."

"There wasn't any scene. But we will not allow a political campaign to be disrupted."

"What campaign? What's this got to do with a campaign?"

"So you want to be educated in the facts of political life? Then let us begin. You know what the international situation is like. We have to lure the youth into the army. You are the most outstanding students of your class. Next year others will follow you to the school. Understand?"

"I understand. We're the most outstanding students. But why offend Vit'ka's father?"

"Let him be offended with himself. We shall not allow anyone to disrupt a political campaign. Is that clear? Now trot on home. I haven't had supper yet."

"We'll go home, but there was no need to insult Uncle Petya," I said and went to the gate.

"Which shirt shall I iron? The blue one?" Alyosha's mother asked from the house.

"Just one more question," shouted Sashka. "To what town and to what school are we going?"

"We'll go wherever they send us . . ."

Alyosha went into the house. When I came out through the gate Sashka said, "You asked that one properly . . ."

The talk with Alyosha did not improve our mood. We saw Zhenya home and then took a streetcar. The streetcar was too crowded, and its brakes screeched on the descent. We pushed Inka and Katya onto the platform, and we ourselves hung on the steps. Inka held me by the arm above the elbow. She squeezed my tensed bicep in her fingers as though she feared I would run away. The streetcar slowly crawled downhill. The poles of the street lights were hidden among the trees, and the lights burning in the foliage looked like pale egg yolks. The stores were closing, and salesclerks in smocks were lowering the night-screens down over the fronts of the stores with hooks.

We got off on Coastal Boulevard. People were wandering along the shore from one end to the other, sitting on benches in the ice cream pavilion, talking and laughing. This produced a light, happy din which hung in the air along the shore. Close up the various separate noises could be distinguished, but in the distance they all blended into one, and this was interspersed once in a while with bursts of laughter here and snatches of conversation there. That evening stocks and aromatic tobacco were in bloom. Their pungent, strong odor hung in the air as the smell of expensive perfume does when a beautiful, but no longer young woman passes by. For some reason the majority of women over thirty wear a lot of perfume.

We lost Sashka and Katya and had no intention of looking for them. We quite immediately forgot about them. The two of us walked together against the stream of passersby, and, when we became separated, we hurried to join each other again. Inka became bored with this way of walking. She walked around a man and woman who had separated us and took me by the arm. I pressed the palm of her hand with my elbow. We had never before walked this way, and I was afraid to look at Inka. My attention was rather suddenly drawn to something I had not noticed before — the men who passed us were staring at Inka. She was wearing a stylish dress and flats which were custom-made by a well-known Greek shoemaker in town, and she walked calmly by under their persistent gazes. I was walking next to her in wrinkled cotton pants with baggy knees, brown canvas shoes with leather toes and a checkered cowboy shirt which was faded and smelled of perspiration. I began intercepting their looks and grinned insolently at them. A noise arose in my ears, and it took me a while to realize that it was the pounding of my own heart.

It was not very dark yet on the shore, but pale rays of light had already begun to emanate from the street lamps.

"Do you want me to be a doctor?" asked Inka.

"Were you thinking about that while we were standing near Zhenya's house?"

"Yes. How did you guess?"

I didn't know myself. It just came by itself. It happened every once in a while that I would suddenly see everything clearly.

"You felt very lonely when we were looking at the poplars, didn't you?"

"I did. But how did you guess?"

"I was thinking that, after we leave, you would be left all alone. But the rest came to me just now."

"So you want me to be a doctor?"

"Yes, I do. But, you know, you have a hard time with chemistry and zoology."

"You think I'm stupid or something. I'm not stupid at all. I'm very talented. You yourself said I was talented."

"You're talented. But your head is full of feathers."

"It isn't feathers. I'm just bored. How many times I've said to myself that this is it, and I shall sit down to work. But then I get bored again. Am I to blame for being bored? I don't want to be bored."

We hadn't noticed that the shore had ended and that we were walking along Stalin Street. This was the main street of the town. It used to be called Simferopol' Street because Simferopol' highway began from it. It was renamed not long ago, and there had been a meeting about it in town. But for a long time people still used the old name. They couldn't get used to the new one.

It was dark. The branches of the acacia touched the roofs of the houses and covered the sky. Street lights were burning on the corners, but the light from them had difficulty in penetrating the thick foliage. Once in a while streetcars passed by all lit up, and then it became immediately visible how many people there were on the street. But they didn't bother us. On the contrary. From the talking and laughter going on in the darkness right beside us we felt less inhibited.

"Inka, why do you like me?"

As soon as I said it I grew deaf from the din in my ears.

"I don't know. Why do you ask?"

I didn't know either. That was something probably no one knows. But I wanted to know.

"You're so pretty, and I scold you all the time . . ."

"Am I really pretty?" she asked, and I felt the warmth of Inka's cheek on my shoulder.

"Very pretty. Everybody on the boulevard turned around and stared at you."

"I know . . ."

"How's that? You weren't looking to the side."

"I just pretend not to look. Actually I notice everything. My eyes probably are just made that way. I look straight ahead, but I notice everything: how people are dressed, what they look like and how they look at me."

I put my hand on Inka's fingers which were still squeezing my elbow. And we walked on and were silent, and we no longer knew how long we had been walking. I took my hand away whenever we passed by a street light, and then I again took hold of Inka's fingers, and they were so tender and soft that it actually became painful for me when I squeezed them.

We passed through a small public garden and crossed a square. Beyond the square began the health resort. It stretched all the way to the Maynaks — a series of saltwater lakes. There was a vacant field to the right of us in the darkness. For two years the town had been trying to build a stadium on it, but so far had set up only the football goals. A passing streetcar lit up the freshly cut crossbeams. And on the left, behind low limestone walls, rose the dark cupolas of the sanatorium parks.

We turned down Morskaya Street. It was three blocks to Inka's house, and we walked more slowly. From morning to night the street was full of people, since it was one way of getting to the beach. But at that moment there was no one on the street besides us.

"A man is interesting because of his future, but a woman is interesting because of her past," said Inka. "It's true, it's true, I read it in some book. What do you think? What does 'past' mean?"

I didn't think one way or the other. Thinking was the last thing I wanted to do. But I was used to answering Inka's questions, no matter what they might be. The main thing was to begin and then something always popped into my head.

"You have a future," said Inka. "You will achieve everything you want. You are very clever, and you can do everything. Mama and Papa also say that. They say that you're still a boy, but that you have a great future ahead of you. So, you're interesting. But what sort of a past do I have? None . . ."

"Inka, why do you want a past? You also have a future. In the beginning all there is is the future. And afterwards it becomes the past. In my opinion the future is more interesting."

The synthetic soles of Inka's flats clopped against the asphalt pavement of the street, but my steps couldn't be heard, since my shoes with their worn-down heels had rubber soles.

There were lights on in the windows of a five-story house behind an iron fence. The house had three entrances and above each one of them a lamp was burning. The light shone through the thick foliage of the trees onto the street, and the iron fence glittered in the dark.

"Imagine that this is our house. Not mine, but ours. Understand? We have been to a concert and have come home . . . That's only the future, right? And you say the future's more interesting. I wish that everything was the past and that you were through with school . . ."

"You've talked about that already."

"Well, what if I did talk about it. I could talk about it all the time."

Two people passed under the street lamp on the corner — a man and a woman.

"I completely forgot," said Inka. "Mama's home alone. Papa's on a night flight, and Mama's at home alone. You know how she dislikes being alone, when Papa is on night flights."

I played with Inka's fingers and was silent. The two people were getting closer. In the darkness the woman's heels clopped lightly and hollowly on the asphalt and next to her came the shuffling of the man's heavy steps. The footsteps of both of them were unhurried and even.

"Such a night was made for love. Are you still angry?" asked the man.

"No, I'm just tired," answered the woman.

As they walked along the fence, spots of light fell on them. They passed by us but we couldn't see their faces. A few steps later there was no one visible, but the smell of perfume hung in the air.

"Let's go back to the sea," said the man.

"No. Everything seems so insignificant by the sea."

Their voices grew distant.

"But I stop feeling insignificant only when I'm in the sea," said the man. We couldn't hear the woman's words, but perhaps she didn't answer him.

"Was that the Tin Man?"

"I think so. It sounded like his voice, anyway."

"Let's go to the sea, shall we? It's all right if Mama's alone. Shall we go?"

"No." The voice was mine. But I wasn't the one who said it. I didn't want Inka to leave.

"Then see me to the door."

I shoved the gate with my shoulder, and it opened easily. We walked along the asphalt path between the flower beds towards Inka's entrance. Inka was holding me by the hand, and, if her mother were looking out the window then, she would have seen us. Inka was also thinking about this.

"It's all right," she said. She opened the door with her free hand and lightly pulled me along after her. The door slammed with a thud, and we became surrounded by the noise-sensitive quiet of the empty stairs. Light trickled down from the second floor, and the stone steps glistened. Inka was no longer beside me, but I saw her eyes shining behind the stairs. I didn't remember her leaving me. Her arms were raised. I don't know how I guessed that because I couldn't see her arms. Her hot and slightly moist hands pressed against my ears, and her lips touched mine. I felt as though I were falling, and I would surely have fallen if my back had not struck against a water heating pipe.

"Does it hurt?"

I didn't recognize her voice. The blow didn't bother me at all, but I felt a pang from the sound of Inka's voice which was alarmed, devoted and tender. My recollection of everything that I did afterwards is very dim. I remember only the sensation of what happened. Inka's arms were resting on my shoulders, but I didn't feel their weight. At that moment I was hugging her legs and touched her knee with my lips; it was soft and warm, as I had imagined there in Zhenya's garden.

"I'll fall," said Inka. Her lips almost touched my ear. It's amazing how much the sound of the voice can say, much more than words. By the sound of her voice Inka had said, "I'm afraid of falling, but you needn't pay any attention to that, if you wish." Everything immediately got back into place, and I again felt my power over Inka. I let go of her legs and stood up. Somewhere upstairs a door slammed.

"That's on the fifth floor," said Inka.

We went to the foot of the stairs, and Inka put her hand on the bannister.

"Don't you dare wear such short dresses anymore."

"But everyone wears them . . ."

"No, not everyone, Zhenya doesn't . . ."

"Zhenya doesn't have pretty legs . . ."

"And yours are too pretty."

"And is that bad? When you really want me to, then tell me, and I won't wear short dresses anymore. Tell me truthfully, you don't want me to?"

I don't know myself what I wanted. I didn't even know whether I wanted Inka to obey me implicitly as she had before.

"Tomorrow let's go down to the *kursaal*. Study till six, and at six I'll drop by for you."

"You didn't answer me."

"Tomorrow I'll tell you."

"No, tonight," she said. Her hand was white against the bannister, and I kissed it. I don't know myself how that got into my head. Someone was slowly coming down the stairs. He stopped and struck a match, probably for a smoke. Inka also listened.

"He's still far away," she said.

"Go . . ."

Inka went up one step, then the next. She had her face turned to me, and her hands were slowly working their way up the bannister. Then she turned and ran up the stairs. Whenever I climbed stairs, I always took several steps at once. Inka ran up, one step at a time, which filled the whole stairwell with noise from the bottom to the top. Inka simply couldn't live without noise.

translated by COLLYER BOWEN

A Summer Rain from the Sea

GALINA KORNILOVA

❄ ❄ ❄ ❄

In the courtyard a young girl is sitting on some logs piled up near the sheds. She has light-colored wavelike braids, a thoughtful air, and in profile looks like the French movie actress Simone Signoret. Tol'ka Suchkov comes out of the neighboring house into the courtyard. He looks at the girl with curiosity and hidden anxiety, but she raises her blue eyes — and in them there is a cold, wise mockery.

I am the one sitting on those logs. My hair is straight and short, my nose is shapeless, and I have gray, widely set eyes. When Tol'ka Suchkov comes out into the courtyard, I turn away so he won't notice how I blush. And if Tol'ka asks me something, I answer him quickly and in monosyllables, and then I turn away again. Apparently he considers me a shallow and stupid person.

But what do I care what Tol'ka Suchkov thinks of me? I know very well what he is like — I can imagine. Even with the adults in our house he speaks in a haughty manner, screwing up his eyes mockingly and condescendingly. Any girl who starts bawling when she is accidentally hit by a ball, he won't allow in the ball game. When our boys start arguing over something, it always ends up the way Tol'ka Suchkov wants it to. He's like an uncrowned king in our courtyard. But, in spite of this, I know that last night the boys decided not to speak to Tol'ka; they've decided to boycott him.

I'm sitting on the logs watching sunbeam reflections playing on all the house windows. Windows are opened, and the sunbeam reflections jump headlong down to the ground, and long-legged Vit'ka Kiselev, walking through the courtyard, steps over them.

Even from a distance you can see that Vit'ka is hot in the brown leather jacket, all zipped up with three zippers, but it's a new jacket, and not everyone has seen it yet. "Hi," Vit'ka says to me, coming up to the logs. He has a fixed and important look.

"Are you in on it?" he asks. "Yesterday we adopted a decision regarding Suchkov. Since we all live in the same house, it means that we are a collective, and one must consider the collective. But Suchkov considers only himself."

Vit'ka isn't making the speech for me alone. My friend Tonya Malakhova has stuck her head out of the second-floor window, and, behind Vit'ka, near the clothesline, stands a fat, sleepy girl — a nurse with a baby in her arms. Vit'ka unzips his jacket with a crackle, puts one foot forward and looks like the statue of Maya-kovsky in Mayakovsky Square. Above his head the wind blows up a flock of light poplar down, although there are no poplars in our courtyard. In our courtyard there is not even any grass, and probably that's because our courtyard is like a deep, narrow well.

"Girls, we want to know," says Vit'ka loudly, "are you going to back us or not? Or are you going to be like strike-breakers?"

Vit'ka stops on the last word and looks at me. He's waiting to hear what I'm going to say. The quiet girl, Zoya Pronina, comes up to the logs and sits down next to me; she's also waiting to hear what I'm going to answer Vit'ka. And Tonya is also waiting at her windowsill. And I say very calmly and clearly, "Of course. Of course, we'll back you up."

Zoya Pronina nods her head, and Tonya says from her window, "Tol'ka has a high opinion of himself. Better to educate him now than later. It'll be too late then."

I know very well why the kids from our house like me. It's simply that I know how to tell all sorts of stories and I dream up all kinds of games for them. After school, if I don't come out for a long time, they all gather in the alley under our windows and call me in turn. And each time I catch it from the neighbors be-cause of this. But they respect Tonya Malakhova for a different reason. She's quiet and just. She easily makes peace among the girls who have quarreled, and, when the women in our courtyard have to go out somewhere, they entrust their babies only to her.

"Yes," Vit'ka Kiselev repeats after Tonya, "Suchkov must be educated. Let him feel what the solid collective is like."

Vit'ka nods to all of us at once, "Then it's set. See you later, girls. I'm going home."

I'm also going home. A dense, gray cloud has appeared above the very rooftops and has covered our well-courtyard. Heavy, transparent raindrops fall on my hands.

"Tonya!" I yell, "Don't go out, it's raining."

And Zoya and I run behind Vit'ka towards the gate. In our rooms the windows are being shut, and it seems that on the street, outside the windows, a garrulous crowd is gathering. It's the rain ringing, muttering, whispering in the alley. And even at night, in my dreams, I hear clearly how someone's bare feet go smacking along the asphalt. I wake up at night and hear the rain ringing outside, and I cry quietly into my pillow. Something terrible has happened to me. I don't know how it happened, but my heart aches and is breaking with yearning.

Early in the morning I'm sent out to the bakery for bread. The front door, swollen and heavy from the rain, opens with difficulty. I open it and remain standing on the threshold. Overnight something has happened to our city, to our alley. In our alley, gray from the gray houses and gray asphalt, it smells of flowers and something else. An unfamiliar, subtle, astringent odor comes up from the wet bridge. This smell is unlike anything else — it almost makes my head swim, and I suddenly guess that it is the smell of the sea. I have never been near the sea, but still I know that that's exactly what it smells like in the morning, when the fog hasn't melted away yet, when the water is still unclear, still unwashed by the sun. It's the rain that has come from the sea and brought this aroma to the city.

I stand and see the doors of the houses open, and people come out into the street. They screw up their eyes sleepily, breathe in the morning air, and suddenly become thoughtful and tender. But then they shake their portfolios as though they're shaking off something; they walk briskly along the sidewalks, and the expressions on their faces change; they become indifferent and tired. I don't want them to go away, I want them to breathe in this odor properly. Then they might, like me, want to go walking through the city, wherever their legs will carry them, look into strangers' windows and sing a song to themselves. But, screwing up their eyes, they walk past me; they hurry off to some specific place they know well, and I remain alone near the front door.

I walk through the alley, look into the windows, and sing a song to myself. Then I turn into our courtyard. It has also changed overnight. The ground in our courtyard is dark, all in tiny pits from the raindrops; the hopscotch marks, drawn in chalk, are barely noticeable. The roofs of the sheds shine like new, and near the wall of the house, sharp and thin grass stems have sprouted. The courtyard is completely empty, except for Tol'ka Suchkov sitting on the green bench near a wet pile of sand. The sleeves of his white shirt are rolled up above the elbows. He's drawing something with a twig on the ground, and his face is indifferent and tired, like the faces of the people passing by in the alley.

I look at Tol'ka, and, just like at night, my heart begins to ache. I know that Tol'ka has sat down on the bench for just a minute. He'll get up soon and will leave the courtyard and will never again come here. Perhaps, he'll even leave the house for good, and we'll meet in a few years, after we've finished school and completely grown up. And perhaps we will never meet again.

I walk along the damp sand and don't even think about what kind of eyes and hair I have; I don't even want to look like Simone Signoret . . . I don't want to look like anyone. It only seems that it's not me who is walking, but that someone is leading me up to the green bench, and I don't have the strength to stop.

Tol'ka turns his head and looks at me. He looks unbelievingly and sullenly, but I don't turn away and am no longer blushing. I walk up to the bench and say to him, "Let them have their boycott. It's all the same to me. They dream up all sorts of nonsense."

Tol'ka smiles ironically and with hatred turns his head in the direction of Vit'ka Kiselev's windows.

"They're fools," he says calmly. "They think I need them. I have a lot of things to do. I still have an exam. Then I'll go away to the Oka, to my grandmother. Maybe they think that I don't have any friends besides them."

"You're going away to the Oka?" I ask.

"Yes. You know, I don't like the Pioneer camps. They won't

let you swim there. As soon as you get into the water it's: 'Children out of the water!' And I love to swim very much. I'll swim across the Oka at any spot I like. You don't believe me?"

Of course I believe him. He's telling the truth. He talks to me as though we were old friends and as though nothing has happened. We talk about simple things, and I think to myself that probably I've never known Tol'ka Suchkov, no one has known him. He isn't proud, he's quite ordinary, and his eyes aren't dark, they're bright, and he has freckles on his forehead.

"And where are you going this summer?" Tol'ka asks me.

I don't know yet. I don't know at all what's going to happen to me this summer. Perhaps this summer a miracle will happen, perhaps this summer all sorts of wonderful things will happen.

Then we simply sit and don't say anything. With his twig Tol'ka is drawing straight short lines on the ground; they look like a row of exclamation points. It seems to me that his face, now, is calm, even happy. He raises his head and wants to ask me something. But I suddenly turn around. It's as though someone was calling me, although the courtyard is very quiet. And I see that behind us, near the sheds, all of our kids are standing: Vit'ka Kiselev and his friend Igor Ryumkin, and Tonya, and Zoya Pronina, and other boys and girls. They look at me and don't say anything. They are still silent when Tol'ka gets up from the bench, extends his hand to me, and says loudly, "See you later!"

He walks past them and whistles as he walks; but they aren't looking at him, but at me. I also get up from the bench and am now standing alone, expecting something.

"You know what you are?" Vit'ka Kiselev asks calmly. He is standing quite close to me. "You are a traitor. No one would have gone on military reconnaissance with the likes of you. You're worse than he is, because you betrayed everybody."

Vit'ka looks at me with his screwed-up eyes, sharp as a razor, and I see that he wants to hit me. And all of them look at me the same way: the kind Igor Ryumkin, and Zoya Pronina, who so loved to hear me talk about books. And even my best friend, Tonya Malakhova, with whom I have been sharing a desk for three years, and with whom I plotted out all my life and she hers — even she looks at me as though she were saying goodbye forever. And I want to cover my face with my hands to avoid seeing how they stare at me.

I am walking through the courtyard, stepping carefully so as not to erase the pale hopscotch marks. Above me swirl the transparent stars of poplar down, although there are no poplars in our courtyard. Like tiny carrier pigeons, they fly upward, toward the sky, but the sky above our courtyard is very, very high, and they cannot reach it. I go out of the courtyard into the alley and stop outside the gates. And once again I catch the now quite faint smell of the distant sea.

translated by ROBERT SZULKIN

Not a Peep

YURY KAZAKOV

❈ ❈ ❈ ❈

I

T HE OLD MAN, master of the barn, came to them that first evening, sleepy, barefooted and began to mumble, pulling up his
falling trousers, "Inasmuch as, of course . . . I've decided . . .
only it being summertime, that is . . . you go ahead, live, what's it
to you — you're just having a good time! Only inasmuch as it's
dry, excuse me, I'm saying this in regards to smoking, in other
words, may God prevent . . ."

And in a minute he was already sitting with the hunters on the
threshold of the barn; he smoked, sighed, kept blowing his nose,
and said that every day the shepherds see wolves, that in the
Zakaznoy Forest there were so many black grouse that you
couldn't get rid of them, and that in the fields, beyond the threshing
barns, the situation with the quail was just horrible.

There were two hunters. To the youngest — Sasha Starobel'sky,
a thin, bashful student, almost a boy still — everything seemed to be
a happy trepidation that first evening.

He had left Moscow only yesterday; all through the journey he
couldn't tear his eyes away from the window; he looked greedily
at the passengers getting on and off at each station. He was going
to Smolenshchins to visit a friend, and he was excited and sociable
from his first freedom, from the thought of the future hunts and
the country life.

But in Vyaz'ma a certain Seryoga Varaksin from Myatlevo came
into the coach; he threw his rolled-up empty sacks, which smelled
badly, on the top shelf, put a watermelon on the bench, cut it open

with a crunch, and began to eat, gulping it down noisily and chok-
ing on it while he looked rapidly at everyone in the coach.

He was thick-lipped and red-eyed, with swollen pink hands. He
had drunk a good deal, and was happy. In Vyaz'ma he had suc-
cessfully sold some pork. He immediately began to call Sasha Starobel'sky "student," and, having found out that the latter was going
hunting, he lit up and began to tell what a wonderful wealth of
wildlife there was in Myatlevo.

"Student!" Varaksin said. "Listen to me now, I'm giving you the
real lowdown. I'm an electrician. Our Sovkhoz is the best in the
area! Where are you going?"

"To Vazuka," answered Sasha happily.

"Eh! I've been there. I've been everywhere; I know the whole
area. You ask me about hunting! Your Vazuka's not worth crap,
I'm telling you true! You want to hunt — you come to us, to
Myatlevo. I've got a friend, a gamekeeper, and we've got enough
of whatever you want; we've got quail, the lake's full of ducks and
geese — I'm telling you true!"

And he told Sasha so much "true" that the latter became so
thrilled that he no longer felt anything, except that he was unusually happy and that life was wonderful.

As for the rest, everything went along naturally. They got off
at Myatlevo at night and immediately started off along the open
fields. Barely had the train left, when Sasha felt that one life had
ended, disappeared, and a new life, differing sharply from the
other, had come — an obscure, mysterious life.

Summer lightning blazed on the horizon as though some spirit
of the forest and the fields kept winking at them. There was no
moon, but the stars were so bright, and there were so many of
them, that they illuminated everything: the thin transparent clouds
above; and below, on earth, the bushes, the fields with the sparse,
narrow boundaries, the haystacks, and the small fir groves near the
road.

The road smelled of earth and dry plantain. Along the sides
something kept creaking, chirping, squeaking. Black telephone
poles appeared, and then a weak but distinct polyphonic sound was
heard, although there was no wind at all, and it was inexplicable
why the poles gave off this sound.

They crossed shattered log bridges, splintered by tractors, which at one time transversed anti-tank trenches, which had long ago turned into ditches overgrown with bushes and reeds. Here and there in the ditches, black, oily, stagnant water shone.

It was, according to him, fifteen kilometers to Seryoga's village. In the train this distance seemed insignificant to Sasha. But here, they had been walking and walking, and, as before, the fields and groves stretched out before them along the sides of the road; they came across common graves with mutely darkening obelisks, and the road disappeared into the darkness just as before. Sasha became tired, and it seemed to him that they had long ago covered not only the fifteen kilometers but thirty, and that there would be no end to this road, to the night, to the mysterious sounds and the slight fear which he had begun to experience.

"Stop," Seryoga suddenly said in a whisper. He held his breath and listened for something. "Hey there, student, take out your gun!"

"Why?" Sasha asked quietly, taking out his gun.

Seryoga didn't say anything, and Sasha began to unpack his rucksack hurriedly, taking out the shining boxes of cartridges with their shining copper bottoms.

"Because I could be killed! I have money, five hundred rubles. You understand?" Seryoga said in a rough tone, with satisfaction from the thought that he was frightening the student, but he was even more frightened himself. "Let's go faster."

Looking around frequently, soon they were almost running along the road, sometimes taking shortcuts away from the path to save time. Because of the heavy rucksack and gun, Sasha was panting, but Seryoga kept pressing on, frequently stamping hard with his boots on the hard-packed soil.

Finally, on the road near the threshing barn, they came across a pile of light hay left over by the combine. They did not go around the hay, but straight through it. It was springy and crackled under their feet.

Just then a river became visible, and beyond the river, the Sovkhoz, its white structures shining faintly in the distance. They crossed the river, jumping from rock to rock. They arrived at

Varaksin's and went to sleep without eating. And in the morning, after the chill, they left for the distant village of Kunino.

II

THE first to wake up was Sasha; he crawled out from under the sheepskin coat and started waking Seryoga. The sun rose slowly; it was brilliantly white, but cold. The hunters walked in single file along the water-meadow, leaving behind them a rich green track. And the closer they got to the small game, where the Zakaznoy Forest began, the quicker Sasha walked; he became pale, stopped, and, long before they got to the small game area, he couldn't hold out and took off his gun and threw up his arms.

And with each step Seryoga kept shaking his meaty cheeks, made faces, yawned, looked at the clear, blue-turquoise sky, and kept stumbling on the mounds.

"Student," he began in a hoarse voice. "You know, you and I are a couple of dopes."

"Why is that?" Sasha responded after a certain pause.

"What do you mean 'why'?" said Seryoga animatedly as he caught up to Sasha. "We're wearing out our boots for nothing. We ought to find ourselves a woman now, a nice piece! Eh? Student!"

"Cut it out," said Sasha with a blush, and he increased his pace.

"Boy, there are some nice women around!" Seryoga coughed and blew his nose. "You grab a hold of one . . ."

"Shut up, you!" Sasha whispered, bending over with a look of suffering on his face.

As always happens at the wrong time, a grouse flew out of the thicket, and it screeched so horribly and wildly among the birch trees that Sasha's body contorted. Sasha shot at it — he missed, of course — and changing his cartridges looked frantically at Seryoga. Seryoga winked guiltily, and the hunters, carefully and efficiently, marched forward in silence.

Toward midday the sun bore down on them; Seryoga plopped down in the shade of some bushes, took Sasha's rucksack and with greedy enjoyment began to gulp down eggs, bread, and cold mutton with the fat already solidified, washing it all down with a bottle of milk.

Sasha, having taken a turn in the forest, and exhausted by the sun, also came over, lay down, and looked at the sky until he became dizzy. After a while he unwillingly took some food, unwillingly and gloomily listened to the satiated Seryoga, who had loosened his belt. The latter, yawning and belching frequently, picked his teeth with a match, fixedly and sleepily looked at a birch tree and said, "Girls — they're nothing. Don't get tied down with girls: there's going to the movies, clubs, dances, and you have to tell them all sorts of fancy things, and you can't avoid their tears or reproaches. I've had enough of them. No, you take a woman, a woman . . . aha! A wo-man!"

"Lay off," Sasha said drearily. "Aren't you ashamed?"

"Listen, stupid, I'm giving you the real lowdown!" Seryoga answered jokingly, and became even more animated; he tossed and turned and put one leg atop the other. "Not even a woman, no, you take a widow, not a young one either, but one about thirty-five — that's the real thing . . . you take a widow or a divorcee, and one that's not too beautiful either. She has no claims on you as regards marriage and things like that, but she'll satisfy your whole soul. Oh, she'll enjoy herself. 'And all night long she loved me,' he suddenly screamed and sat up, smoothing his thighs.

"Student," he started again, squinting at Sasha, his eyes bloodshot. "Oh, but we're bad, you and me! Eh? Dopes! There are plenty of women in the villages . . . Let's go home!"

"Go to hell!" Sasha said. He took his gun and went off into the woods, and Seryoga, thinking for a while, dragged off after him.

III

ON the fifth day Seryoga did not go on the evening hunt; he cleaned his boots, put on his jacket and set off for the club.

Sasha wandered by himself along the golden-pink stubble under the low, dark sun; he frightened the quail, kept shooting with relish, ran to pick them up — firm and warm — put them in his sack, and smiled exhaustedly, wiping away his perspiration with his sleeve.

Soon it got dark and cold. Coming out towards the river, Sasha got undressed behind some bushes, his tender, slim body showing white; he made a running start, screamed, threw himself in the water, and swam for a long time, stirring up the dark waters near the shore.

Refreshed, and feeling lighthearted, he arrived in the village, gave the quail to the mistress of the house, refused to eat and only drank some fresh milk, went to the barn, daydreamed a bit, as was his habit, and soon fell asleep.

Seryoga came back late at night; puffing, he climbed up to the hayloft, took off his boots, undressed, stretched out, yawned, and crawled under the sheepskin coat where Sasha was. Having worked up his pillow, he settled himself, warmed up, and nudged Sasha.

"Well, did you get anything," he asked in a friendly way.

"Some quail . . ." Sasha said inattentively, as though through a dream.

"Well! As for me, brother, I went strolling today." Seryoga lowered his voice. "I had me a real nice chick! Third house from the corner, did you see her? That's where she's from. Nineteen years old, the devil . . . She finished ten years of secondary school."

"But I thought you didn't like girls," Sasha couldn't help saying, and he laughed caustically in the dark, completely awake now, and sniffing with satisfaction the smell of the pillow and the hay.

"That all depends on what kind of girls," Seryoga was quick to answer.

"How did you meet her?" Sasha asked after some silence.

"Well, that's nothing to me! Setting up the love routine and writing letters — it's as easy as spitting!"

He sat up, found his pants in the dark, got out his cigarettes, lit one, lay down again and continued, "Say you're writing to some girl. Let's call her Lyuba, for example . . . So you write: 'With warmest regards to you, Lyuba, your unknown-to-you, first-class electrician, Sergei Varaksin. Inasmuch as we are carrying on the heroic struggle for the good of the entire Soviet nation, I am quite interested, Lyuba, in knowing all about you in your everyday life and your studies.' "

Seryoga burst out laughing at the style in which he was speaking, and raised his voice: " 'You wrote in your letter, Lyuba, that you believe in pure friendship. You, of course, do not know me; however, you will soon get to know me through this correspondence, and, perhaps, even through a personal meeting. And on this contemporaneous question I am completely in agreement with you and propose to you my passionate and faithful friendship. Lyuba, please write your opinion on this matter. As for now, Lyuba, I am sending you my photograph, and hope for the same from you . . .' And here's what you should write on the photo," he added, laughing: " 'Love me true, as I do you, and we'll be friends forever,' or 'May this dead imprint recall my living image.' "

"What nonsense," Sasha said, also smiling. "You better tell me what happened tonight!"

"It's not nonsense at all!" Seryoga answered with animation. "You're still a snot-nosed kid, you don't understand. These words work like acid on the girls. You, with your philosophy, yes, and your poetry, will remain a fool forever. You ought to mix with our people, they'd take you in hand. You're not a bad-looking lad . . .

"As for today, here's what happened. I came to the club. Well, their club is nothing at all! Our club is new, with columns — took two years to build it. But theirs is just a big house, four walls with no stove and no partitions.

"I come in, light a cigarette, case the place. People are coming in, but at first just girls, no guys. The accordion player comes, starts screeching on his instrument, and the girls start dancing. I go over to one of them. 'Permit me,' says I, 'to take a couple of turns with you!' We dance. I immediately drop a hint on the crowded situation, that, as a matter of fact, it wouldn't hurt her any if she were to give some consideration to some more suitable situation.

"And the girl! . . . Such nice tight hips, and how her cheeks shake! Oh, you little Buddha, I think to myself, you're just what I want! Well, she answers me that she agrees with me and does give some consideration, only not to the likes of me. Of course, this means I didn't make it with her. Well, okay then . . . I see she's taken; it's a dead deal. I keep quiet again and look around.

"Suddenly I see one . . . young, beautiful . . . She keeps blinking her eyes, small red lips, black hair, and me, I don't go for blondes at all. And, most important of all, she's hanging around with the girls, giggling. The ones that aren't taken always hang around in the same herd.

"Well, I noticed how she looked at me once, twice. Then I go up to her and take her aside . . . Just then the generator starts up, the lights go on, and she seems even more beautiful in the light.

They put on some records, I dance a couple of times with her and am interested to know who she is. She says she takes care of the calves on some farm. Well, okay . . . I suggest we get some fresh air. We go out into the entryway, then onto the stoop. Of course, there are some guys there; they're all Komsomols, a conscientious bunch, parasites, smoking in the entryway, and they shout to her, 'Galya, Galya!' — that's her name, Galya. They have some lanterns, and I whisper to her, 'I want to tell you something . . .' Well, she starts shaking. These girls always start shaking when you take them by the hand or when you grab hold of them, so she starts shaking.

"Well, she's shaking, and I'm leading her along the road; I look around, can't see a soul; I press close to her and cough, but don't say a thing — I make like I'm very embarrassed. 'Why are you shaking?' I say. 'You cold?' 'I don't know,' she says. Well, I immediately put my jacket on her shoulders. And that, student, is the first thing — give her your jacket. As soon as I put it on her, she became just like a little mouse.

"So I accompany her up to the yard, and above all, I'm glad that it's on my way. Cause if she was from Gorok, why, you can go crazy accompanying 'em. But in this case it was nothing, just neighbors. We went out to the yard, to the back part of it, sat down on a log, and I tell her about my life, pour out my soul. I talk to her sensibly, like in the papers — they love this sort of thing. And then I begin to embrace her. At first she kicks up a fuss, but then it's okay — she's thrilled. She whines and trembles, the little bitch! In a week you'll see, there'll be full order in the Kolkhoz — I know how to deal with 'em."

"You're a scoundrel!" Sasha said.

Seryoga burst out laughing and lifted up his legs, smacking his buttocks.

"You wanna bet? Well?" he continued joyfully. And not waiting for an answer, still smiling, he turned away, sniffed his hands, fidgeted, making himself comfortable, and fell asleep, flinching several times.

IV

IT was raining off and on, and everything was quickly becoming autumnal.

The roads were soggy and wet, the roofs and walls of the barns became dark, and slow, dense clouds came from the North; it grew cold, the hay in the loft got damp, and it was terrible to crawl out from under the sheepskin coat in the morning.

But soon the rains ended, and everything again began to shine with the last beauty of late summer. The cobwebs gleamed golden in the stubble and in the bushes; the sunsets again became blood-like, then yellow, then green. In the mornings dew fell again, the air was sharp, and more and more often a crisp hoarfrost covered the roofs and the grass.

In the gardens, in the fields, and in the rowan trees, starlings flew about like clouds. In the threshing barns, people were thresh-ing and winnowing, the air was full of sharp sounds of motors, automobiles and trucks were constantly going to the city carrying grain, and a very thin dust hung in a dry fog above the road.

Seryoga would be gone for a long time on walks. He had com-pletely forgotten about hunting, and Sasha went alone; he went persistently in the morning and in the evening, although he himself couldn't stand it any longer and wanted to go to the club. Now he didn't have anyone to say a word to, and he frequently fell into deep thought, became thinner, more distinct in his face and cheek-bones. His eyes became more limpid; now he looked at the girls he met more frequently and more attentively.

And Seryoga would return late at night, would make noise, lie down, begin to wheeze, twist and turn. He smelled of perfume and powder. If Sasha was asleep, Seryoga would wake him and begin to torture him with stories about Galya.

And then, once, Seryoga returned just before daybreak and did not undress as usual but sat down near the edge of the loft, took off his boots, dangled his legs, lit a cigarette, and shouted out, "Student, you asleep or not?"

"What do you want?" Sasha responded roughly.

Seryoga was silent, coughed, then said:

"You owe me a bottle, student! You lost the bet . . ."

"You're lying!" Sasha said and sat up.

"Why should I lie? I'm not under police interrogation." Ser-yoga's reply was indifferent, and, from the inertness with which he objected, Sasha knew he wasn't lying.

And for some reason he began to put on his boots, feeling a pain in his heart and feeling sorry for himself, as though something bad, shameful, had happened to him. And Seryoga flopped down on his back, put his hands behind his head, stretched out, laughed and said, "Three days ago I noticed she was sleeping alone in her hayloft. But I don't let on, I keep on persuading . . . No, not at all! Hey, where are you going?"

"Nowhere," said Sasha, standing still, searching for something in the hay with his trembling hands.

"And I thought you were . . . Well, today we said goodbye and everything was on the up and up, she went to her place, I remained behind the gates . . ." He suddenly burst out laughing. "They have a neighbor, a crazy old man, guards his garden. Comes out in a sheepskin coat with a gun and goes around like a night watchman. There was noise in the village, then it quieted down. Why don't I get myself an apple, I think to myself . . . I crawled over, jumped over the wattle fence, but not too well, caught my legs in the brushwood. The old man started screaming, 'Who's there? I'll shoot!' — and he cocks the gun! I hurled myself down and stayed there nose so much in the ground that my back got cold. Well, thinks I, now I'm really in trouble. If he hits me in the behind, my whole love is gone! But nothing happened; he stood there, then left. Then I picked five apples and started back. I wanted to bring you a couple, but started dreaming and ate them all myself.

"So I'm sitting on the log, chewing on the apples, thinking over the situation, my arms and legs are about to fall off, I'm so tired, and all around me — darkness! I finished the apples, took off my boots and arose. I went into the entryway, like some kind of thief, all trembling. I'm climbing the ladder, not breathing — in other words, not a peep out of me . . . I stretch out my head and look — where is she? I look, she's lying there right under the eaves. I crawl over to her over the hay . . . Hey, where are you going?"

"Go to hell!" Sasha shouted in a shrill voice and found the crossbeam with his foot. "You pig! Idiot! Ooo!"

In his undershirt and boots, he went out of the barn, went over to the road, sat down on a log near the small bridge across the stream, hunched over, shaking from the cold, the depression, and the disgust.

In five minutes, fully dressed, Seryoga came out in the street, looked around, saw Sasha, went up to him and sat on the other end of the log.

"What's the matter with you, student?" he asked humorously. "Are you jealous? You dope, I told you a long time ago — lay off this hunting. Everything in its time and place. You want, I'll introduce you to someone? Gal'ka has a friend; she's lonely, and pining away. Of course, she's not as beautiful, but she'll do for you . . . what do you say?"

Sasha turned away and didn't say a thing. He felt bitter and lonely. Voices could be heard beyond the village, then dark figures appeared — they were coming in a crowd along the road, illuminating the scene with their cigarettes. Coming up to the small bridge, they grew silent and stopped, looking.

"Is that him?" someone asked, not sure.

"Let's take a look . . ."

And all of them turned and come up to the hunters. Seryoga got up spread his legs and put his hands in his pockets. Not understanding anything, but having a premonition of something terrible, Sasha also got up.

"Got a smoke?" asks one of the approaching men.

"In the barn . . ." Seryoga said as though not in his own voice.

"Stop!" said one small boy in a military cap, and then he tenaciously grabbed Seryoga by the sleeve. "Do you know Gal'ka?"

"What's the matter with you? Lay off!" said Seryoga weakly.

"Do you remember what we told you in the club, you bastard?"

"What's the matter, boys . . ." Seryoga mumbled, beginning to tremble. "I'm one of you, I'm a country boy! Don't, boys! And I won't see her anymore . . ."

"Oh, you won't see her!" the one holding him repeated with rage and kept inhaling.

"If not, may I be . . . Honestly, I'll leave tomorrow."

"Oh, you'll leave!" a thickset one repeated again, senselessly, getting infuriated.

But now, coughing, another one approached them, a tall, lanky man in riding breeches and boots, with a bunch of some sort of white flowers sticking out of his jacket pocket.

"Stop, Petya!" he said, affecting tenderness and pushing the thickset one aside. "I know him! He's one of our own. You mustn't hit him . . ."

And bending over with a controlled gasp, he hit Seryoga in the solar plexus. Seryoga fell heavily, then jumped up, but two others immediately threw themselves on him and again beat him down to the ground.

Sasha wanted to stop them, but a healthy lad grabbed him and hit him lightly, just hard enough so that Sasha's head was ringing; then he grabbed him by the shirt collar with his strong, knobby hand, began to choke him, and mumbled quietly, "Quiet, quiet . . . or you'll have some bloody teeth . . . quiet!"

And everybody was looking into the darkness. And there, pushing one another, and being in each other's way, they were beating and beating something which would burst out screaming and wheeze with every blow. The tall boy with the white flowers in his jacket pocket was especially adroit. He kept speaking and puffing, "Don't . . . Lay off, boys!" as he jumped up and beat Seryoga about the head and in the stomach.

"What are you doing?" a surprised woman's voice shouted from a neighboring yard.

The boy who was holding onto Sasha and shaking him energetically, dropped him, turned to his friends, pushed them apart, and they all ran off into the darkness along the damp meadow.

Alone, Sasha stretched and grew rigid looking at Seryoga, who was lying near the small bridge. And when people came running, putting on their flashlights and asking who he was and why he was beaten, he couldn't say anything, and his teeth chattered and his knees knocked.

They brought Seryoga to the barn, sat him down on the threshold, put the light on him, felt and examined his head and body. Turning his face, Seryoga spat blood and cried.

"It's nothing, he's okay!" someone said cheerfully, having examined Seryoga and having wiped his hands with some straw. "He'll be okay."

Breathing hard, the doctor's assistant in a white dressing gown came and washed, smeared, and bandaged Seryoga's head. Then they threw down some hay and his pillow from the hayloft. They put Seryoga to bed, and soon everybody left.

All night Seryoga groaned, blew his nose, spat blood, swore at Sasha, Moscow, and hunting. And in the morning Galya came running, and Sasha, seeing her for the first time, almost gasped; so beautiful, so open and bashful was she in her love.

"What have they done to you? What is this? Oh God!" she whispered passionately, looking with fear at Seryoga's bandaged head.

"Here, look," Seryoga answered, undoing the bandage, showing his black face and looking maliciously at Galya with his swollen eyes. "Did you see? All because of you, you bitch. I'm leaving today, I don't give a crap about this kind of provincial farce!"

"Seryozha . . ." she said, going down on her knees. "Don't, don't say that. We'll complain to the police about them . . ."

"Get away from me!" Seryoga said, turning away.

Galya looked at Sasha and blushed painfully; tears appeared in her eyes. Sasha grabbed the gun, jumped out of the barn and set out across the fields for the forest once more, feeling yesterday's depression, insult, envy . . .

And, as if out of spite, the day was magnificent, especially peaceful, especially tender, a perfect summer day, but pale and sad like autumn.

The entire day, getting angry with himself, Sasha walked and kept shooting, trying to forget himself, to drive away the depression by tiring himself out, but he couldn't think about anything else except Galya.

"Not a peep . . ." he remembered with a caustic smile. And again he stumbled on some hummocks, crawled about in the ravines, ate raspberries and wild currants, getting drunk on their stiffling odor, and kept shooting. The echo resounded loudly and sharply in the forest, and the smoke fell in a shroud on the grass.

Exhausted, drawn, he returned to the village, opened the door to the barn and immediately understood with contempt: Seryoga had left. "Oh, the beast," Sasha said. He put his gun on the straw and went to see the master of the house. The old man had just gotten up, was sitting on the bench with a puffed, senseless face, rubbing his dark hand along the oilskin, driving away the flies.

"Sergei?" he asked.

"He left. Yes . . . he took off in the daytime, he was very distraught. He left two rubles," he said with a sad laugh. "That's right, two rubles, I say . . . What about you, are you staying? Well . . . See for yourself. The barn has all the hay you want. Who beat him up? Was it the Levoshkin bunch? I saw the police going there. They really gave him a good beating!"

He climbed up on the Russian stove, took out some brownish-green, home-grown tobacco leaves and started crushing them in the palm of his hand.

"I planted a garden by myself . . ." he mumbled, yawning. "Well, how was the hunting, eh? Didn't get anything? That's the way it happens with amateurs, of course. Did they really get together? You don't know? Well . . ."

He lit a cigarette, let out the smoke sweetly, and began to cough so that his bald head became red; he screwed up his eyes, wiping away the tears with his rough hand.

"Nastya!" he suddenly shouted into the entryway. "Pour out a couple of cups of home brew . . . No, not from there!" After listening, he again shouted, "The one near the pail!"

And when it became completely dark, the slightly drunk, distraught Sasha returned to the barn, climbed up onto the hayloft, plopped down and began to rub his face which had become numb. He suddenly wanted to go home. "To hell with it, I'll leave!" he gloomily decided. "In Moscow there are fellows and girls, football . . . I'll leave!"

He started to think about Moscow, about girls he knew, and soon his face became hot from the agitation. And the life which he had been living all these days, the hunting, the bashful but already wanton face of Galya, as it seemed to him, Seryoga, the sound of the threshing machines, the night fight, the beauty of autumn — all of this immediately became distant, disappeared somewhere exactly as his previous life had disappeared when, late one night, he got off the train at Myatlevo.

translated by ROBERT SZULKIN

To the City

YURY KAZAKOV

❈ ❈ ❈ ❈

I

EARLY ONE MORNING Vasily Kamanin was walking along the
road to Ozerishche. His boots were caked with mud, his
brownish neck was long unwashed, his eyes with their yellow
whites looked out turbidly, and a gray bristle had begun to form just
below the eyes. His walk was uneven; his legs kept straying apart
and were somehow falling behind his body, which was straining
forward. A cold wind blew at his back; dark, endless mounds of
autumn plough-land were seen on the sides of the road. Here and
there water glistened, lead-gray between the mounds — it had already been raining for a week. Reddish-brown sorrel, spattered
with mud, fluttered in the wind along the sides of the road.

The day before Vasily Kamanin had drunk a great deal at his
father-in-law's. Today his head hurt, and his whole body ached as
it did only when bad weather was approaching. There was an unpleasant taste in his mouth. Vasily, spitting, lifted his heavy head
and gloomily looked ahead. But up ahead there was only a muddy,
miry road, dolefully dark haystacks, and, up to the very horizon, a
low gray sky without the least ray, without any hope of sun. Vasily
lowered his eyes. He picked out the drier spots by habit, but later,
absorbed in thought, he again walked helter-skelter, slipping, moving his legs with difficulty, bending his thin body forward.

Vasily Kamanin lived in Mokhovatka, in a large old house which
sat aside from the others. Before the war, Mokhovatka had been a
big village, and the Kamanin house stood in a row with the others.
But when the Germans were retreating, they set the village on fire,
and it burned to a cinder; only the Kamanin house miraculously

survived. After the war, the village was rebuilt, but it was a far cry from what it had been, and Vasily's shack found itself on the outskirts of the village gates. It was suggested to him that he move his shack, and he himself had made preparations for it, but somehow he never got around to it, and so he continued living at a distance.

His three daughters had married one after another and had left to live in the city. The house became empty; Vasily more and more often took on work on the side — he was a good carpenter and he made a lot of money, but, with the years, he began to get bored and started drinking; he became gloomy when drunk, and beat his wife.

Vasily hadn't loved his wife Akulina for a long time. Before the war he somehow wound up as a recruit on a big construction project, worked there the entire summer, and from that time on the thought of moving to live in the city never left him.

Every year, around autumn, when there was little work, he was suddenly seized with longing; he became indifferent to everything; for long periods of time he lay about in the yard, his eyes closed, and thought of city life. He couldn't stand city people — he considered them all a bunch of parasites — but city life — the parks, restaurants, movies, stadiums — he loved so much that even his dreams were only about the city.

Several times he made preparations and would have left, even sold the cow, but at night Akulina kept whispering to him about the soil, their relatives, the farm, about how she would die of boredom in the city, and he thought it over and stayed.

Everyone in the Kolkhoz knew about his passion for the city and laughed at him.

"What's this, haven't left after all?" they would ask him.

"He who laughs last . . ." he would answer, smiling gloomily and harboring a hatred for his wife.

In the spring Akulina fell ill. At first they thought she would get over it. Then Akulina started visiting the medical center and took prescribed powders and mixtures willingly. Believing that she would get well, she drank the bitter medicine; but she did not get well — on the contrary, she got worse and worse. Then she tried secret methods. Old women took to visiting Akulina at her home, bringing phials with magic potions and homemade brandies. But

these didn't help either. Akulina's eyes became hollow, her temples
sank, her hair began to fall out. She became progressively worse;
she was going down fast. People who had seen her healthy not too
long ago, in meeting her now, would stop and follow her with
their eyes for a long time. It was terrible to sleep with her, she
was so emaciated and groaned so much in her sleep. Vasily began
to sleep in the yard, on the fresh hay.

He spent whole days in the fields, worked on mowing the hay,
fought with the brigadier and, knitting his large, dark brow,
thought about his wife and kept assuring himself more and more
that she would die soon. And in the evening he would bring the
hay home and drag in sacks full of seeds which were given to him
in advance for the work days. He returned home tired, his face
brown from the sun, sat down on the bench, supporting himself
with his crackling hands on his knees, and looked sullenly at his
wife.

Horrible, emaciated, with a frantic look in her dark eyes, but still
beautiful, Akulina would serve dinner. Later, leaning against the
wall, she breathed with difficulty, her black mouth open. Abun-
dant perspiration appeared on her face.

"Vasya," she asked, "for Christ's sake, take me to the city! Take
me there! I'll drop dead soon . . . my strength is gone, I'm as sick
as I can be, Vasya!" Vasily gulped his soup in silence, afraid to
look at his wife, afraid to give away his secret thoughts.

"Take me, Vasya," Akulina said very quietly and sat down on
the floor near the wall. "I can't eat anything, it all comes back up.
Can't even drink milk now . . . We have the cattle, Vasya, they
need looking after, it's hard for me . . . I'm on all fours . . . I
crawl . . . it's easier for me that way. And inside of me it hurts,
oh, it hurts so much! Take me to the city, let the professors look
at me. I don't believe anyone here anymore, and it's bad, oh, it's
bad!"

And so now Vasily was going to Ozerishche, to the Kolkhoz
chairman, to ask for a horse for his wife, and at the same time to
ask permission to leave the farm permanently.

He was in a bad mood, his head hurt from a hangover; spite for
his wife, the brigadier, and the neighbors was overflowing in him.

He swore and kept thinking how to speak to the chairman so that he'd let him go to the city.

II

VASILY arrived in Ozerishche in an hour, but he was so tired that his legs almost gave way under him.

The chairman's house was distinguished by its size, its porch with small columns, its metal roof, and a big barn covered, not with straw as was everyone else's but with shingles. Beehives could be seen in the garden under the apple trees. Carefully cleaning his boots on the mud scraper, Vasily looked sideways at the beehives and thought for the hundredth time: "I ought to start a bee business, it's a good business!" But, remembering why he came, he only grunted, and feeling an unusual agitation and uneasiness, he opened the door into the dark, cluttered entryway.

In the house things were in disorder; it was dirty there and smelled of boiled milk and sour cabbage. A sewing machine stood on the table, pieces of cloth were scattered about the floor and socks were hung on the wires from the lamp to the radio. The master of the house was not at home. His wife Mar'ya, a strong, dark-haired woman with a shapely posterior, was standing near the oven, hotly illuminated, and was moving the oven prongs, legs spread wide, continually bending down.

"Hello!" Vasily said sullenly, pulling off his hat. "Where's Danylich?"

"What do you want him for?" asked Mar'ya, also sullenly, and without looking at Vasily.

"I got business, of course."

"He's in the fields. Been gone since daybreak."

"Be home soon?"

"Said he would for breakfast, but I dunno . . ."

"Then I'll wait!" Vasily said decisively, and he sat down heavily on the bench, his face to the oven.

He took out his tobacco and was about to light up, when he remembered that Mar'ya didn't like it if people smoked in the house, and so he stashed away the tobacco pouch. And he didn't even want to smoke anyway. He felt an unpleasant weakness in his body, and his head buzzed.

Vasily lowered his head and began to think. He thought about his wife dying soon; he'd have to make a coffin, and it would be better to get hold of some good boards ahead of time. He would have to slaughter a ram, if not two, for the funeral dinner; the relatives would be knocking down the door, and they just love to stuff themselves . . .

Then he started thinking to whom and for how much to sell his house and property, and where to go. At first he could go to Smolensk, to his oldest daughter, and, once there, he'd see. Thank God he'd have money and could be on the lookout for some small house in the city.

Then he began to pick out more convincing words so that the chairman wouldn't object to his leaving. In his thoughts everything came out in order, and the chairman wouldn't in any way be able to stand up against him.

"What did you come for?" the housewife asked, putting the oven tongs in the corner and sitting down at the table.

Vasily didn't immediately understand what he was being asked, he had been so lost in his thoughts. Blinking, as though half awake, he looked at Mar'ya's beautiful face, her full lips and her light blue, slightly protruding, impudent eyes.

"My wife's very sick," he finally said. "It's about a horse that I came. I'd like to take her to the city. Then, of course, too, I've got my own business."

"How old is Akulina?" Mar'ya asked disinterestedly.

"How old?" Vasily thought for a while. "You figure it: I'm fifty-five, and she's two years younger."

"Oh," was the only thing Mar'ya said.

She was silent for a while; she was also thinking about something. Then she bent over the sewing machine, bit off a thread, spread out the material, and a measured, even whirr filled the house.

Vasily closed his eyes again. He wanted to lie down on the bench, cover himself up to the head and not think about anything, just sleep . . . The thought that he had to wait for the chairman, to speak and to prove that he could no longer remain in the Kolkhoz: this thought filled him with revulsion and cold. Something was twitching between his shoulder blades, and the skin on his chest and arms felt as though it were tightening up.

Vasily soon forgot himself under the whirr of the sewing machine; he no longer was thinking about anything, and he started when he heard heavy footsteps in the entryway, and the master of the house came in.

He was a big man with a small, pale face on which grew barely discernible whitish little bushes, as on a eunuch. He had come on horseback, and, coming into the house, he first of all wiped his thighs, knit his brow, and, bending down, looked out the window at something.

Vasily also turned around and looked: a small boy was leading a tall, bony colt with a bobbed tail along the fence. The colt's legs strayed apart, and he kept lifting his head.

"How did everything go?" Mar'ya asked loudly, going up to the pot storage compartment in the oven and again taking up the oven tongs.

The chairman, still bending down, turned his head in her direction, and was about to say something, but, seeing Vasily, he remained silent and extended a cold, damp hand to him. Then he walked through the room, sighed like a very tired man, sat down on the bench with his back to the window and began to pull off his boots.

Having taken off his boots, and moving his bare toes, he looked at his wife, and his face gradually assumed a sleepy and mysterious expression. Vasily also attentively examined Mar'ya, saw how she strained moving the cast iron pots in the oven; he looked at her strong back and involuntarily thought, "Eh, devil, she's a smooth one!"

"Well, how are things going?" asked the chairman. "Are you bringing in the hay?"

"We're bringing it in," Vasily answered hastily, taking his eyes off Mar'ya. "We're bringing it in, but we'll never finish on time . . . The rains came too soon; it's very wet. And there aren't enough people — they're all sitting home."

"What does that brigadier of yours use for a brain?" said the chairman knitting his brow for a moment. "How many times has he been told to bring in the hay? He had to wait for the rains! Just wait, I'll get to him."

The chairman looked at his wife and sighed again. Vasily coughed and began to fidget on the bench.

"Is it gonna be ready soon?" the chairman asked his wife.

"Be ready in a minute," Mar'ya said indistinctly.

Vasily was tormenting himself. The chairman didn't ask him why he had come, and to begin first was awkward. All the words which he had thought of while he was sitting and waiting had suddenly disappeared, and Vasily again felt that he was thoroughly sick, that the most important thing now was to sober up and go to sleep for a while.

"We were looking over the Bukatinsky fields," the chairman said, and became animated, "with a reporter from the regional newspaper. The flax should be good. He promised to write something about our girls."

Without turning around, he began to feel around on the windowsill behind him, found a folded newspaper, tore off a piece, stretched out his right leg in front of him, took his tobacco out of his pocket and lit up.

"Well . . !" Vasily feigned surprise and also lit a cigarette hastily. "They'll write something all right! That's their business — writing."

"You've smoked up the room," Mar'ya said frowning and went outside banging the door.

"Why did you come to see me? Some business?" the chairman asked, winking as he followed his wife, and he smiled to Vasily.

Vasily tucked his legs in under him, made himself more comfortable and bowed his head.

"My wife's very sick," he began. "I want to take her to the city. But the roads are in bad shape, it's impossible to go by car. I need a horse, Danylich . . ."

"A horse?" the chairman groaned, scratching his head. "What about the medical center, has she been there?"

"She has. Only I think she needs an operation."

"Well, it's already too late today, but I'll tell them tomorrow to give you one. You'll go in the morning."

"As a matter of fact, my health's not been any too good lately either," Vasily began again, making a sad face. "You ought to drop by and visit me one of these days," he suddenly interrupted himself, remembering that such deals aren't made just like that. "I've got some home-brewed beer; my daughter sent me a package from the city — sugar. We'd have something to drink, my home brew is good, the wife made up a batch the other day. It's not bad at all. I've got some fatback too, the suckling pig came out over three hundred pounds . . . You ought to drop in."

"Why not," the chairman said, smiling.

"You know what, Danylich?" the overjoyed Vasily was quick to say. "I've decided, that is, to say goodbye to the Kolkhoz permanently."

"What do you mean 'say goodbye'?" The chairman had stopped smiling.

"Here's what I mean," said Vasily, plucking up his courage and moving his eyes. "Fact is, I don't want to work here anymore. My wife's sickly, the daughters keep writing, asking me to come . . . What have I got here? Then, also, I've been meaning to for a long time . . . The old chairman had given me permission, ask anybody! Let the others work for a while, I've had enough. I'll always find some carpentry work in the city. What have I got here?"

"What do you mean?" The chairman looked at Vasily as though he had seen him for the first time. "What's the matter, have you forgotten what the management board said?"

"But what have I to do with the management board?"

"Wait a minute, and no 'buts.' Haven't you got work to do? In the fall we'll be putting up a new calf-shed — how about that? Then we have to rebuild the clubhouse, isn't that work? And installing the hotbeds — that's not work?"

"That's true, but let the others do it. And don't you hold me back, or I'll go anyway. I still know my rights."

"Oh, you know them, do you? And that there aren't enough people in the Kolkhoz — do you know that?"

"What's that to me? That's for you to watch out that nobody runs away from the Kolkhoz. You don't run away from something that's good! And maybe I want to live some, I'm not a hundred years old to be lying around the house. And what have I got from the Kolkhoz? Culture? There's no place to drink even."

"Oh, so you're bad off, is that it?" The chairman bent over

rapaciously and began to get yellow in the face. "Have you killed yourself on Kolkhoz work?"

"Don't you raise your voice at me!" Vasily said and moved his eyebrows. "Don't you shout! Don't you pick on me! What I've got, I've got by my own hard work; and as for your Kolkhoz, you couldn't get a handful of snow in the winter out of it."

"So . . . work people, break your backs, and you want to go to the city?"

"My wife's dying." Vasily's head began to buzz; he was finding it difficult to breathe. "She has to be taken to the city. How am I going to do that?"

"We'll give you a horse," said the chairman, and he got up.

"In other words, you won't let me go?" Vasily asked, also getting up.

"Looks like you've grown rich, eh?"

"The devil won't toss any money on my stove," Vasily emphasized seriously.

"That's a fact!" said the chairman, and he began to breathe loudly. "You're a master at grabbing side jobs. Why don't you build us the calf shed, the clubhouse, and the hotbeds, and then we'll see."

"Calf shed? Maybe you want this?" Vasily made a coarse gesture.

The chairman turned to the window.

"Our conversation is finished. Get out! You know the party rules. You're literate. That's all there is to it. We'll call you to the management board; we'll hash it out there!"

"Okay." Vasily pulled his hat over his eyes. "Okay, and give this to your mother! We'll see! There'll be a noose for your neck, too."

Banging the door he tumbled out into the entryway and rumbled off the porch. Blowing through his nostrils from the insult, gritting his tobacco-stained teeth, he walked along the street rapidly, frightening the chickens standing around the wattle fence.

"Well, we've spoken, you mother . . ." he muttered, wiping the perspiration from his face. "Of course, what kind of a talk can you have without a bottle!"

And all the way back he was sorry that he had come to the chairman without a bottle.

III

THE next day, having had some home brew in the morning, Vasily went to the stables and returned on horseback half an hour later. Having tied up the horse near the stoop, he brought out some hay from the barn, kneaded it up and put it in the cart, then thought for a while, threw some to the horse, and went into the house. He had decided to slaughter the ram in the morning; there was a market day in the city, and the ram had been coughing for two weeks.

Telling Akulina to get ready, he took a thin, narrow, German bayonet and went outside. He could barely drag the big old black ram with a white spot on its neck out from the cattle shed: he wouldn't go but stood firm and trembled.

"You feel it, eh?" Vasily mumbled and smiled in an evil way. He rested for a while, then took hold of the warm, twisted horn. The ram looked at the open door with his limpid eyes.

"Well, pray to God!" Vasily said, and he threw down the ram, put his knee on the soft underside and grabbed the ram's muzzle with his hand. The ram kicked and squirmed out from under Vasily's knee. Vasily, breathing heavily, again put the ram under him and turned its head back, stretching tight its neck with the white curly spot. Then, clenching his teeth, he took aim, and, with excessive force, he cut along the white spot.

The ram trembled and became soft under his knee; almost-black blood burst out from the widely spreading wound, covering the hay and the fertilizer and dirtying Vasily's hands.

A slight tremor went through the ram's body; his eyes, looking out into the light as before, screwed up and grew turbid. The calf, sniffing with curiosity from its corner, suddenly began to puff and banged against the wall several times.

Vasily got up, threw down the bayonet, carefully pulled out his tobacco pouch and began to roll a cigarette with his bloody fingers, wetting the paper with his saliva and not taking his eyes off the ram.

The ram began to shake; it stretched out, eyes now completely closed, the hind legs twitching even more, and in a minute the entire body pulsed in a strong and even beat; the legs kicked out joyfully, as though running, and kicked up the hay and the chicken droppings on the ground.

Waiting until the ram grew still, Vasily then put it up on a hook and began to take off the hide quickly and adroitly, cutting under the dull-gray pellicle membrane and through the leg tendons.

Cutting up the stomach, from which steam burst out, he took out the hot liver, cut off a piece and chewed it up, smearing his lips and chin with the blood.

Akulina came out on the stoop, freshly dressed, with a bundle in her arms. There was a change of underwear in the bundle, in case she was put in a hospital. Somehow managing to crawl into the cart, she covered herself with the oilskin and began to wait for Vasily. She looked at the dark fields and the river below with longing and love; then she looked around as though she was bidding farewell to her home and village forever.

In a while Vasily came out of the barn, holding the ram's carcass, already cut up and wrapped in a sack, like a child.

He put the carcass in the front of the cart, went off to give some feed to the cattle, and then to lock up the house. And Akulina suddenly caught the sweetish odor of the freshly slaughtered ram. At one time she liked this smell. It always filled the houses just before holidays. But now she felt bad, and she closed her mouth and nose with the edge of her kerchief.

Vasily took another gulp of home brew, locked up the house and came out on the stoop, girdling himself. In the morning he had washed and shaved, put on a new shirt, and now he looked happy, as though he had become younger.

"Vasya," said Akulina, "look at the beauty . . . I'll probably die in the city. I'm very sorry to be leaving. It weighs on my heart . . ."

Vasily also looked around at the fields with the dark haystacks and the black plough-land, the river, the village roofs darkening from the rain; he spat and said nothing.

Then he untied and bridled the horse, pulling and tearing at the horse's lips in the process; he fixed the hay in the cart again, sat down and moved off. The frightened horse started at a fast pace, and the cart began to roll from side to side in the wide ruts.

Akulina sat in the back, hunched over, holding her hands to her chest, looking longingly at the houses on both sides and watching the birch trees and the rowan trees already filling up with their saffron-red berries.

She looked and remembered her whole life on the Kolkhoz — both her youth and her married life, her children, loving this all the more strongly and sharply, knowing that perhaps she would never see her native places and none of those close to her. Tears rolled along her sunken cheeks. She only wanted one thing: to die at home, in her own village and to be buried in her own cemetery.

Some women, who happened along on the street at that moment, stopped, and, silently looking at her, bowed. Akulina smiled through her tears with a tense, bashful smile and also bowed, willingly, low, almost touching the cart slats with her head.

Vasily kept screaming "giddy-up" to the horse. His red face was tensely expectant and happy. He thought that once he put his wife in the hospital he would go to the market, sell the ram, drop over to his relatives, and then go to the restaurant at the railroad station.

He would sit there and drink light wine, looking out the window at the trains passing through. Waitresses in small white aprons and caps would serve him, an orchestra would be playing, it would smell of food and good cigarette smoke.

And once there, he would take counsel with his relatives and decide what to do: how best to leave the Kolkhoz and come to the city, and how to sell his house and property at the highest possible price.

translated by ROBERT SZULKIN

The Smell of Bread

YURY KAZAKOV

I

THEY RECEIVED the telegram January 1. Dusya was in the kitchen, so her husband went to open it. With a hangover and in his undershirt, he yawned irrepressibly, and, signing for the telegram, he pondered who else could have sent New Year's greetings. Still yawning, he read the brief, funeral telegram announcing the death of Dusya's mother, a seventy-year-old woman in a distant village.

"What a time for this!" he thought, stunned, and called his wife. Dusya didn't break out crying, she only paled slightly, entered the room, readjusted the tablecloth, and sat down. Her husband glanced dully at the unfinished bottles on the table, poured a drink for himself and drank it down. Then he thought a bit and poured one for Dusya.

"Drink it," he said. "Christ, I've got a head. Oh God. Well, we've all got to go sometime. What will you do – when will you go?"

Dusya was silent, rubbing her hand back and forth along the tablecloth. Then she drank, went over to the bed, as if she were blind, and lay down.

"I don't know," she said after a slight pause.

Her husband went up to her and looked at her plump body.

"Well, fine . . . What's to be done? What are you going to do?" He didn't know what else to say, and he turned back to the table and poured himself another one. "May she rest in peace. We've all got to go sometime."

The whole day Dusya went about the apartment sluggishly.

Her head ached, and she did not go visiting. She would have liked to cry a little, but somehow she couldn't bring herself to cry. She was simply sad. Dusya had not seen her mother for about fifteen years; she had left the village more than fifteen years ago and seldom remembered anything from her past life. And even when she did recall something, it was more apt to be from her early childhood, or how she was accompanied home from the community club when she was a little girl.

Dusya began to look through some old photographs and again was unable to cry: in all the snapshots her mother had a strange, strained face, bulging eyes and heavy, dark hands lowered along the seams of her dress.

At night, lying in bed, Dusya talked to her husband for a long time and, towards the end, said, "I won't go! What's the point in going? It's cold there now . . . And if she's left any stuff, the relatives have probably taken good care of it. There's no shortage of relatives there. No, I won't go!"

II

THE winter passed, and Dusya completely forgot about her mother. Her husband had a good job, they enjoyed their life, and Dusya became even plumper and prettier.

But in the beginning of May, Dusya received a letter from her nephew Misha. The letter was dictated by him and was written on a small sheet of paper in a slanting hand. Misha sent greetings from the numerous relatives and wrote that Grandmother's house and possessions were still intact and that Dusya should come without fail.

"Go!" her husband said. "Get a move on! Don't make any special fuss over the price, just sell whatever is there as soon as possible. Otherwise someone else will get it, or it will all go to the Kolkhoz."

III

AND Dusya set off. She hadn't taken a trip for a long time, and it was pleasant to be riding. She succeeded in enjoying herself on the way as one should and spoke with and met many people.

She had sent a telegram that she was leaving, but for some reason no one met her. She had to walk, but even the walking was enjoyable to Dusya. The road was well-paved, and her native Smolensk fields with a light blue copse on the horizon spread along the sides of the road.

Dusya arrived in her village in about three hours. She stopped on the new bridge across the small river and looked about. The village had been built up a great deal and had spread out with its white farmhouses. For some reason Dusya did not like these changes.

She walked along the street, glancing sharply at everyone she met, trying to guess who he was. But she recognized almost no one, although many recognized her, stopped her, and were surprised at how she had grown up.

Dusya's sister was overjoyed at her arrival; she burst out crying, and ran to set up the samovar. Dusya began to take out presents from her suitcase. Her sister looked at the presents, began to cry again, and embraced Dusya. Meanwhile Misha sat on a bench and wondered why they were crying.

The sisters sat down to drink tea, and Dusya found out that many of the things had been taken away by relatives. The cattle, the suckling pig, three young sheep, the goat and the chickens her sister had taken for herself. At first Dusya secretly begrudged her this, but then she forgot about it, all the more since much was left and, most important of all, the house remained. Having drunk a good quantity of tea and having had a long talk, the sisters went to look at the house.

The farm acreage had been ploughed, and Dusya was surprised, but her sister told her that the neighbors had ploughed it so that the soil should not go to waste. And the house seemed to Dusya not at all as large as she remembered it.

The windows were covered with boards, and a lock hung on the door. Her sister tried for a long time to unbolt it, then Dusya tried, then her sister again, and both managed to wear themselves out before they finally did open it.

It was dark in the house; light barely penetrated the boarded windows. The house had become damp and had an unlived-in look, but it smelled of bread, a smell dear to her from childhood, and Dusya's heart began to beat quickly. She walked about in the room, looked around, getting used to the dim light. The ceiling was low and dark brown. Photographs still hung on the walls, but the icons, except one which was not hung, were no longer there. Not even the embroidered cloths on the stove and chests were there.

Left alone, Dusya opened a chest — it smelled of her mother. In the chest were the old woman's dark shirts, *sarafans*, a worn-out sheepskin coat. Dusya dragged all this out, looked it over, again walked about the house, glanced into the empty yard, and it seemed to her that a long time ago she dreamed all of this, and now she had returned to her dream.

IV

HAVING heard about the sale, neighbors began to come round to Dusya. They looked at everything painstakingly, felt everything, but Dusya asked cheap prices, and the things went quickly.

The main thing was the house! Dusya consulted about house prices and was surprised and overjoyed at how much house prices had gone up. Immediately three buyers appeared — two from her own and one from another village. But Dusya did not sell right away — she was worried that her mother might have hidden some money somewhere. She looked for it for about three days. She tapped the walls, felt through the mattresses, crawled about in the basement and the garret, but didn't find anything.

Having agreed with the buyers on a price, Dusya left for the regional center, registered the sale of the house with a notary, and put the money in a savings account. When she returned, she brought some more gifts for her sister and began to prepare to go back to Moscow. In the evening her sister left for the farm, while Dusya prepared to visit her mother's grave. Misha accompanied her.

They left at sundown and went by the meadow. Here and there dandelions had already appeared, the grass was tender and green. The sky had been threatening and overcast in the late afternoon, but toward evening the clouds disappeared, and only on the horizon, where Dusya and Misha were going, there still hung a bank of ash-pink clouds. It was so far off and unclear that it seemed as though it stood behind the sun.

The river made a sharp loop about two kilometers from the village, and in this loop, on the right steep shore, as though on a peninsula, there was a graveyard. Once it was surrounded by a brick wall, and one entered it through a high, arched gate. But after the war the destroyed wall was taken away for building purposes, leaving, for some unaccountable reason, only the gate, and the pathways toward the graveyard ran from all directions.

On the way Dusya questioned Misha about school, work on the farm, the chairman of the Kolkhoz and the harvest; she was calm and collected. But now the old graveyard appeared, crimson in the light of the setting sun. Along its boundaries where once a fence had stood, where bushes of sweetbriar grew, there were many old graves which had long since lost the appearance of graves. Alongside of them in the bushes could be seen freshly painted fences with low wooden obelisks — common graves . . .

Dusya and Misha passed the gate, turned right, then left through the blooming birch trees and the acridly smelling bushes. Dusya's face kept turning pale, and her mouth half opened.

"Here's Grandma's . . ." Misha said, and Dusya saw a hillock in a sunken place covered with sparse, sharp grass. Loamy soil was visible through the grass. A small, gray cross, still not fixed since winter, stood crookedly.

Dusya turned completely white, and it was as though a knife had been suddenly stuck through her chest into her heart; such a dark and bitter grief pierced her soul. She began to choke, to shake, to scream violently. She fell down and crawled to the grave on her knees and began to sob, using such strange words that Misha was terrified.

"O-o-o-," Dusya wailed in a low tone, having fallen with her face on the grave and sinking her fingers deep into the damp earth. "My priceless Mama . . . dearest Mama, my darling, beloved . . . O-o-o- . . . Akh, now we'll never see each other in this world, never! How will I live without you, who will caress me, who will calm me? Mama, Mama, what have you done? . . ."

"Aunt Dusya . . . Aunt Dusya . . ." Misha whimpered in

fright, and pulled her by the sleeve. But when Dusya, having become hoarse, began to bend down and beat her head on the grave, Misha took off for the village.

In an hour, already in deep twilight, people from the village came running to Dusya. She was still lying there, having completely lost consciousness, and could no longer cry, speak, or think; she only groaned through her tightly clenched teeth. Her face was terrifying and black from the earth.

They picked her up, rubbed her forehead, began to calm her, to reassure her, and took her home. But she understood nothing. She looked at everyone with her large, swollen eyes, and all of life seemed to her to be darkness. When they brought her to her sister's house, she barely managed to reach the bed — and immediately fell asleep.

The next day, all ready to leave for Moscow, she drank tea with her sister in parting, was gay and described what a wonderful apartment and what luxuries they had in Moscow.

And so she left, gay and calm, having given Misha, in addition to her previous gifts, a gift of ten rubles. And in two weeks her mother's house was opened, the floors were washed, things were brought in, and new people began to live in it.

translated by ROBERT SZULKIN

Lots of Luck, Kid!

BULAT OKUDZHAVA

This is not an adventure story. This is a story about how I fought in the war, how they wanted to kill me, and how I made it through all right. I really don't know who to thank for this. Perhaps no one. So don't you worry. I'm alive and well. Some people will be happy to hear this, and then, of course, there will be those who won't like it at all. But I'm alive. There's nothing to be done. After all, you can't please everyone.

HAYSEED

IN MY CHILDHOOD I did a lot of crying. As I grew older I cried less. Later, when I was in my teens, I only cried twice. The first time was one evening just before the war. I said to this girl I loved—and I said it with feigned indifference:

"Well then, if that's it, then it's all over . . ."

". . . If that's it, then it's all over," she agreed with unexpected calmness, and walked away. It was then that I burst out crying because she was leaving me. And I wiped away my tears with the palm of my hand.

I'm crying for the second time right now: here in the Mozdok steppe. I'm carrying a very important message for the regimental commander. Where the hell is this regimental commander? These sandy hills all look the same to me. It's night. It's only my second day at the front. And if you don't carry out orders, they shoot you. And I'm eighteen.

Who said they shoot you? That was Kolya Grinchenko, just before I left. He smiled sweetly when he said it.

"Take care. If you don't, it's the firing squad . . ."

They'll put me up against a wall. But there are no walls here. They'll take me out in the fields . . .

And I'm wiping away the tears. "Your son showed cowardice and . . ." That's how the telegram will start out. But why did they send me with the message? There's Kolya Grinchenko — he's a real strong, smart fellow. He would have found the place a long time ago. By now he'd be sitting inside the warm headquarters dugout. He'd be drinking tea out of a mug, winking at the girls who operate the radios and smiling pleasantly at them.

Supposing I step on a mine. They'd find me in the morning, and the regimental commander will say to the battery commander, "Lieutenant Burakov, why did you send a green kid? You didn't give him a chance to look around, get used to his place. And it's because of your indifference that we've lost a good man."

"Your son died in action while carrying out a very important mission . . ." That's how the telegram will start.

"Hey, where are you going?"

That's me they're shouting at. I see a small trench, and someone is waving at me. What the hell do they care where I'm going?

"Halt!" someone shouts behind me.

I stop.

"Over here!"

I go over, and someone pulls me into the trench by the sleeve.

"Where are you going?" they ask angrily.

I explain to them.

"Don't you know that there are Germans here! Another thirty yards and . . ."

They explain it to me. This, it turns out, is our advance observation point.

Then they take me to a dugout. The regimental commander reads the message, looks at me, and I feel small and insignificant. I look at my not terribly venerable, thin legs, all wrapped in leggings, and then at my sturdy army boots. I suppose all this is very funny to them. But no one's laughing. And the beautiful radio operator looks past me. Now, if I wore knee boots and a nice officer's coat . . . If only they'd give me some tea. I'd like to sit down at the makeshift table and then say something to the beautiful girl that would . . . Of course, the way I look now . . .

"Return to the battery," the regimental commander barks. "And tell your commander not to send any more of these reports."

He emphasizes the words "of these."

"Okay," I say, and I hear the quiet laugh of the radio operator. She glances at me and laughs.

"How long have you been in the army?" the colonel asks.

"A month."

"In the army you don't say, 'Okay,' but, 'Yes, sir!' . . . and also, you've got your toes together but your heels apart . . ."

"A hayseed," says someone in a dark corner behind me.

"I know it," I say and walk out. I'm almost running.

The steppe again. It's snowing, and it's quiet. I can't even believe that this is the front, an advanced post, that there's danger nearby. I won't lose my way this time.

I can imagine how absurd I must have looked to them: feet spread apart, hands in my coat pockets and cap over my ears. While this beautiful girl . . . They didn't even offer me any tea . . . When Kolya Grinchenko speaks to officers, he sort of smiles. He salutes smartly and says: "Yes, sir!" But I can hear him saying: "Go ahead and order, I see right through you." And he does see.

My ankle boots are good and strong. That's really fine. A heavy masculine foot. I wish I had a fur cap with ear flaps, then I wouldn't look so pitiful. At any rate, I'll be back soon, give my report. I'll drink a lot of tea and then get some sleep. Now I have a right to it.

I'm carrying a submachine gun across my back, two grenades on one hip and a gas mask on the other. I look real belligerent. Very much so. Someone once said that belligerence is a sign of cowardice. But am I a coward? When I had an argument with Volod'ka Anilov in the eighth grade, it was me who shouted first: "Let's fight it out!" And I became terrified. But we went behind the school, and our friends stood around us. He hit me first, on the arm.

"So that's it," I shouted and poked him in the shoulder.

Then we kept swearing at each other, neither one wanting to start first.

And suddenly it all seemed very funny to me, and I said to him, "Listen, I'm going to belt you right in the kisser . . ."

"Go ahead," he said, and put up his fists.

"Or you hit me. There'll be blood. Well, what's the difference?"

He suddenly calmed down, and we shook hands according to all the rules. But after that there was no friendship between us.

Am I a coward?

At sunrise yesterday we stopped in these hills.

"Everyone's here," Lieutenant Burakov said.

"Where are we?" someone asked.

"It's the advanced post."

It was his first time at the front, just like the rest of us, and that's why he spoke so solemnly and so proudly.

"But where are the Germans?" someone asked.

"The Germans are over there."

"Over there" we could see small hills, overgrown with patches of withered scrub.

And I thought that I wasn't at all terrified. And I was surprised at how simply the lieutenant had figured out the enemy position.

NINA

"Oh, but you're handsome," says Sashka Zolotaryov.

I'm shaving in front of a broken piece of mirror. There's nothing to shave. It's colder in the trench than outside. My hands are red, my nose is red, and the blood is red. I'm cutting myself to bits. Can I be handsome? Ears set wide apart. Nose like a potato.

Why am I shaving? We've already been at the front lines for three days, and we haven't heard a shot, or seen one German, or had anyone wounded. Then why am I shaving? Yesterday evening that same beautiful girl from headquarters stopped at the entrance to our trench.

"Hello!" she said.

And I looked at her, and I knew that I was unshaven. I saw myself in her eyes. It's as though I was reflected in them. She has such large eyes. I forget their color. I nodded to her.

"How's life?" she asked.

"I'm living," I said sullenly.

"Why are you so sullen? Haven't they fed you?"

I took out my cigarettes.

"Well," she said, "cigarettes."

"What's it to you, haven't you anything better to do?" I said.

"Let's have a smoke," she said and took a cigarette out of the pack by herself.

We smoked and didn't say anything. Then she said, "You know, you're just a small fry."

"What's that?"

"That's a fish that's just spawned."

I crawled into the trench and could hear her laughing behind me.

"Did Ninka come over?" Kolya Grinchenko asked later.

"Yes. Do you know her?"

"I know everybody," he said.

Now I'm clean-shaven. I still have some cigarettes left. I feel that she'll come. I've unbuttoned my shirt collar. So what if I look bad. I've unbuttoned my coat and put my hands in my pockets. And I'm standing behind the shell crates, so that my leggings won't be seen.

Who am I? I'm a soldier. A mortar man. We're the regimental mortar battery. I've risked my life. Maybe it's a miracle that I haven't been wounded yet. Come on, you radio operator you, you headquarters rat. Come on, I'll treat you to some cigarettes. Come — perhaps tomorrow I'll be lying with my arms stretched out . . .

"Oh, but you are real handsome," says Sashka Zolotaryov. I spit and turn away. Maybe he's laughing. But my lips are twisting.

Sashka is scraping the mud off his boots with a stick. Then he smears them with a thick layer of lubrication grease.

Will Nina come or won't she? I'll say, "Hi, small fry . . ." I'll have a smoke with her. Then it'll be evening. If this is war, why isn't there any shooting? Not a single shot, not a single German or anyone wounded.

"Why aren't there any higher-ups here?" I ask.

"They're in conference," says Sashka.

It's a good thing I'm tall and not fat like Zolotaryov. If only my coat fit!

Kolya Grinchenko comes over. He smiles winningly and says, "The sergeant's a beast. He makes omelets for himself, but gives me concentrates to eat." Kolya looks at Sashka and me.

"Don't make so much noise," says Sashka.

"This isn't the home front," Kolya continues. "They don't do much talking here. They give it to you in the back of the head, and it's goodbye. They won't even recognize you."

"Why don't you go and tell him that," says Sashka.

The sergeant is standing behind Kolya. He has a grease spot on his chin.

"Okay," he says.

Nobody says anything. He turns around and goes into his trench. Everyone is silent. Sashka's boots shine like the sergeant's greasy chin. My hands are sweating. Kolya Grinchenko smiles sweetly. The smell of fried eggs comes out of the sergeant's trench.

"Fried eggs are good with onions," says Sashka.

Shongin comes over. He's an old soldier. A famous soldier. He has served in all armies and in all wars. In every war he winds up at the front lines, and then he gets diarrhea. He hasn't fired a single shot, nor been in a single attack, nor ever been wounded. He has a wife who has seen him off to all the wars.

Shongin comes over. He's eating a radish and doesn't say anything.

"Where'd you get the radish?"

Shongin shrugs his shoulders.

"Give me a radish," Sashka says.

"It's my last one," says Shongin.

It's a good thing there are no big shots around here. No one is giving any orders or driving you. I really carried that message. The devil only knows why . . . as if they couldn't have sent Kolya Grinchenko. When my father was seventeen, he organized an underground Komsomol, and here I am, round-shouldered, ridiculous-looking, and I haven't done a thing. I just brag about my noble character, which likely doesn't even exist . . .

Shongin keeps pulling radishes out of his pocket. The red little balls fly into his mouth and make a crunching noise.

"Shongin, give me a radish," I say.

"It's my last one," says Shongin.

I make a wager: if Shongin pulls out another radish, Nina will come. Shongin puts his hand in his pocket and pulls out his tobacco pouch. She won't come. Suddenly Kolya says, "Here's Ninochka."

I turn around. She's coming down a small hillock. With her is another girl I don't know. Nina has a light step. Her coat is buttoned up all the way. She's wearing a fur cap with ear flaps. A bit cocked, the cap, and what a cap! Hi, small fry! Everyone looks in her direction. She's coming.

"Aaa!"

That's Shongin screaming.

"Aaa!" and he falls down. Sashka too, and Kolya Grinchenko. "Down!"

I throw myself face down. Somewhere off in the distance there's an explosion. A short one. There is some rustling noise, and then everything is quiet.

Someone's laughing. The sergeant is standing at the trench entrance.

"That's enough lying around in the dirt, boys."

Silently we get up. Kolya is gone. He's running towards the hillock where Nina was. From a distance I see her get up from the dirty snow. The other girl lies there motionless. Face up.

Slowly and silently we go over there. Other soldiers too. That was our first mine. The first. Ours.

WAR

I'VE gotten to know you, war. I've got large welts on the palms of my hands, and a buzzing noise in my head. I want to sleep. Do you want me to forget everything I've gotten used to? Do you want to teach me to submit myself unquestioningly? The screams of the commanding officer — run, do, bellow "Yes, sir!" when you reply, fall down, crawl, fall asleep on the march. If there's the sound of a mine — bury yourself in the ground, dig with your nose, head, feet, your whole body, at the same time not experiencing fright, or even thinking. A tinful of barley soup — secrete gastric juice, get ready, grumble, stuff yourself, wipe your spoon on the grass. If comrades die — dig a grave, cover it with earth, fire mechanically into the air . . . three times.

I've already learned a great deal. I pretend I'm not hungry. I pretend I'm not cold. I pretend I'm not sorry for anyone. I only want to sleep, sleep, sleep . . .

Like a fool, I've lost my spoon. An ordinary aluminum spoon. Tarnished, with a jagged edge, but still, a spoon. A very important item. Now I have nothing to eat with — I drink the soup straight from the tin. And if it's *kasha* . . . I've adapted a piece of wood. I eat my *kasha* with a piece of wood. From whom could I ask one? Everyone guards his spoon. No one's a fool here. And me, I have a hunk of wood.

Sashka Zolotaryov makes notches on a stick. One notch for each casualty.

Kolya Grinchenko smiles crookedly.

"Don't worry, Sashka. There'll be enough dames for everyone."

Zolotaryov doesn't say anything. I'm silent. The Germans are silent; today at least.

Lieutenant Burakov goes around unshaven. I'm sure it's for show. We've not been ordered to open fire. There's some sort of conference going on. Our commanding officer's making the rounds of the mortar crews. The mortars are in the trenches, in a hollow. The trenches have been dug according to all the regulations. But we don't study the regulations.

The gunner Gavrilov comes over and sits down near me. He looks at the cigarettes I've rolled.

"Why are you smoking so much?"

"What of it?"

"The wind's blowing the sparks all around. It's already dark, they'll notice it," he says and looks about.

I put out the butt on the sole of my shoe. The sparks start flying around like fireworks. Suddenly a six-barrel mortar opens up on the German side. The shells land with a thump somewhere behind us. Gavrilov is crawling in the snow.

"You mother . . ." he suddenly screams. Explosion after explosion. Explosion after explosion. Closer and closer. My comrades are running past me to the mortars. And I'm sitting in the snow. It's my own fault . . . How will I ever be able to face them? Here comes Lieutenant Burakov. He's screaming something. And the shells keep falling.

Then I get up too, and start running, shouting, "Lieutenant, lieutenant!"

The first mortar roars, and suddenly it's more comfortable. It's as though we found some powerful, quiet friends. Then the shouting dies down. All four mortars are now firing into the air from

the hollow. Only the telephonist, the young and scrawny Gurgenidze, shouts, "A hit! A hit!"

I do what I'm supposed to do. I drag the crates with the mortar
shells out of the shelter. How strong I am after all! And I'm not
afraid of anything. I just keep dragging the crates. Rumbling.
Shouting. The sharp smell of explosives. Everything's all mixed up.
Now this is a fight for you. A real battle. Clouds of smoke . . .
But I'm making it all up. Not one shot has been fired at us. It's us
making all the noise. And I'm at fault. And everyone knows it.
They're all waiting for me to come and say that it was all my fault.

Now it's getting darker. My back hurts. I barely have time to
grab some snow and swallow it.

"All clear!" Gurgenidze shouts.

I'll tell the company commander everything so they won't think
I'm hiding anything.

"Lieutenant . . ."

He's sitting on the edge of the trench and running his finger
over a map. He looks at me, and I understand; he is waiting for
me to say I was at fault.

"It's my fault. I didn't think. You can do what you want with
me . . ."

"And what am I supposed to do with you?" he asks thought-
fully. "What have you done?"

Is he kidding? Or has he forgotten? I tell him everything. I get
it off my chest. He looks surprised. Then he just shrugs his shoulders.

"Listen, go take a rest. What's your cigarette got to do with it?
We just launched an offensive. We simply had to do some shooting. Go, go!"

I go away.

"Watch out you don't fall asleep, or you'll freeze to death," the
lieutenant calls after me.

In an hour we're on our feet again. We're shooting at the Germans again. An attack. But I can't see it. What kind of an attack
is it if we're sitting in one spot? Is this the way it's always going to
be? Rumbling. The smell of explosives. Gurgenidze screaming,
"It's a hit! It's a miss!" And this damned hollow from which you
can't see anything. But there's an attack somewhere else. Tanks

rolling, infantry, cavalry, people singing the *Internationale*, dying without letting their banners out of their hands.

And when there's a lull, I run over to the observation point. I'll take a look, even if it's out of the corner of my eye, and see what an attack is like. I'll breathe it in. Why, the OP's nothing, just a hilltop, with observers lying on their sides, their heads slightly raised, and battery commander Burakov looking through a stereo-telescope. I crawl up the steep hill and raise myself waist high. And I hear birds singing. Birds!

Someone pulls me down by the feet.

"Tired of living?" the battery commander hisses. "What in hell are you doing crawling around here?"

"I just wanted to see," I say.

The observers laugh.

"Where did the birds come from?" I ask.

"Birds?" repeats the commander.

"Birds . . ."

"What birds?" asks the telephonist Kuzin from the trench.

"Birds," I say, and I no longer understand anything myself.

"Do you think those are birds?" the commander asks wearily.

"Birds . . ." Kuzin laughs.

I'm beginning to understand what's up. One of the observers puts his hat on a stick and lifts it above him. The birds start singing right away.

"Get it now?" the commander asks.

He's a good man. Anyone else would have started stamping his feet and swearing. Our commander is a good man. I would have been killed if it weren't for him. He was probably the one who pulled me down by the feet.

It's getting darker and darker. A gray dusk is enveloping the hill. I hear a machine gun firing in the distance.

"Machine gun," I shout. No one pays any attention to me.

"They're ours," says commander Burakov. "We'll start any minute now." Then he says to me, "Here, take a look."

I squat down near the telescope and look. I see the steppe. At the extreme edge of the steppe, against a background of gray sky, a settlement stretches out in a line. And there, just like fireworks, multi-colored lines of tracer bullets stretch out from one end to the other. And I hear the rattling of machine guns and the staccato of submachine guns. But I don't see the attack. I don't see any people.

"Let's go, let's go!" someone screams behind me.

"Where? Where to?"

And suddenly I see — solitary figures, hunched up, running across the steppe. But only a few of them.

"That's enough," says the battery commander. "Back to the battery."

I roll down the hill. I'm running. A jeep comes toward me. A general is sitting in it. I don't know what to do: run past or march past and salute . . .

The general is red in the face. He doesn't see me. He's waving his arms. And the jeep is getting closer to the observation point. The commander is already standing at attention. And the men too. And the telescope, also, is standing motionless on its tripod.

The general jumps out of the jeep and runs up to the commander.

"You're firing on your own men, your own men!"

The commander is silent. Only his head moves from side to side.

Then the general looks into the telescope, and the commander explains something to him. The general shakes his hand.

"There are miracles," I think to myself.

"Cease fire!" Kuzin screams into the telephone.

The battery is silent; as though everyone were listening for something. And the mortars, like dogs, sit on their hind legs and are also silent.

"What's the matter with your hands?" asks the sergeant.

My hands are bloody. I don't understand where the blood came from. I shrug my shoulders.

"That's from the shell crates," says Shongin.

They'll bandage them for me in a little while.

The sergeant turns around and goes away. He probably went to get the medical orderly. I stand there with my hands stretched out in front of me. They really must have bled. They'll bandage them, and I'll write home . . .

"Go wash off your hands," says the sergeant. "We're changing our position now."

THE LITTLE BELL — A GIFT FROM VALDAI

HELP me. Save me. I don't want to die. Just a small piece of lead in the heart, or head, and it's all over. And my hot body, will it no longer be hot? I don't mind suffering. Who said I was afraid of suffering? It was at home that I was so afraid. At home. But now I've gotten to know a lot of things. I've tried it all. Isn't this enough for one person to know? I'll be set for life. Help me. You know, it's ridiculous to kill a man who hasn't had time to do something in life. I didn't even finish tenth grade. Help me. I'm not speaking about love. To hell with love. I'm content not to love. When you really come down to it, I've already loved. If you really want to know, I've had enough of that. I have a mother. What's going to happen to her? Do you know how tenderly a mother strokes the head of her child? I haven't had time to get unaccustomed to it yet. I really haven't been anywhere yet. For example, I haven't been to Valdai yet. I really must know what this Valdai is like. Someone once wrote: "The little bell is a gift from Valdai." And I can't even write such lines. Help me. I'll go through everything. To the end. I'll shoot at the Fascists like a sniper, I'll fight tanks single-handed, I won't eat or sleep; I'll suffer . . .

To whom am I saying all this? Whose help am I seeking? These logs which hold the dugout together maybe? Even they aren't happy about being here. After all, not so long ago they were rustling pine trees. Remember the warm shelter when we left for the front? Of course, I remember. We stood in the open doors and sang some solemn song. We held our heads high. A troop train stood on a siding. Where? At the Kursk railroad station. We didn't get home leave. I only had time to phone home. No one was there. Only an old neighbor, Irina Makarovna. An old witch. Boy, did she get on my nerves! She asked me where the train had stopped.

"Too bad your mother won't be able to see you," she said without feeling.

I hung up and returned to the troop train. An hour later Irina Makarovna turned up at the train and shoved a bundle into my hands. And later, when we were singing, she stood among a group of women spectators. What is she to me? Farewell, Irina Makarovna. Forgive me. How was I supposed to know? I'll never be able to understand it . . . Perhaps, you're the very person one should ask for protection? Protect me then. I don't want to die. I'm saying this honestly and without shame.

There were some dried biscuits and sunflower-seed oil in the bundle. I made a vow to save one biscuit as a souvenir. But I ate it. I couldn't even do such a simple thing as that. And wasn't it me who stood in full view when the Heinkel swooped down and everyone took cover?

"Take cover!" they screamed at me.

But I didn't hide. I walked alone and laughed out loud. If they only knew what was going on inside of me! But I can't tremble in view of everyone. No one must know that I'm afraid. But can I myself face the truth? That's what I mean. I'm my own judge . . . I have a right to do this. Me, I'm not Fed'ka Lyubimov. Remember Fed'ka Lyubimov? Of course, I do. Fyodor Lavrent'evich Lyubimov. My neighbor. When the war broke out, he'd come out into the kitchen every evening and say: "Those German bastards are really pushing . . . Everyone should stand up to give protection. Wait and see, as soon as my arm gets better, I'll volunteer."

"You'll be called up anyway, Fed'ka," they'd say to him.

"It's not a joking matter. Everyone will be called up. When the country is in danger you shouldn't wait. You should join up your-self."

"Do you love your country?" he would ask me.

"Yes," I said. "I learned that in the first grade."

Once I ran into him in the recruiting office. I was delivering telegrams at the time. He didn't see me. He was speaking to some captain.

"Comrade captain, I've brought my exemption certificate," he said.

"What exemption?"

"Reserve. As a specialist I've been exempted from the service. They won't release me from my job . . ."

"Go in there and register. If you're exempt, then you're exempt. That's all there is to it," the captain said.

If you're exempt, then you're exempt. That's Fed'ka for you. What kind of a specialist is he, a watch repairman on the Arbat?

And Fed'ka went in and registered. He passed by me, noticed me, blushed, and stopped.

"Did you see?" he asked me. "That's the way it is. Who wants to die?"

He's probably still exempt. As though he were some well-known engineer or great actor.

We didn't build this shelter. It's a good shelter. True, it's smaller than headquarters, where Nina is, but still, it's not bad. It looks like someone left it in a hurry. Somebody lost a photograph of a woman. A young, unattractive woman smiles at me from the photograph. But someone must love her. Why did he forget to take her picture with him?

"Hey, Sashka, did you get an exemption?" I ask.

"Who's going to give it to me. Not everyone can get one," Sashka replies.

"If you slipped something to the right person, you would have gotten one," says Kolya Grinchenko.

"Probably costs a lot, doesn't it?" Sashka asks.

"Three thousand. You could have sold some stuff to get the money. You could have saved up enough."

"Sure I could. My desk alone is worth three thousand."

"Then you could have given it to them."

"Akh," says Sashka and waves his hand. "Go to hell."

"Why didn't you slip them something and get exempted?" Shongin asks angrily.

"I didn't have any money," laughs Kolya.

"You blabber too much," says Shongin.

LUCKY

OUR mortars have been at it for eight days now. We have three wounded men. I haven't seen them. When I returned to the battery, they had already been taken away. We keep moving from one place to another, so that not only do we not have any trenches, but we also don't have any communications trenches. There's no time for it. It's an attack. When it began Kolya Grinchenko said: "We're in luck, boys. Now we're in luck. Now we'll eat well. We'll live off captured goods now. We've had enough of canned goods for a while."

At that time we all believed him. But it was in vain. The artillery and we always get there last, when everything is already gone.

It's canned goods again. And it's dried biscuits again. And Kolya Grinchenko says to the sergeant, "Sergeant, this canned goods stuff is crap. Where's our front rations?"

"Do you remember, kid, how you were threatening me?" the sergeant asks.

"Prove it," smiles Grinchenko.

"You'd better shut up," says the sergeant.

Now he has something on Kolya. And I see that Kolya is afraid of him. But sometimes he forgets that he's afraid, and he starts in on him again. This can be very funny.

I remember when we entered the first village — it was the same one I had seen from the observation point. It was destroyed. The huts, which were already being repaired, were full of cavalry men; they were dressing, sleeping, playing harmonicas, and, in one hut, they were even making pancakes. Well, of course, we're late everywhere. Where are we supposed to go?

"Let's go," says Grinchenko.

Sashka Zolotaryov and I follow him. We go into a hut. It's hot there. The stove is on. It's empty. Only a Cossack is there, bent over a frying pan. You can tell he's a Cossack from his uniform trousers.

"Hi," says Grinchenko from the threshold. "Welcome some guests."

Kolya really knows how to speak to people. He's really quite at home with them. He smiles when he speaks. He smiles in such a way that you can't help but smile back at him. The Cossack now turns around, and I see a face with high cheekbones and slanting eyes.

"So you're a Cossack!" says Kolya. "Where are you from?"

"What do you want?" the Cossack asks.

"You're a Kalmuk, probably, not a Cossack. A Kalmuk, right?" And Kolya says to us, "Let's get settled, boys. Oh, you Kalmuk Cossack!"

And Kolya puts his field pack on the bench. The Kalmuk picks it up and throws it on the threshold. He stands in front of the tall Grinchenko; he is so small, with his high cheekbones and wide shoulders.

"What's the matter? You don't like Kalmuks? Go away!"

"Why, you swine . . ." Kolya's face turns red.

"Go, go!" the Kalmuk says calmly.

"I've shed blood, and you're throwing me out in the cold?" Sashka takes Kolya by the arm.

"Don't be cute, Mykola."

"Take your friends with you," the Kalmuk says.

"Please, don't get mad," I say.

"Get going . . ."

Suddenly the door opens, and some Cossacks come in. There are three of them.

"What's the trouble?" asks one of them.

The Kalmuk doesn't say anything. Sashka and I are silent. Kolya also keeps quiet. Then Kolya smiles, and asks the Kalmuk, "Why are you silent, Kalmuk?" and then he says to the Cossacks, "See that bastard . . . he lights the stove for himself and sends Russians out into the cold!"

"What's with them?" the Cossack asks the Kalmuk.

"Come on boys, take off," says the other Cossack to us. And the third one says to the Kalmuk, "Come on Dzhumak, let's eat."

We leave the hut in silence. Into the cold. It's twilight. If Grinchenko says something now, it'll be sickening. It seems to me that I've insulted a man. Kolya is silent. He "shed blood" . . . He hasn't even gotten a scratch.

Now we're already beyond this populated point. Fire, mortars, fire! Blow, wind! Pour, you, half-rain, half-snow! Get wet, you back of mine! Hurt, you hands of mine!

What can I do so my feet won't freeze? Boy, do I need a pair of boots! Wide ones. Three sizes too large. So I can really wrap my feet . . . so my foot will be just like in a nest. I must walk some more. But we almost never walk. We have to change positions all the time. This means, get into the trucks, and get rolling. It's raining. It's coming down from the sky in a straight line. Now it's snowing. It comes in at a slant. The wind's blowing from all sides.

Day and night we get soaked. Towards morning it starts freezing up. You don't feel like moving.

I'm thinking about Nina. And it seems to me that she's somewhere on one of the trucks. The telephonist Kuzin is dead. Caught a bullet right in the mouth. It was a spent bullet, a weak one. But somehow it managed to pierce him, and he died.

CONVERSATIONS

THIS is probably the first night that we've been able to sleep normally. We're lying on the floor of an abandoned hut. We're on our coats. It's impossible to cover up. It's hot. Shongin has heated up the stove. We've really crowded into the hut. It's dark. Only the red glow of Shongin's cigarette hovers about slowly and constantly.

"Give me a smoke, Shongin," says Sashka Zolotaryov.

Shongin is silent. The red glow is flying around.

"Give me a smoke, Shongin," I say. We continue the gag, slowly, as we always do.

"He's asleep," says Kolya Grinchenko.

The red glow hangs suspended in the air, pitiful and motionless. I stare into the darkness, and it's as if I can see the smile on Grinchenko's face, and as if I can see Shongin's clenched lips and his blinking eyes.

"I want to smoke," says Sashka. "Should I wake him or not?"

"Don't wake him," says Kolya. "Let the man sleep. Take it yourself. Take as much as you want."

"He's got his tobacco in his gas mask," I say.

"I'll give you 'take it yourself,'" says Shongin. "I'll give you some myself."

"See, you've awakened the man," says Kolya.

You can hear Shongin groaning.

We lie there and assiduously inhale the bitter cigarette smoke.

It's quiet. Then someone says in the darkness, "It'd be nice if Nina would come here. We could talk to her."

Sashka Zolotaryov laughs.

"I like plump girls," he says, "and girls that are taller than me."

"Ninka has a husband," I say.

Sashka laughs.

"I have a wife, too. Maybe Ninka's husband is with my 'dumpling' right now."

"It's war," says Kolya. "Everything has been mixed up. And then, if you want to speak about love, then in that case you can't order . . ."

Sashka laughs.

"You're a bunch of animals," says Shongin, and he turns over to the other side.

"I wouldn't marry someone like her," someone says in the darkness.

"But I would . . ."

"I had a girl, Katya was her name. What a beauty. Braids down to her waist. Now Ninka, well . . ."

"No one is forcing her on you," Kolya says angrily.

"If you don't like her," I say, "you don't have to take her. Right, Kolya?"

"Your Katya probably has a nose like a belly button," laughs Sashka. "You like 'em like that. A nose like a belly button and smelling of dough."

"You won't be laughing for long, Zolotaryov," someone threatens from the darkness.

> *You're still alive, my old girl,*
> *I'm alive too. Regards to you, regards.*
> *Above your roof, let there swirl . . .*

It's Kolya singing.

Suddenly the door opens. The commander's voice cuts into the darkness:

"Who's spreading pessimism here?"

And then it's quiet again.

What will happen tomorrow? Where are we going to wind up? No letters from home. There's no more room for notches on Sashka's stick. If I'm wounded, I'll be put in a hospital. I'll eat my fill. I'll go home on leave. I'll go over to the school. And everyone will see my crutches. I'll have a stripe on my chest. For my wound. And perhaps I'll get a medal, and they'll see that, too. And Zhenya will come out. And she won't be laughing this time. And everyone will look at her, then at me. And I'll say to her, "Hi, Zhenechka."

And I'll walk, walk along the corridor. And she'll catch up to me. "Why don't you drop over and visit me at home. I've missed you."

"At home?" What do you mean? Why, what do you mean?

"There's no reason. A lot has changed." And I'll walk along the corridor. And the girls will tell her quietly: "You fool, Zhen'ka. It's your own fault."

"I've got a stomachache from the pumpkin," says Sashka.

"When I was a civilian, I never even saw one," says someone.

Kolya advises Sashka: "You know, Sashka, you ought to go and take a load off your mind."

"You fool," says Sashka. "A pumpkin is a good thing, only not if it's raw."

"And I like borsht," someone says in the darkness. "A thick one, so that when you put your spoon in it, it'll stand upright. I don't need any dumplings."

And I don't have a spoon. Being without a spoon is like being without hands. They laugh at me and my piece of wood. I'm laughing myself . . . But I don't have a spoon . . . And I don't have boots. If only I had a pair of boots, we'd talk differently, Nina . . .

Nina, you're so slim. Look, here we are, you and me, walking through the city. Here's Zhenya coming towards us. She understands everything. And she's silent. And I'm wearing black slacks and a white shirt with a turn-down collar, and there's a Leica across my shoulders. And there's no war.

"And I'd like to eat some sour cream, too," someone says in the darkness.

NINA

No matter how many times I come to regimental headquarters, no matter how many times I look at Nina, she doesn't notice me.

But her own people, the ones from headquarters, speak to her very simply: "Nina, give me the mug . . ." "What's the matter, dear, tired? . . ." "Let's have a smoke . . ." "Hi, Ninochka . . ." "Good to see you again! . . . ," and they embrace her. And she — she hands them the mug, smiles, smokes, sitting on the crate, and kisses those who return right on their unshaven cheeks.

That's because they're "her own." But who are they, these "her own"? They're headquarters rats, and I come from the battery. I risk my life. My hands are cut to bits, my coat is burned, my lips chapped. But they're — "her own."

I crawl into the headquarters dugout. It's warm there. A joyous, potbellied stove is burning. It smells of bread. There's no one there. Only Nina is sitting with her earphones near the receiver.

"Don, Don, this is Moscow. Over. Don, Don, this is Moscow. How do you read me? Over."

"Hi, Nina," I say in an offhand manner.

She nods to me. It's so friendly, so nice. It's so unexpected.

"How do you read me? Is it better now? Over."

She takes off the earphones.

"Sit down, warrior. Rest up."

"No time," I say, and sit down on the boards. And I look at her. She smiles.

"Well, why are you staring?"

"Oh, nothing. It's been long since I've seen a woman smile. There are no women at the battery, you know. Sashka Zolotaryov sometimes smiles, and Kolya Grinchenko, but there are no women."

She smiles again.

"Your Kolya comes here often. He keeps telling me about his heroic deeds. I don't like braggarts."

"Come to see us . . ."

"Where?"

"At the battery."

"To drink tea?"

"We'll sit a while, smoke . . ."

"We'll sit a while, smoke." She smiles.

How daring I was when I first walked in. How daring! Even the flame of the lamp trembled. But now it's not moving.

"If you want, I'll give you some tea."

"I don't drink tea," I say ironically.

"Oh, I get it," says Nina. "You've gotten used to stronger stuff."

"Accustomed or not, I prefer it. We'll get our fill of tea when we're civilians again."

She looks straight at me, not blinking, and smiles.

"You're a strange one. Our reconnaissance men are good kids

too, but they don't refuse tea . . . You're a real strange one. But I'll come to the battery, okay? We'll sit a while, smoke, eh?"

"Really?"

"Yes . . . you know, you have nice eyes."

White wings sprout on my back. White. White. They make everything light, like a rocket flare at the front. Delirium.

"I still say you're lying about the 'stronger stuff.' "

She says this from afar. I don't see her. Only two large eyes. Round. Gray. Derisive.

Some people come in. They stamp their feet. They speak words. But I hear: "Don, Don . . . you have nice eyes . . . I'm signing off, Roger."

"Are you from Lieutenant Burakov?" they ask me.

"Yes, sir!"

"Here, take this . . ."

I take a piece of paper, put it in my pocket. I go over to Nina. "You'll come, then?"

"Where? Oh, the battery? We'll sit a while, smoke. Right?"

"Come."

"But I don't smoke," she smiles. "We'll just sit, okay?"

"Hey, Ninochka, what are you doing, entertaining the handsome soldier boys?" I hear behind my back.

". . . Everything is calm, quiet, but I feel kind of bad. I have a feeling," says Shongin, "and I'm not happy about this silence. No, I'm not happy about it."

The small, scrawny Gurgenidze stands in front of Lieutenant Burakov. A drop hangs from the tip of his nose. He's waving his arms.

"Let me go home for four days. My house in Kvareli. I bring all kind *purmarili*, food, wine, *khachapuri*, *lobio*. This porridge no good."

The lieutenant laughs.

"And who's going to do the fighting?"

"I will," Gurgenidze bows. "Who will? I will. No war here now."

"And how will you get there?"

"What?"

"How will you go?"

Gurgenidze looks at the lieutenant regretfully.

"Give me leave. I'll get there."

The commander looks at us.

"Well, what do you say, shall we let him go?"

"Well, you see how it is, comrade lieutenant," says Shongin, "it'd be okay to let him go, but supposing it suddenly starts? How are we going to get along without a communications man?"

"You see how it is," says the commander. "We can't get along without you."

"Why not?" Gurgenidze becomes worried. "Sure you can. No fighting four days."

"Listen, Gurgenidze, why don't you go over to the Germans and ask them when they are going to begin. Perhaps you can even go after all," Sashka suggests.

Everyone laughs. They can't hold back. Gurgenidze tries to understand what happened. Then he shrugs his shoulders.

"Eh!" and he himself laughs.

And the drop, no longer being able to hold onto the tip of his nose, falls to the ground.

And the commander says, getting serious, "Rest. All of you. We'll be working this evening." And he goes away.

In the evening, again, nothing happens. I asked her to come to the battery. Why should she? Why? What is she going to do here? I invited her as though for a walk in the park. If she only saw my hands, covered with scabs and calluses; my hangnails, my hands which are impossible to wash clean, so deep has the dirt eaten itself into the flesh . . . I'll say to her, "Listen, why fool around? You see everything, you understand. Well, come on then and let it be simple: you and me. That I might know that you visited me. Let everybody see. Come on, what do you say? Listen, we're the same age. It's a lot of nonsense that the man must be older. I've known you for a long, long time. Well, please don't pretend that it's all the same to you. I know that the reason you laugh at me is because you're embarrassed." And when I say this to her, the white moon will come out, and the snow will glisten, and there won't be anyone around us, and my leggings won't be showing.

"Why aren't you resting?" asks Kolya Grinchenko.

What am I going to tell him?

"Yesterday I made a date with Ninochka. She'll come today."

"You're still lying," I say, relieved. "Boy, do you ever lie."

"You'll see," he says. "Wait."

Kolya stands before me. He smells of perfume. He shaved. Shaved? Is she really coming? Why, of course; she smiled, and I . . .

A white rocket flare goes up over the German trenches. Somewhere in the distance a machine gun rattles, lonely and sadly, and then it falls silent.

Kolya Grinchenko blows cigarette smoke into his cupped hands. He smiles.

"Yes, Ninochka will come, we'll talk . . ."

"But, she's married," I say. "You won't get anywhere with her."

He smiles and continues smoking. Then he walks off. And he doesn't say anything. If he's quiet, it means he's telling the truth. It means she will come. Fool that I was, fool. I asked, begged. One must do it the way Grinchenko said. Yes, that's the way. Embrace her, squeeze her till her bones crack so she can't say a word; so that she feels here's a man! They like that, yes. But conversations, who needs 'em? Oh, you gray-eyed Nina, you! Now I know what to tell you . . .

Beyond the dugout a jeep rumbles. And a female voice is heard. And I see Kolya heading in that direction. She's come. And I hear her voice:

"Hello, hello!" What a smile, what a smile. I can't stand it . . . "See, I came to visit you. Just for a minute. I asked the major to take me with him. Well, how are things? Well, look now, you've even got Germans nearby. Why are you so quiet, Kolya? You even have time to shave. Listen, you have a boy here, a dark-eyed one, where is he?"

"What dark-eyed one?" asks Grinchenko.

I hear her quiet laugh. She laughs well. Should I go over? But why should I? Why must it be me she's talking about? Gurgenidze is dark-eyed, so is the platoon leader Karpov, and so's the battery commander.

Her dark, slim silhouette swims out from beyond the dugout like a dark moon. She has stopped and is rocking back and forth lightly.

"There you are, warrior . . . We'll sit a while, smoke, right?"

She comes nearer, closer.

"Now that's really something," she says. "I have a date in the middle of the war. Why are you so quiet? Oh, oh, you probably filled yourself with that strong stuff, right?"

"I didn't drink anything . . ."

"Well, tell me something . . ."

"Let's go over there, near the shell crates. We'll sit."

"Aren't you something! Head for the corner right away."

"Why do you say that?"

"Because everyone wants it. And even more so at the front. What's going to happen tomorrow?"

"I like you, Nina."

"I know."

"You know? You're simply convinced of it?"

"Why what do you mean? What do you mean, my boy? Grinchenko told me that you speak to me in your sleep."

"He's always lying!"

From beyond the dugout someone shouted: "Nina! Nina Shubnikova, let's go!"

"Well, it's time. You haven't really told me anything. Who you are, what you are, what we're going to do," she says and passes the palm of her hand over my cheek.

"Well, goodbye. It's war. Perhaps we won't see each other."

"I'll come to see you tomorrow. I like you."

"Many people like me," she says. "I'm the only one here, you know."

She runs to the car. She runs quickly and flares go up more and more often above the German trenches.

OH, TOBACCO, TOBACCO . . .

JUST as thunder roars out of the calm, so unexpected colors appear in a gray morning: red on gray; saffron on gray; black on white. Flames, rusty, warped metal, motionless bodies.

Nina went off with the major to headquarters. The last rocket over the German positions is like the last flower. Nina is probably screaming into the telephone: "Volga, Volga, this is Don, how do you read me? Over!" And I have such a fat, little, peaceful shell in my hands. I'll pass it to the loader. Then the mortar will groan, sitting back on its hind legs.

I know how it's going to be. Boy, am I ever experienced now. And the palms of my hands don't hurt anymore.

And Kolya Grinchenko is sitting on the mortar base plate. He smiles pleasantly. And he sings quietly to himself:

"*Oh, tobacco, tobacco* . . ."

"Did you hear? The Germans broke through," says Sashka.

"Infantry?"

"No, tanks."

"Are they heading this way?"

"They're behind us . . ."

"How many?"

"They say about forty."

German bombers are flying high over our position. They don't want us. They'll drop their bombs behind our lines.

"The medics will have plenty of work," Sashka says.

And Kolya sings:

"*Oh, tobacco, tobacco* . . ."

And then a German shell explodes on the hill, to the right of us. Our mortars send them a friendly answer. All four of them. Then another one. And again.

And behind us red balls of fire burst up. I can feel the hot wind on my back. The back of my head aches. The German artillery keeps pouring it on.

"They're onto us," someone says.

I keep bringing more and more shells. I don't stop to think about anything. Each movement is as automatic as hell. Ten steps back. Pick up a sixteen-kilo, cold suckling pig. Ten steps forward. You can do it with your eyes closed. A couple of round trips. And the fingers themselves unbutton the coat. And they pick some snow and shove it in the mouth. And suddenly I get a stupid idea: after the battle, I'll take some sugar, mix it with snow, and I'll get ice cream . . .

Ten steps forward. Ten — back. There are less and less "suckling pigs." How much time has passed? Happy people never notice time pass . . .

A shock wave hits me in the back. I can't stand up. I fall.

"Aaa, aaaa," someone screams. And then again, but weaker this time, "a-a, a-a-a-a-!"

It's me screaming. I see the backs of my comrades. They're shooting. They don't see me. Thank God, everything is okay. No pain. Why did I scream? Supposing there was a direct attack . . . But that's impossible. Why me especially? And why not? And suddenly there is an especially violent explosion. And there's a scream again. But it's not me, it's someone else this time. The way he screams — you can't bear to look. I see Kolya run up to him, and then he covers his face with his hands and runs back. And before reaching his mortar, he stops and bends over.

Who was on the first mortar? I can't remember anyone. No one. Absolutely no one. And there's no more room for notches on Sashka's stick. The platoon commander Karpov shouts at us to change our position. And everyone's as busy as hell. Quicker, quicker! If we don't get a move on, the Germans will clobber us. The mortars are already hitched to their carriers. And we crawl out of the dugout where our position was. Where will our new position be? What's going to happen? Everybody's quiet. Now I see four spots in the snow and a figure in a long coat approaching us. And I don't want to think about it, but it won't leave me, and I can't get rid of it for anything.

"Number one is gone," says Sashka.

"Gone," I say.

"A lot of the boys are gone," says Sashka.

"Shut up!" says Shongin. He's sitting, hunched over.

The trucks keep moving. And I don't notice the shooting anymore. I only see Kolya's pale face. He is looking somewhere off in the distance and not moving.

"Hey, Kolya!" says Sashka. "Better say goodbye to Ninka. They'll be transferring us to another division."

Kolya doesn't move.

"Shut up!" says Shongin.

"As if it wasn't enough, now they have tanks crawling up our back," says Gavrilov.

We pass some sort of fire. Probably a barn. Burned to the ground. Some logs are still smoldering. Smells terrible. A smell of burning, of burning . . . but that's not the word.

From the new position we can see the firing on the enemy. Three of our mortars keep pouring it on somewhere over the hills. I keep bringing more and more shells.

But it could hit our mortar. Not number one, but ours. And I wouldn't be carrying shells. Maybe I'd be walking slowly along the fields, just barely moving, and then I'd fall. So far it's quiet here. They haven't spotted us yet. There it is again: "Retreat!" And again into the trucks. And into the night, and into the darkness.

We're stamping our feet in the darkness near the trucks. We hitch up the mortars. And somewhere up in the sky the bombers are droning on.

"Ours."

"You never see them in the daytime."

"It's better than nothing."

Second Lieutenant Karpov, our platoon commander, comes over. He's rubbing his hands and cheeks. Our platoon commander is either frozen or he's worried.

"Are we moving again?" Sashka Zolotaryov asks.

"What do you mean," says Karpov. "We're moving up, boys! Enough of this sitting around."

"Sitting around," says Shongin. "Look how many men we've lost."

"That's war," says Karpov quietly. "And what's an old soldier like you, Shongin, talking like this for?"

Everyone is quiet. Words — that's really funny. It really is war. What are you going to do? Is it Karpov's fault? Look at him; young, red-cheeked, energetic . . . Is it my fault? Kolya's?

We're sitting in the trucks. Miserable road. The truck keeps rocking like a boat. We rock from side to side. It's a good thing we're riding. Otherwise, the road would have become so muddy. You try and pull a truck through the stuff. We're riding. It's half raining, half snowing. We gradually get soaked. At first it's even nice: it's cooling after the heat. And the cold raindrops run down inside your collar comfortably. But now it's no good anymore. Enough. I know, in a minute we'll be shivering. Then try and get warm. And the feet freeze. Quickly and certainly. We're moving to a new battle sector. You can already clearly hear the explosions and the song of the automatics. And a lit-up sky swims out from beyond the hill.

"AND WHERE IS YOUR DAUGHTER?"

How well everything is going. Tomorrow I'll write home. I'm alive. What's left of the battery? Two mortars and no more than thirty men. And I'm alive. Didn't even get a scratch. I'll write tomorrow. Home.

"Let's see what's there," says Sashka Zolotaryov.

Night. Some sort of a hut. The windows are dark.

I knock on the shutters. "Lady, would you be so kind as to. . . ." No answer. "Lady, I made it, I'm alive. Oh, if you only knew what it was like!" I knock on the shutters. "The boots — here; the uniform — in the closet; the sword — on the chair . . ." "Thank you . . . But where is your daughter?"

"Sleep, sleep, sleep . . ." says Kolya.

I knock on the shutters. "Grouse? . . . Cheese? . . . Wine? . . ." "Oh, thank you. A small piece of cold veal and some rum. I'm a soldier, lady." I knock on the shutters.

"We'll freeze to death."

"Let's go to another one."

"Knock again."

I knock on the shutters. Sashka knocks on the shutters. Kolya knocks on the shutters.

"Here's your room. Good night." "Good night, lady. But where is your daughter? . . ."

"What do you want?"

A woman is standing in the doorway. She's all bundled up.

"We'd like to spend the night here, lady."

"We made it, we're alive," I say.

"Big deal . . ." says the woman. "That's all I needed."

"Can we come in?" asks Kolya.

"It's very cold," says Sashka.

"We'll just stay overnight and then leave," I say.

It's cold in the hallway. Inside it's warm. A lamp is burning and smoking up the place. Someone is tossing and turning on the Russian stove. It's a small room. How are we all going to fit in there?

The woman takes off her kerchief. She's very young.

"Lie down here," she says to Kolya, pointing to the corner. Kolya's got a good place. "And you, over there," she says to Sashka.

Zolotaryov spreads his coat under the table and lies down on it. Kolya undresses silently. She puts me on a bunk near the stove. I can only lie on my side. What the hell — as long as I'm lying down. The woman herself lies on a bed. A folding bed. There's a rag of a blanket on it. She crawls under it without taking off her outer coat.

I put my coat on the bunk. The blue flame of the lamp goes out. A hand strokes my hair.

"Come up here," says a quiet voice from the stove. "It's warm here."

"Who are you?"

"What's the difference. Come on. It's warm here . . ."

"Man'ka," the woman says indifferently, "watch out . . ."

"Who asked you," says Man'ka from the stove. And her hand keeps stroking me, stroking me.

"Come on over here."

"Wait, let me take my shoes off."

"Come on, what's the difference?"

Supposing they hear? . . . "Where's your daughter, lady?" Supposing they hear . . . now there's a daughter for you . . . It's warm near Man'ka. If I just touch her, the whole thing will be shot. Man'ka . . . Is that really her name?

"What's your name?"

"Mariya Andreevna."

Now there's something for you. How can . . . She has a hot, flabby stomach and small, clutching hands.

"How old are you?"

"Sixteen . . . Why?"

"Sh . . . !"

"Why? Why?"

"They'll hear us."

"Let 'em . . . come closer."

"Man'ka," says the woman, "you'd better watch it, Man'ka."

"Never you mind," says Man'ka.

Down below, Sashka Zolotaryov coughs, and Kolya says: "Lady, aren't you cold?"

And Man'ka wraps herself around me, and I don't know which is me and which is her. Everything is all mixed up.

"Your heart is really thumping." She laughs right in my ear. "What's the matter, are you afraid?"

And Kolya asks, "Aren't you cold, lady?"

Is that how simple it is? And will it be the same with Nina? With everyone?

"What's the matter, are you dead or something?"

"Leave me alone."

"I'm just kidding, silly . . ."

"Let me go, Mariya . . ."

"Mariya," says the woman. "Hey, Mariya, you're not Mariya, you're a towheaded fool."

"Let go of me, or there'll be trouble."

"Come on, let's just lie here, okay?"

"Let go . . ."

"Go back to your bench if you think it's too crowded here."

The bench is cool. Sashka's coughing.

"Lady, you must be freezing under that rag. Want me to cover you with my coat?" says Kolya from the corner.

. . . Someone's walking around in the hut. And he's whispering something. It's a quiet, hurried whisper. I can't make out the words. It's probably Mariya on the stove. And maybe it's the woman. And perhaps it's not a whisper, but just the stillness. But someone is sobbing. How difficult it must be in this small village. And tomorrow I'll be a laughingstock. They'll make fun of me for sure . . . Serves me right. She herself asked, begged . . . They'll laugh at me. I'll get up early in the morning and go to another hut, or to headquarters, or to the trucks. She's hot like fire, that Mariya Andreevna. She'll be the first one to laugh. Sixteen . . . Kolya calls them "peaches and cream." But someone really is crying. Or is it outside the window?

"Who is it?" I ask.

"Don't shout," says the woman. "Lie down and sleep."

I must be in a delirium. They'll laugh at me, really laugh at me.

And still, someone is crying. Could it be that it's Mariya laughing?

In the morning Sashka Zolotaryov says, "Looks like we'll be eating here. The battery commander's eating potatoes. The trucks broke down."

Sashka has already washed. He has an air of cold about him. His cheeks are just like children's cheeks, crimson. He's had time to find out everything. And Kolya is sleeping. And the woman and Mariya are gone.

"What's going to happen now?" I ask.

"Nothing," says Sashka. "We'll wait for some new equipment, and then we'll start again."

"And the trucks have broken down?"

"Completely."

"Is the kitchen operating?"

"What kitchen?"

Sashka takes out three packages of powdered peas from his field pack.

"Here's what they gave us. We'll cook it. Better wake Kolya. Get up Mykola!"

And suddenly the woman comes in. She takes off her kerchief. And I see that she is very young. And beautiful.

"Get up, Mykola," says Sashka. But Kolya sleeps.

"What are you waking him for?" the woman asks. "Let him sleep — he's tired."

She speaks very severely. And she keeps looking at Kolya.

"Give it to me, I'll cook it," she says, taking the powdered peas from Sashka.

We're sitting at the table. We're silent. We're eating the pea soup. With wooden spoons. But I don't have a spoon. As soon as we leave this place, I'll get my piece of wood . . . For now, I'll use the wooden one. I haven't had a spoon for a long time . . . We eat the pea soup; there's no bread. Kolya eats slowly. Occasionally he looks up at the woman. She's sitting directly opposite him. And she also looks up at him from time to time. And that's all. And I'm waiting for Mariya to start laughing at me. But she won't even look at me. It's only that I haven't really looked at her. She's pug-nosed. And she has a wide face. And a funny lock of hair hangs down her forehead. And she has several large freckles or birthmarks on her nose.

"Well now, freckle-face," Sashka says to her, "what's going to happen to us?"

"We'll get along," says Mariya.

"It's tasty soup," says Kolya, and he looks at the woman.

"How come you don't look alike?" asks Sashka. "You live together, you're like sisters, but you don't look alike . . ."

"But we're not sisters," says Mariya. "We just know each other and live together."

"You know, the soup's not bad," says Kolya. And he looks at the woman. But she doesn't say anything.

Suddenly Shongin comes in.

"Here we go again, another one," the woman says loudly.

And Shongin sits down on a stool.

"There are a lot of dead," he says, "and wounded. They've taken them away." And he takes out his tobacco pouch.

"Are we gonna smoke?" asks Sashka.

"What is there to smoke?" says Shongin. "There's not enough tobacco for me," and he shows the pouch.

"Where did you sleep, Shongin?" Kolya asks.

"I didn't sleep," says Shongin. "There were a lot of wounded. By the time we picked them all up, it was morning."

"I'd love a smoke now," says Sashka.

"Here smoke, smoke," says Shongin, and he takes a drag. He blows out large clouds of smoke. "I just dropped in to see how you were," he says.

Meanwhile, the woman is pouring milk into some cups. And Kolya says, "Listen, Shongin, that powdered stuff wasn't enough. Would you like some milk?"

"It's goat's milk," says Mariya.

"I've eaten," says Shongin. "I've eaten. Gurgenidze was wounded. I made some soup for both of us."

Poor little Gurgenidze. Just a boy. With an eternal drop hanging from the tip of his nose. "It's a hit — it's a miss."

"Is he bad, Shongin?"

"Nothing much," says Shongin. "He's in the truck. The last one. They're going to take him away."

I'm running along in the fresh snow. To the truck. Soldiers are walking around it. Gurgenidze is lying on some straw in the back of the truck. In a burned coat. He raises his bandaged head. A drop is hanging from the tip of his nose.

"I got hit," he says with a sad smile.

We weren't even friends. Just knew each other. And his red eyelids keep flinching.

"Where'd you get it?"

"I get it in the head, the stomach, in the leg. Shongin carry me on his back."

"It's okay, Gurgenidze. Now you'll rest up. Everything will be okay."

The motor turns over. Gurgenidze falls back on the straw. His hands are folded on his chest.

"What's our section?" he asks. "What number?"

"Special mortar battery, friend."

"No, which regiment?"

"229th, I think."

"What division?"

"Why do you want to know?"

"They might ask me in the hospital."

The motor is even. The back of the truck shakes.

"What division?"

"Who the hell knows," I shout after him.

The truck rumbles along the fresh snow. Gurgenidze's arm is sticking out from the back of the truck. He's saying goodbye to us. He has left, gone. And I forgot to ask him for his spoon.

"Get them together. It's time. We've rested," the battery commander says to me.

There's no one in the hut. Kolya and the woman are sitting on a log in the back of the hut. She's silent. She's resting her head on her hands. Her eyes are red. Her lips are pouting, just like a little girl's. And Kolya is smoking and is also silent.

"It's time, Kolya," I say. "The battery commander ordered . . ."

"I know," he says and stands up. And he looks at me.

I wait for him.

"I know," he says.

I go away. Let them say goodbye.

THE ROAD

"DID you see the German trucks?" Kolya asks. "They have tarp covers and all that stuff. They're real comfy, just like at home. But our stuff . . ."

"I can't feel my feet anymore," says Zolotaryov. "I'd love to have me some boots. Fur-lined ones. To hell with the face, the main thing is the feet. Maybe I've already lost my big toe, eh? If I take off my shoes, it'll probably fall out."

I don't want any fur-lined boots. Just an ordinary pair of boots would do. With wide tops, and like boats. If I got into water nothing would happen. If I got into snow nothing would happen. Even if I stood there all night. No matter.

Steppe, steppe, steppe. When are we going to stop? Our battery keeps moving from position to position. First we're sent to one section, then to another. Who knows where the regiment to which we were attached is now? And Nina is there. Nina, Nina, you smiled so sweetly for me. And I can't forget you. Who are you, and where are you from? I don't know anything. Where am I going to look for you? Everything in the past has grown dim and hazy. Zhenya is somewhere in a fog, in the distance. There's only you, Nina. And why did you speak so nicely to me?

"Do I talk in my sleep?" I ask Kolya.

"Once, to Ninka Shubnikov."

"What did I say?"

" 'Sit next to me, Nina, sit. We'll sit down, have a smoke,' that's what you said. Great fun."

"Did she say anything to you about me?"

And why did I ask? He'll laugh in a minute. Or maybe he'll make up some story . . .

"No, she didn't," says Kolya with a frown. "What's there to say? She's living with the regimental commander. You remember — that tall major."

I remember. I'd have felt better if he hadn't said anything. If I ever meet her, say, purely by chance — it could happen — I'd say to her . . .

"When I was serving in the cavalry," says Shongin, "now that was really terrible. I'd come back from a march, and I wouldn't be able to sleep. First I had to unsaddle the horse, then feed it, and then, if there was any time left over, then I could rest."

"The English soldiers have waitresses serving them," says Kolya, "and they get cognac with their dinner."

"You're lying, Grinchenko," Shongin mutters.

The trucks have stopped. A traffic jam. It's getting dark.

"Get down, boys. Warm yourselves."

No letters from home. I wonder what's happening there.

"Shongin, ever get any letters from home?" I ask.

He looks at me attentively.

"Of course, I do," he says, and pulls out his tobacco pouch and offers me a smoke.

"Here, warm up."

If we stay here like this until morning, we'll really catch cold. What eyes that Shongin has. They're tender and kind. Yesterday, when we were cooking the powdered peas, he came over to me and Kolya and put a handful of millet in our mess tins. The millet made the soup thick. He came over himself: "Here, boys, I'll put something extra in . . ."

"Shongin, let's have a smoke," says Sashka.

Shongin is stamping his feet up and down, warming them.

"You'll get along without it," he mumbles.

When it gets dark, you can't see the snow. It feels warmer. The platoon commander Karpov comes over. He always has red cheeks. You can even see them in the dark.

He's laughing.

"What's the matter, warriors, you frozen?"

"You'll freeze too," says Kolya. "The sergeant's warm, though — he warms himself on the truck radiator. Maybe we can start a bonfire, lieutenant, what do you say, eh?"

"No bonfires," says Karpov.

Like a guard, Shongin stomps his feet in the snow and bangs his mess tin with his hand.

Gavrilov comes over and says quietly, "Boys, there are some trucks up ahead, full of groats, and the drivers are asleep . . ."

"So what?" asks Shongin.

"Nothing," says Gavrilov. "I was just saying that the drivers are asleep . . ."

"You know, it wouldn't be so bad if we could get us a potful of groats," says Sashka Zolotaryov.

And he goes off into the darkness, in the direction where the drivers are asleep. And everyone follows him with their eyes. And everybody is silent.

If it's millet, we can make some thick soup. If it's buckwheat, it's good with milk. If it's pear-barley, that's nice with onions. Will I last until morning or not? I'm soaked through and through. Supposing I catch pneumonia?

No letters from home. Where are you, military post?

KIDS

I'M loading machine-gun magazines. I'm loading, and I'm silent.

"Why so sad, kid?" the sergeant asks.

I can't answer him. What can I tell him?

"Oh, nothing," I say, "just reminiscing about home . . ."

You've got it good, sergeant. You eat omelets. And we eat cold pea soup. You've got it good, sergeant. And we don't get any decent sleep for days on end.

"We've reached Rostov," the sergeant says.

. . . You have a pleasant face. And there're less and less of us. And this Mozdok sand screeches in my teeth and in my soul. You ought to give me some boots, sergeant, or something. The artificial soles on my American knee boots have cracked. When it's cold, I shove my feet in the bonfire. And the knee boots are a beautiful red. But what's left of them? . . .

"You ought to grease those shoes, kid. Just look at them, they're no good."

. . . And what kind of shoes did I wear before I got into the army? I don't remember. Did I have stylish chocolate-colored shoes with a white edge, like ocean surf? Or did I just dream about it? I probably wore plain black shoes. And in the winter I put galoshes over them. Yes, yes, galoshes. At the last Komsomol meeting I forgot them at school. I forgot them. I came home without galoshes. And the war had already broken out, and no one noticed my loss. That's the way I left. And they were new galoshes. Shiny ones. Now I don't know . . . will I ever have another pair like them?

And when we had the last Komsomol meeting, Zhenya was sitting in a corner. While we each took our stand and swore to die for our fatherland, she didn't say anything. Then she said, "I'm sorry for you boys. You think it's so simple to fight? Wars need silent, sullen soldiers. Wars don't need noise. I'm sorry for you. And you . . ." she pointed to me. "You still don't know how to do anything except read your books. There's death out there, death . . . and it loves young people like you."

"And you?" someone shouted.

"I'll go too. But I won't scream and suffer. What for? I'll simply go."

"We'll also go. Why are you lecturing us?"

"You must be mentally prepared . . ."

"Shut up, Zhen'ka . . ."

"Otherwise, you won't be of any service."

"Shut up!"

"Enough," said the Komsomol organizer. "Why are we shouting like this? Like a bunch of kids?"

And when I kissed you at the gate so that you moaned and embraced me, what was that? Does that mean I don't know how to do anything except read books? . . .

"Tomorrow we'll go get some mortars," says the sergeant. "You can take it easy for another night, kid."

"What mortars?" I ask.

"Don't sleep. We'll be getting some replacements tomorrow. You'll be teaching those babies."

"But how can I?"

"What's the matter, do you need three years fighting to teach our business to a bunch of school kids?"

Our business? My business? Does he mean the mortars? I'll be teaching?

"Okay, I'll teach 'em," I say.

School kids. But I was a school kid too. Does this mean I'm no longer a school kid? But at that meeting I was a school kid. And when everybody made noise, I made noise too. Zhenya said, "You're making noise, just like a school kid. You can't do that there. You need severity there."

And she looked at me. I looked at her, too. Someone told me that, if a girl loves you, she won't hold out a "stare." She'll blush and lower her eyes. That means she didn't love me. She didn't love me.

"Let's all go together, the entire class," someone shouted.

"Let's all go!" I shouted.

"Shut up," they told me. "Shut up, you jerk!"

Then the school director came in, and the Komsomol organizer said, "Okay, we'll continue the business of the day."

And on the agenda there was but one question: Komsomol studies.

". . . When you finish with the machine-gun magazines, come into the smokehouse," says the sergeant and goes away . . .

. . . And after the meeting we were all walking along the Naberezhnaya together. And Zhenya was walking with us, but she didn't look at me. It was dark and tense.

"We won't see the tenth of the month, boys," someone said. And a siren suddenly started wailing. And I found myself next to Zhenya.

"So, we're school kids?" I asked.

"Of course," she said calmly.

"In other words, we won't make good fighters?"

"Of course."

"To be a good fighter, you have to be broad-shouldered, right?"

"Yes," she laughed.

"And indifferent, right?"

"No," she said, "I didn't say that."

"Let's go over there," I said, pointing to a dark side street.

We were walking along the side street. It was even darker and even more tense there. And suddenly a window opened. With a bang. On the third floor. Laughter came out of the window. Then music. The phonograph was playing an old prewar tango.

"As though nothing ever happened, right?"

"Right," I said.

The window closed. The music died down. And the siren started again . . .

. . . I loaded all the magazines. I'm walking to the smokehouse.

It's not a smokehouse, just a simple hut where the sergeant is staying.

The sergeant is warming his hands near the stove. And the platoon commander Karpov, so pink-cheeked, is shaving near the window. Even through the white, foamy lather, you can see his pink cheeks.

Sashka Zolotaryov is standing at attention in front of the battery commander.

"In other words, you stole someone else's millet?" the battery commander asks.

"I stole it," Sashka says.

"You ate someone else's gruel! When you stole, did you think that someone else would go hungry? Did you?"

"Yes, comrade lieutenant!"

"Well?"

"I was hungry, too."

"You know what you can get for this?"

"Of course, I know," Sashka says quietly.

"He gave some to everybody," I say from the threshold.

The battery commander looks at me piercingly. Will he hit me? If he only hit me.

"They're a bunch of hooligans, not a battery," he says.

"They've gotten out of hand," says Karpov. "Grinchenko is their leader. They're continually talking about love and stuffing their faces . . ."

"Okay, Karpov, go on with your shaving," says the battery commander. "I have other business."

And I want to ask Karpov where he was when we were raw troops, just beyond State Farm #3, when we took part in our first battle. He was eating food at school.

"About face!" the battery commander shouts at me.

I'm walking to my place. Maybe Zhenya really is right. Maybe I really am a school kid. The winter will be over soon. Soon we'll be returning to the front lines. Then we'll see what kind of a school kid I am . . . And I'll meet Nina again. "Hi, small fry," she'll say. "Haven't seen you for a long time. Let's sit a while, have a smoke, right?"

CONVERSATIONS

WE'VE been at this destroyed village for four days and nights. There was a state farm here. A big, shredded windmill, like some sad bird, looks at us from above.

Shabby batteries, battalions drained of blood, regiments thinned out in attack; all of these have gathered here. Depots have sprung up in former dugouts, and tired commissaries, who haven't had enough sleep, distribute, give out and supply us with all kinds of goods.

The roads to the North pass through here. The offensive has gone that way. We can hear the deafening cannonade from there. New units hurry along these roads to the front. In new uniforms. Spic and span. On new trucks. And they look at us with curiosity and respect, with fear and envy.

I haven't seen Nina for a long time now. I'm already forgetting her face. Her voice. How quickly everything happens in war . . .

Kolya Grinchenko has had a good night's sleep and has cleaned up. He's happy again. Every two hours Sashka Zolotaryov cooks something for himself in addition to the rations. And he sleeps. His eyes are very, very small. His cheeks are even more crimson. I can't tell now whose are more crimson, his or Karpov's. And Second Lieutenant Karpov walks around like a conqueror in his sheepskin coat, cocked hat, and with a twig in his hand. He keeps hitting his boot tops with this twig, just as a calf drives away flies with its tail. His voice has become clearer, more ringing. And for some reason, we clash more with him.

"He's got nothing to do," says Kolya Grinchenko, "so he keeps poking his nose in everything."

"He's a commander," says Shongin.

"Didn't even hear a word out of him at the front," says Sashka, "but he'll start educating us soon."

"He's a commander," says Shongin. "He's got to do it."

"He'll get around to us soon," I say. "See how he keeps looking at Kolya?"

"He doesn't like me," says Kolya. "The battery commander does, but not that one . . ."

"Now the battery commander, that's altogether something different," says Shongin. "He's not about to walk around with a twig in his hand."

"He's smart," says Sashka Zolotaryov.

Second Lieutenant Karpov comes up. He's hitting his boot tops with his twig.

"Grinchenko, why are you wearing a navy belt buckle? We're in the artillery," he says to Kolya.

"Yes, sir! The artillery," says Kolya and smiles.

"Then take off that buckle and put it away as a memento."

"Yes, sir! Take off that buckle," Kolya salutes and smiles.

"I mean it," says Karpov with great restraint. "No joking around on the front."

"Yes, sir!" says Kolya and smiles.

Karpov looks at us. We're not smiling. Sashka looks aside. Shongin stands at attention, but I can't. Both legs just keep buckling under me. Now one, now the other.

"Take it off, and bring it to me," says Karpov. He hits his boot tops with his twig and leaves.

Kolya quickly takes off the belt buckle. It's a beautiful buckle with anchors on it.

"But I didn't argue with him," he says. "What got into him?"

"He's a commander," says Shongin, "and you're a jerk. That's why."

Kolya walks off swinging the belt in his hand.

"He'll get it yet," says Sashka Zolotaryov.

Whom does he mean: Kolya or Karpov? I don't know. We also walk away. To our hut. It's warm there.

Kolya's sitting on the bench. He's changing buckles.

"I'll transfer to reconnaissance. They're okay," he says.

We sit and keep quiet. Tired of sitting and being silent — of speaking. No replacements.

"Why don't they send us out a little farther; as it is, we don't do anything," says Sashka. "We'd go into some small town . . . On leave. An orchestra probably would be playing in the park. Soon the apple trees will begin to bloom."

"Karpov would surely let you have it," says Kolya.

"The apple trees will bloom without you," says Shongin, "and there are no orchestras now. What good are they . . . now?

When I left for the front, there was an orchestra playing."

"That was the last one," I say. "Then everybody became a machine gunner. They all became machine gunners."

"Eh, bull . . ." says Shongin.

"Yes. No orchestras are playing now. Now they only play when we liberate a city."

. . . And when I left, there was no orchestra playing. It was autumn. It was raining. Seryozhka Gorelov and I were standing at the streetcar stop. We had rucksacks. And we had a packet from the enlistment office. And our orders sending us to separate mortar divisions.

"You'll get there on your own," the head of the second unit told us. "You're not children."

And we left.

No one saw us off. Even Zhenya didn't come. We rode through Moscow in the evening, and we were silent. And at the Kazan' railroad terminal it was terribly crowded. And we sat down on the floor. And we liked it. Seryozhka smoked and kept spitting on the floor. We played at being soldiers, and we liked this game. And I kept looking around all the time. Perhaps I'll see Zhenya. No, an orchestra did not play at our farewell. There was just a piano on a raised platform, and some drunken little sailor sat down and played an old waltz. And everyone fell silent and listened. And I listened, but kept looking around all the time: maybe Zhenya was coming.

It was some kind of unfamiliar waltz, but you felt that it was old. Even the crying children suddenly stopped crying. And the sailor was rocking on his chair, and his long forelock hung down and touched the piano keys.

"Well, now we're soldiers," Seryozhka whispered to me.

The sailor was playing an old waltz. Everyone listened. Women, children, old men, soldiers, officers . . . And I was happy that I was sitting on the floor, that next to me I had my rucksack, that I was a soldier, that perhaps tomorrow I'd be given a weapon.

And I was happy that I was with them, that the drunken little sailor was playing the piano. And I wanted very much for Zhenya to come and see us in this world to which we have attached our-selves and which is so unlike our homes, our former life.

And the little sailor kept playing the old waltz. It was stifling in the waiting room. But no one made any noise. Everybody listened to the music. They had all heard music before. And probably better than this. But this music was special. And that's why everybody was silent.

And the waltz went on and on. And an officer with a red armband and two soldiers from the commandant's patrol were also listening. The officer — sullenly, the soldiers — wide-eyed.

"Well, now we're soldiers," Seryozhka said.

And the sailor continued to play. And his long forelock kept flopping on the piano keys. Then he suddenly dropped his arms. They slipped down and were just hanging there, and his head hit the keys, and the piano gave forth a strange, sad sound.

Everyone was silent. And the officer with the red armband walked over to the sailor, saluted, and said something to him. Suddenly, everyone who was close by started to shout at the officer.

"What's all this, boys . . ." said the sailor. "What if the Krauts burned my mother?"

"He sits at home," said Seryozhka. "He ought to be there, then he'd know how to walk around with an armband . . ."

"What's with him? . . ." some women said.

And then I ran over there and shouted at the officer, "You headquarters rat, why don't you leave the people alone!"

The officer didn't hear me. And one of the patrol soldiers said to me in a tired voice, "Go home, kid!"

. . . The front twilight crawls in through the windows. We don't put on the light.

"When I was in the cavalry," says Shongin, "we'd come back from a march, feed the horses, and then start cooking some thick millet soup."

"And today the sergeant shortchanged us again on the sugar," says Kolya.

"I'm beginning to dream about my wife," says Sashka Zolotaryov. "We won't see any passes, lads."

"When I was in the eighth grade," I say, "we had a very funny math teacher. As soon as he'd turn around, we'd start talking. And he'd give a 'D' for it, but never to the kid who did the talking."

THE ROAD

WE'RE setting off for the army base to get some mortars. We — that's Second Lieutenant Karpov, the sergeant, Sashka Zolotaryov, and me.

Karpov gets in front with the driver, while the three of us take our places in the back of our one-and-a-half-ton truck.

And we're off. I'm tired of this stupid sitting around in the village. It's better to be riding. Everyone's tired of it. Sashka and I smile and wink at each other.

The sergeant has settled down up front on a soft seat made of empty American sacks. He leans against the cabin with his hands on his stomach, his short legs stretched out, and closes his eyes.

"We're off, boys, don't fall off while I'm asleep."

We're moving.

Perhaps I'll meet Nina someplace. Because of the frost, the truck moves well. It speeds from hill to hill. And up ahead — more hills. And beyond those — still more. We've only got to go forty kilometers. Nothing to it. Now I'll see how they live in the rear.

The road's not empty. Trucks, trucks . . . Tanks go by, infantry. They're all on their way to the front.

"The Siberians really took care of the Germans near Moscow," says Sashka. "If it weren't for them, who knows what might have happened."

"The Siberians are all the same height," I say. "Six feet. They're specially selected."

"Fools," says the sergeant without opening his eyes. "What's that got to do with it? It was equipment that did it at Moscow, equipment . . ."

What's the use of arguing. Let him talk. I know what happened at Moscow. I was told by eyewitnesses. When the Siberians started moving up, the Germans ran West without stopping. I know. Because the Siberians stood ready for death. They're all hunters, bear trappers. They face death from early childhood. They're used to it. And us? Sashka and me, for instance. Could we do it? Supposing tanks come at us — we'd just shut our eyes . . . And not because we're cowards. We're simply not used to it . . . Could I face a tank? No, I couldn't. With mortars it's simpler. The front lines are far from here. You can fire away, change your position. But face to face . . . it's a good thing we're not the infantry.

Suddenly the truck stops. Up ahead the road seems empty. Only far off in the distance a lone soldier stands and is looking in our direction. The sergeant is sleeping. Sashka and I jump off the truck. Second Lieutenant Karpov is asleep in the front. His lower lip droops like an old man's. The driver has raised the hood.

And the soldier is running toward us. A little soldier. You couldn't think of a smaller one. He's running toward us and waving his arms.

"Look, look," says Sashka. "A Siberian."

I laugh. The soldier is really very small. He runs up to us, and I see that it's a girl. She's wearing a long coat, neatly girdled. She has sergeant's insignia on her shoulders. Her face is small, and she has a nose like a button.

"How about a lift, boys. I've been standing here for an hour. All the trucks are heading for the front lines, not a single one the other way. And I have to get there desperately," she says and gestures by drawing her hand across her throat.

I help her to get into the truck. Sashka and I give her our canvas coats, and she sits on them.

"Where are you boys from?"

We nod towards the front lines.

"Has the fifteenth left yet?"

Sashka and I look at each other and shrug our shoulders.

Our truck finally moves. The sergeant sleeps. He even snores, just a bit.

"That's great," says our traveling companion, and laughs. "He snores as though he were home on the stove."

"He loves to sleep," says Sashka.

When she laughs, her lips turn up at the corners. Like a clown. A sergeant! And I'm only a private! Where is she going, such a tiny one, such a slim young girl? What happened? Everyone has been taken by it, carried away, all mixed up . . . School kids crawl about in the trenches, they die of wounds, they return home, armless, legless . . . A girl . . . a sergeant . . . what's happened?

"Day before yesterday, the base was raided by forty Junkers," she says. "It was something. We were swept off our feet . . ."

"And what would you have done at the front?" Sashka asks. "It's even worse there."

"I probably would have cried," she says, and laughs.

. . . What could you expect . . . of course, she would have cried. After all, even I almost cried. Before the war, I saw a movie. All the soldiers were like soldiers in this movie: adult, experienced, they knew what was what. But I don't know, Sashka doesn't know, this girl doesn't know . . . The sergeant's asleep, and Karpov . . . But they knew what's what. Yet I don't know, Sashka doesn't know, and our commander, although he's sullen . . .

"My name's Masha," she says. "I'm a sergeant in the medical corps. In school I beat all the boys."

"And you like to brag a little, eh, sarge?" says Sashka.

The sergeant wakes up. He looks at Masha for a long time.

"And where did you come from?" he asks, using the familiar form.

"May I ask you not to be so informal?" Masha says calmly.

The sergeant's cap slides onto the back of his head.

"Who do you think you're talking to?"

"It's amazing how uneducated a man can be," she says to us.

I want to laugh. The sergeant looks at Masha for a long time, and then he notices her shoulder bands.

"I'm asking you, comrade sergeant, where are you from?"

The truck stops again. The driver again raises the hood. Karpov comes out.

"How are things up there," he asks us.

"While you were asleep, your soldiers froze here," Sashka says.

"Oho," says Karpov. "What a nice passenger. And you, did you freeze?"

And he invites her up front.

She jumps out lightly from the back of the truck. She waves goodbye to us.

How warm it must be up front. Hot air from the radiator, soft seats, the whole road spread out before you.

Karpov climbs in after her.

"No, no," she says, "perhaps I'd better go back, comrade second lieutenant."

"Sit down," Karpov says coldly. He gets into the back of the truck.

"Why have you spread out your legs like that, Zolotaryov?" he says. "Can't you sit like a human being."

. . . We're riding. It's getting dark already. If we don't get to the base in half an hour, I'll freeze to death. Sashka is all bundled up; only his nose is visible. A big red nose.

"A man needs a bed, not the back of a truck," he grumbles, "and a warm stove, and good food, and love . . ."

"And who is going to work, kid?" the sergeant asks.

When I return home, I'll study hard. I'll go to sleep at ten. In the winter I'll put on a fur coat, so that nothing can get to me . . .

We stop some truck. We ask. It turns out that it's still some eighty kilometers to the base.

"What do you mean?" Karpov asks, surprised. "They said forty."

"You should have taken another road," comes the answer from the truck.

"He missed the road, the devil," Sashka hisses.

"We'll freeze," says the sergeant.

Masha comes out of the cabin.

"The first turn off, State Farm #7," she says.

"Really?" says Karpov, overjoyed.

"For your information, I always tell the truth."

. . . Not many houses have remained intact at this state farm. Not many. But when you consider it in terms of fingers and lips numb with cold, and legs as though they were made of wood — what's the difference how many houses? There are houses, and they let you in, and it's warm inside, and you can drink some tea.

Karpov picks out a house that's bigger and more intact than the others and invites Masha there.

"You'll be more comfortable there."

And he turns to us.

"And you go there, friends, where the windows are lit up."

"I'll stay with the truck for a while," says the driver. "You can relieve me later."

I can only hold out for another minute. Sashka and I run to the

house. A girl opens the door for us. She's wearing felt boots and a
kerchief.

"Who's there?" someone asks from the inside.

"They're ours, Mama," says the girl.

The girl's name is Vika. Her mother is also wearing a kerchief
and a shawl. She looks like my mother. Very much so. She invites
us in. We take off our coats.

"You wouldn't happen to have some tea?" I ask with my frozen
lips.

We put our dried biscuits on the table.

"That's all we have, lady," says Sashka. "We'd be glad to . . ."

"That's okay," she says, "I'll get you some food right away."

"And Karpov has gone off after Masha," says Sashka, "and he's
having the sergeant run errands for him."

We're sitting at the table. Vika is also there, and she looks at us
with her big eyes. And her mother puts the frying pan on the
table. Meat pies are steaming on the frying pan. Gosh, how like my
mother she really is . . .

"The hospital stops here," she says. "They gave me a bottle of
vodka. Drink it, boys, warm yourselves."

She has big black-and-blue marks under her eyes. We don't refuse the vodka. I drink my glass and feel that I can't catch my
breath. I sit with my mouth open. She laughs.

"You should have exhaled, before swallowing. I completely forgot to warn you. Wash it down with the meat pie."

I eat it. But she really does look very much like my mother. My
head is swimming. It's really swimming.

"I made it from your dried biscuits," she says.

"Another one?" asks Sashka.

"Yes, let's belt one down," I say.

She pours the vodka for us.

"You ought to take one, lady," says Sashka.

She laughs and shakes her head. And my head is swimming,
swimming.

"Mama mustn't," says Vika.

"Just a little bit?" Sashka asks.

"Mama mustn't," I say, "why are you so persistent?"

She pats my head and gives me another pie. My head is swimming. I'm hot. Sashka has moved far off in the distance. So has Vika . . . and Mama . . . that's so I won't be so hot.

"Are you local?" asks Sashka.

"We're from Leningrad," says Vika.

"How nice," I say, "and I'm from Moscow. What a coincidence . . . What a meeting . . . at the world's end . . . I'm very happy, very happy . . ."

"If you go to Leningrad via Moscow, please give me a call at my home . . ."

Sashka is eating a pie. While he's eating, I'll sleep for a while. I'll put my head on the table and sleep.

"Wait," says Sashka, "I'll go with you."

He puts on the coat which he had spread out.

"For some reason, I'm tired," I say.

"Sleep, my boy, sleep," says Mama. She's standing over me.

"Mama," I say, "I'm alive and well. I'll return soon, with the victory . . ."

. . . In the morning it's quiet in the room. The driver is sleeping in Sashka's place. No one home. I put on my coat. I run to the truck. Sashka is walking around it with an automatic around his shoulders.

"And me?" I ask. "Why didn't you wake me?"

"You slept so — I couldn't get you up," says Sashka. "You really drank last night. You were worn-out."

"And you're walking like this? Alone?"

"I've slept enough," says Sashka. "Here, you take it for a while. I'll go warm up, and then I'll come back."

Me — I'm a scoundrel and a villain. If I were in his place, I would have tried until I woke him up. I wouldn't do more than I had to probably. I'm a swine. I ought to be taught a lesson. I'm a traitor. If anyone would come for the truck though, I'd cut his throat in short order.

The sergeant comes out of the house.

"Well, kid, everything okay?"

I don't answer. He doesn't need it. He gets into the back of the truck and yawns.

"Go call the boys. We have to go."

. . . "Wait a minute," Vika's mama says to us, "I'll make some potato pies."

"Thanks, we have to go," I say.

"You and your daughter eat it, eat it to our health," Sashka says.

We go over to the truck. Masha is sitting in the truck. She smiles at us.

"I've got it right now. It's another thirty kilometers to the base," says the driver.

"That's amazing," says Masha.

"Everybody in?" Karpov pokes his head out of the front seat.

And suddenly I see Vika is running from the house. She holds out a bundle. I manage to take it on the move.

"That's the pie," she shouts. "Goodbye!"

"How did you sleep, Masha?" Sashka asks.

"The lady of the house and I slept fine," she laughs, "but I don't think the lieutenant slept."

"He slept," says the sergeant.

"Well, that means you didn't," laughs Masha. "Someone kept waking us up, three times during the night, knocking on the door. 'Masha, I have to speak to you!' "

"I didn't knock," says the sergeant.

NINA

KARPOV comes out of the division headquarters. We look at him.

"The replacements have already left," he says. "We missed each other. They didn't wait."

"All the better," says the sergeant. "Less worries."

"We'll be getting an American armored car," says Karpov. "That's not a bad deal either. Sergeant, take the boots for the depot, load up the one-and-a-half-tonner and get going! We'll go in the armored car."

Boots! So there they are. Real boots. Now things will really begin. Boots. The way I am now, I walk around like a cart driver, with rags around my feet. I'm even ashamed. A submachine gun and rags. Now we'll do some fighting!

Karpov goes off to various sections.

"You can wrap all sorts of rags around your feet when you have boots," says Sashka. "No frost can get to you."

"And they won't let any water in," I say.

"It's okay," says Sashka. "Smear them with some lubrication grease and you're all set."

"And you can stick your spoon in the top," I say.

"To put 'em on is just sheer pleasure," Sashka says. "One pull, and you're all set."

"You have to pull 'em by the boot tab," I say.

"Of course, by the boot tab," says Sashka. He goes off to look for some friends. Fellow-townsmen. I'll take a walk too. My submachine gun is getting rusty. I haven't used it once.

"God, where did you come from?" I hear someone say behind me.

It's Nina! She's wearing an athletic shirt. She has an empty mess tin in her hand. It's really Nina . . .

"Did you come for a visit?"

"I looked for you," I say. "I've been looking since that first time."

She laughs. She's happy. I see it.

"Oh, you darling . . . There's a real friend. So you didn't forget?"

She's cold standing there. There's a frost, and it's windy.

"Let's go eat. We'll talk, okay?"

She pulls me by the hand. I'm following her, following her.

We sit in the headquarters mess hall. In a barrack. No one around.

"Everyone has eaten already," she says. "I was late. Let's ask Fedya for something."

"Fedya," she says into the window to the cook, "give me some soup, Fedya. I have a friend up from the front lines . . ."

And Fedya pours a full tureen of soup for me. And Nina breaks off a piece of her bread for me.

"Well, we've managed to scrounge up a meal for you," says the black-mustached Fedya from his window.

"It's warm here," I say.

"Well, how are things going there?" she asks. "How's Kolya?"

"Nina," I say, "you know I really did look for you. I thought and thought about you . . . Why were you silent?"

"Well, we'll eat now, and then have a smoke, right?"

"Why were you silent?"

"If I didn't go out to eat, I probably wouldn't have run into you."

"Now I see what color eyes you have. They're green. I tried, but just couldn't remember what color they were. What color were they? Now I finally know."

"Eat! It's going to get cold. Do you have it tough there?"

"You know, I once even imagined how we'd meet after the war. You were wearing a rose-colored jacket, and no hat . . ."

"None at all?"

"We walk along the Arbat . . ."

"Eat. Your soup's probably cold, isn't it?"

"I have to go back soon. If you want, I'll write you a letter."

"And I told the girls here: 'I've got a friend there,' I said. Dark-eyed. He's the only one, all through the war. But they didn't believe me. They laughed. But you remembered me, didn't you?"

"Why the only one? Don't you have any others?"

"With the others it's something else . . ."

The black-mustached Fedya looks at me attentively. Why is he staring? Maybe he's sorry he gave me the soup. Maybe he's one of those "other ones"?

"Listen, I mean it seriously. I really did think of you. I never thought about anyone like I did about you."

"Well now, you too . . ." Her lips twist. "How nice it was then . . ."

. . . And on the edge of the tureen, a solitary noodle hangs there just like a tiny worm. A white, sad, little noodle. And Nina has rested her head in her hands and looks past me. And I see the barrack windows in her green eyes. And beyond that, green twilight approaches.

"You don't even hear any shooting here," says Nina. "We've only been bombed once."

"Listen, Nina," I say. "If you want, I'll write to you, all right? Nothing much. Just how things are . . . Otherwise I'll lose you. Where am I going to look for you then?"

What a fool she is. Doesn't she understand? What am I, some seducer or something? . . . It's war. It's not Zhenya. Then everything just seemed to be, seemed to be. But this is more real. Doesn't she see? I understand everything now. What a little fool . . .

"What do you think, that I'm like the others? If you want, I'll prove it to you. If you want, I'll write home about you right now. You can send it off yourself . . ."

Black-mustached Fedya keeps looking at me. Doesn't he have anything else to do?

"Well, we'll have another date, right?"

". . . and when the war is over, we'll go together . . ."

"Right smack in the middle of the war we have a date. The only thing that's missing is ice cream. Fedya," she says, "you don't happen to have any ice cream, do you?"

"For you, Ninochka, I have everything," says Fedya, "only, the ice cream is hot, it's almost boiling."

"Before the war, when I used to go for a walk with some boy, he'd always buy ice cream for me. There was one boy who didn't. I got rid of him fast . . . We had a park in town . . ."

"Nina, I have to go soon."

"I'm sorry for you," she says. "You shouldn't be fighting. What are you going to get for it? Just don't get angry, don't. I don't mean that you can't fight. Just simply, why do you have to?"

"And you?"

"Well, I'm already used to it. Now Fedya there, he worked in a restaurant. The Poplavok. Is that right, Fedya? He made salads, cooked chops . . ."

"I have to go," I say. "Tell me, are you going to write me? It'll make it easier for me."

"I'll write," she says. "I'll write."

We head for the exit. The spoon clatters in the mess tin.

"Listen, Nina, that major, what was he . . ."

"Major?"

"Yes, that major . . ."

"Oh, so you noticed him."

We stop again, near the door. She stands next to me. Very close. How really small she is. Frail and thin. How defenseless she is. I'll take her by the shoulders, her little round shoulders . . . I'll stroke her head with my hand. It's okay if she doesn't explain. I didn't want to ask, I didn't . . .

"Are you feeling sorry for me, is that it?"

"No, but don't feel sorry for me either, Nina."

"What are you going to do now?"

"I'll wait for your letters."

"Supposing you don't get any? Anything can happen."

"I'll get them. You promised."

"What do you need it for, you dope . . ."

Boy, I am a dope, a real dope. I said something I shouldn't have. I didn't say what I wanted to.

"You have a bread crumb on your cheek," I say.

She laughs. Wipes off the bread crumb.

"It's time to go. They'll miss you."

"Let 'em miss me," I say. "Let 'em. It's all the same . . . One problem after another."

"How daring you are," she says with a laugh. And she strokes my head.

We go out into the lobby. I touch her back.

She pushes my hand aside. Very gently.

"Don't," she says. "It's better this way."

And she kisses me on the forehead. And she runs out into the storm, which is just starting.

. . . The armored car is standing near division headquarters. Sashka is walking around it. He looks around.

"We'll be off, right away," he says.

FUN

An armored car is a very convenient vehicle. It's just like a gray beetle. It can go through everything and get out of everything. It's comfortable and warm. The electric heater works. You can even sleep on the go.

I'm not sleeping. I'm just dozing. What's going to happen in the evening, when we catch up to our division? Maybe there'll be a big battle. Maybe we won't find anyone alive . . . We'll arrive, and I'll wait for Nina's letters . . . And Sashka is sleeping. Really sleeping. And Karpov is sitting next to the driver; he's either sleeping or staring motionless at the broken road.

. . . And the sergeant has brought the boots. But what if I don't get any?

"Comrade lieutenant," I say, "if the road was good, we'd probably really move."

But Karpov doesn't answer. Karpov is apparently asleep.

"Fedos'ev," I say, "now we really have a good vehicle . . ."

"But I'm not Fedos'ev," he says, "I'm Fedoseev. Fedoseev is my name. Everyone mixes me up with someone else. They call me Fedoskin, and all sorts of things. In the war you really can't stop to figure it out: Fedoseev or Fedos'ev? No time for it. I was once even called Fedishkin. It's really funny. But I'm really Fedoseev. I've been Fedoseev for forty years. From the day I was born, as they say."

We're carrying a barrel of wine. That's for the whole battery. The front-line ration.

"There's a smell of wine here," says Fedoseev.

He has protruding pink lips, white eyebrows, and his teeth are large and have gaps in them. He speaks in a singsong tone of voice. He probably never loses his temper. He makes you feel comfortable and secure.

"There's a smell of wine here," he says.

It's a big barrel. The opening is closed with a wooden stopper. Very tightly. It can't be knocked out. And even if you could, it's all the same, how would you get the wine out? At the battery they're taking on replacements now. Rookies. Young kids, probably. They're standing around, looking. It's funny. Schoolboys. Kolya Grinchenko is probably standing around in front of them. Show-off. And Shongin is probably smoking and saying to Kolya, "You just love to talk, don't you, Grinchenko!" The sergeant has brought the boots. Supposing I don't get a pair?

"Fedoseev, supposing you were to give it the gas, what would happen?" I ask.

"The speed would increase," says Fedoseev. "An increase in speed. That's if you give it more gas. But you can't here, the road's bad. If I give it the gas, it'll shake . . ."

"Let it then . . ."

"But why?"

"It'd be interesting, when it shakes . . ."

"A pity to ruin the car. And people are sleeping. Let 'em sleep. You and I aren't sleeping. But they are. Let 'em."

What if I don't get any boots? Why shouldn't he feel sorry for me? You ought to drive faster, Fedoseev. Maybe I'll make it on time yet.

"It smells of wine here," says Fedoseev.

It really does smell of wine. A sweet aroma comes out of the barrel. And I'm hungry. But we can't drink the wine; it's in the barrel. And the stopper is as big as a fist.

"We could pull out the stopper," Sashka whispers in my ear.

Supposing Karpov hears of it. He'll really let us have it.

"Of course you could," says Karpov, without turning his head.

"Just say the word, nothing to it," says Fedoseev.

We turn off the road and stop near a solitary pole. We pull out the stopper. It's easy. It comes out of its nest, just like out of butter. And a cloud of wine vapor breaks through the frosty air. Stronger and stronger.

"Each one take his ration," says Karpov. "No more."

"It'd be nice to have a bite with it," says Sashka.

"We'll grab a bite at the battery," says Karpov.

Fedoseev does it very simply. He takes a rubber tube used for siphoning gas, and he puts one end in the barrel.

"Hold out your tins," says Sashka, "so you don't spill any."

The golden wine runs into the tin. Sashka takes aim. We look at him.

"It stinks of gas," he says.

"That's nothing," says Karpov, "nothing."

He takes a few gulps.

"Pure gas," he says, and spits it out.

"Can't do without it," says Fedoseev. "It's the tube. Here, let me try it . . ."

We drink up our samples. It's strong wine. You can feel it right away.

"Don't breathe when you drink," says Sashka.

"Gas fumes are very useful," says Fedoseev. "They prevent all sicknesses. You just have to get used to it. It doesn't bother me. Nothing to it. Here, let's have that tin . . ."

"Well now, pour out the rations in full," says Karpov.

"What is the ration?" I ask.

No one can tell what the ration is.

"As long as we keep drinking," I say.

"Now that sounds like double-talk," says Karpov.

I know what's going to happen. I'll drink, and the fiery liquid will go through my body. I'll feel hot, weak and strange.

"Don't drink too much, Fedoseev," says Karpov. "You have to drive."

"It's like water," says Karpov. "I could drink two liters full of this stuff and not bat an eyelash. It's like water."

"Yes," says Sashka. "This isn't vodka, buddy, it's water."

I can't drink anymore. There's still plenty left in my tin, but I can't anymore. For some reason my lips have become tight. I can't open my mouth very easily. And Sashka's chin is all covered with wine. He just manages to catch a breath, and he's at the tin again. And Karpov holds onto the armored car.

"Damn it, I'm weak from hunger," he says.

"It's time to go," says Fedoseev and gets into the cab.

"A fine place to stop," says Karpov. "Right smack in the middle of a bumpy field. There's no place to put your foot. There's a more level place over there."

"You've really belted it down," says Sashka to Karpov.

"That's nothing — I can do it with pure vodka," says Karpov.

"What's your first name," asks Sashka.

"Aleksei," says Karpov.

His cheeks are bright red, Sashka's too. They're like brothers.

We crawl into the car.

"You want some more, Alyosha?" Sashka asks.

Karpov shakes his head. Sashka sucks the tube. Wine pours into the tin.

"Here, drink." Sashka pushes the tin at Karpov. "Drink, Alyosha. It's like water."

Sashka has short arms. They're like two stumps, and instead of a head he has a barrel. Now there's a head for you.

"But where are you going to put the stopper," I laugh, "not in your mouth?"

Sashka merely shakes his head and doesn't say anything.

"Where's the tube?" Fedoseev asks.

"In the barrel," says Sashka.

"It's swimming," I say laughingly.

"Swimming?" asks Karpov. "I didn't see it."

"Oh, you Alyosha," I laugh.

He's okay, this Alyosha. I shouldn't have been teed off at him. He has such a hurt look on his face. I tickle his neck.

"Hey, Alyosha," I say. "Don't be sad."

Sashka has put his head on the barrel and is sleeping. Let him sleep. He's okay, too. Everybody's okay. And when they give me a pair of boots, I'll really show 'em how to fight.

"Sashka," I say, "close up the barrel. It's sickening."

But Sashka is crying. Large, childlike tears flow down his cheeks.

"Where am I going?" he sobs. "What the hell do I have to go with you for! Klava is waiting for me . . . Where are you, Klava?"

What a sickening smell. A combination of gasoline and wine. Suppose you mix perfume and peaches? It's still bad. And suppose you mix roses and shoe polish . . . If he just whined quietly and softly, soft like a mosquito, it'd be easier.

"What's the matter, kid," asks Fedoseev, "you sick?"

But I don't feel sick. It's just that the smell is sickening. And I can't stretch my legs. It's crowded.

"Come and see me. I'll show you my dog," says Karpov.

"Where?"

"Eight Volga Street."

"Funny," says Fedoseev.

And Sashka is weeping huge tears. He remembers his Klava. And he wipes away his tears. But I don't want to cry. Why cry? And again Sashka has a barrel instead of a head. It whirls and whirls, this barrel. There's no help.

"Because of the Krauts, you'll forget me Klavochka . . . Buy a pack of Nord for me as a memento . . . We'll say farewell on the threshold. Klavochka, buy yourself a bright kerchief . . ." is heard from the barrel, "I'll even give you money . . ."

But I'm not crying. It'll be better if I just whimper. It's easier to breathe that way. Because this damned smell . . . Forgive me Nina, so slim, so small, and so strange . . . so unknown . . . forgive me.

"Where are we going?" asks Karpov.

"To the battery," says Fedoseev. "They're on their way, flying, flying."

"Are you drunk, Fedoseev? . . . Who's flying? Rockets? Are you driving us to the front lines?"

"That's right. There she is, over there."

"What do I want it for, Fedoseev?"

". . . there's nothing to do there for me."

"Better turn off, and let's have a cup of tea at my place . . ."

"I could take a cup myself, but this damned smell . . ."

. . . I open my eyes. Our armored car has stopped. Firing can be heard distinctly up ahead. My head's all fuzzy. Sashka is asleep. Karpov is asleep. Head thrown back and mouth open. We've been drinking. Repulsive.

"Why have we stopped?"

"We've arrived, but the battery is gone. No one is here," says Fedoseev. "The front has moved. We have to catch up . . . You were okay. How did you like it?"

The car moves on. The headlights are out. Very thick snow is falling. It lights up everything around us. It's transparently light. I'm dreaming. Or am I drunk? The offensive is under way, and we got drunk. I'm delirious from the drinking; up ahead there is a white figure. It stands in our way. It has raised its arms. It holds a submachine gun in one hand, and a lantern in the other. The small yellow flame doesn't illuminate anything.

"Fedoseev, stop!!" I say.

The car stops. Karpov has awakened. He looks at the figure. He reaches for his holster.

"They're ours," says Fedoseev. "Let's find out what's up."

Supposing they're Germans? Where's my submachine gun? It's gone. It's probably under the barrel, someplace. Under the wine barrel. The figure comes closer and closer. Fedoseev flings open the doors.

"Boys," the figure shouts, "help us, quick. Some of our friends have been killed. We have to bury them . . ."

The figure comes up to the car. It's a soldier. He is completely covered with snow. One side of his coat is torn off.

"How did they get it?" Karpov asks, and he yawns.

He yawns as though he just got out of bed. He yawns and our boys are lying there, dead. Karpov is drunk.

"Bullets," I say.

"Mind your own business," says Karpov. "Where are the dead?"

The soldier waves his lantern.

"Over there, over there," he says. "All seven of them. Two of us made it. Help us, boys."

"There's fighting going on," says Karpov. "We can't be late for the battery."

"We're already late," says Fedoseev.

"We shouldn't have drunk so much," I say, and am surprised at my daring.

But Karpov looks at me and doesn't say anything. He doesn't say anything, because there is nothing to say.

"We got drunk like a bunch of swine, while the fighting was going on," I say loudly. "Let's go, Fedoseev."

We climb out of the car. Karpov too. Silently. Then the sleepy Sashka. We take the spades and a pick and follow the soldier.

"You've never seen anything like it," he says, and continues walking. "Nothing like it from the very beginning. We pounded each other for six hours. Then we went forward."

We are walking across the bumpy, snow-covered ground. No, it's not a dream. Up ahead the terrible fighting is going on. I can hear it well. Well, Ninochka, your warrior has distinguished himself. Beneath a low hillock, a solitary soldier is hacking away at the frozen ground. And the one who came with us says, "Here, Egorov, I've brought some help. Now we can do it quickly. You go on hacking. We'll all help you in a minute."

A little to the side lie the seven bodies of the dead men. They're all sprinkled with powdery snow. Their coats and faces are white. Seven white men lie there in silence. What dream is this? They're dead men. Ours. And we drank wine.

"Not a bad commander," I say to Sashka. "He got drunk and let us get drunk, too."

"Shut up!" says Sashka.

"Grab the spades," says Karpov.

"Everybody should," I smile ironically.

Sashka and Fedoseev look at me.

"I'll take one, too," says Karpov calmly. "I also have a spade."

And the seven lie there motionless, as though they had nothing to do with it. We dig in silence. An hour or two. The ground doesn't give very easily. But we manage. We'll be burying the dead in a minute. How will I be able to look at them?

"Put out that lantern," says Karpov.

Egorov puts it out. But nothing changes. It hardly gave off any light anyway. And why did Karpov suddenly think of putting out the light? . . .

It's a deep grave. And the first soldier gets into it.

"Well, come on, Egorov," he says. And I know what he means. And Egorov gives us the sign, and we follow him. Am I really going to pick up dead bodies with my own hands and bring them to the grave? Sashka and Egorov take the first one. They carry him. Fedoseev bends down for the second one. Karpov looks at me. And why shouldn't I take one? I'll take it by the feet. At least it's not the head. I must. Yes, me. Not Karpov, but me. I pick up the dead man by the feet. We carry him.

"Careful, boys," says the first soldier from the grave. "Don't drop them."

"Certainly not Lenya," says Egorov, going by.

"That's our Lenya," says the first soldier. "Let's have him."

He takes Lenya's body from us and carefully lays it down.

Then we drag over another one, and another.

"Saltykov on top. He was young," says the first soldier. "It'll be easier for him to lie like that."

"Can't you keep quiet?" asks Karpov.

"They don't mind it, lieutenant," says the soldier, "and, naturally, I can keep quiet."

We put them all in. Carefully. They lie there in their coats. All of them have new boots. We work with the spades in silence. We do everything that's necessary. Now even the boots are hidden under a layer of earth. And a helmet is lying on the hillock. Whose — I don't know.

We're off in the same direction again. Towards the firing. We're silent.

OPEN SCORE

. . . AND who has counted how many times we've changed our position? Who? And how many shells I passed to our loader Zolotaryov? And how my hands ache . . . We don't just change our position. If it were only that. We're going forward. Mozdok is somewhere behind us. Come on! Come on! Now I'll probably get a spoon. I'll have a nice new spoon. And as soon as the fighting is over, the sergeant is going to give me a pair of boots . . . That is, when it is over. But when is it going to be over? . . . Kolya Grinchenko keeps bending down. He looks through the sights. Then he stands up. He is tall.

"Platoo-oon!" shouts Karpov. He waves his twig. He stands there so pale. "Fire!"

Sashka Zolotaryov has thrown off his coat. The padded jacket has come apart. His lips are white. He just keeps throwing those shells into the mortar barrel. And he groans each time. And the mortar groans, too.

Through the shouting and the explosions, you can hear the German "Vanyusha" mortar begin to snort. And its terrifying shells land somewhere behind our battery.

"I hope they don't close in," says Shongin. He's actually screaming, but he's barely audible. "If they zero in on us we're goners."

"Retreat!" shouts Karpov.

"Thank God," Sashka laughs pleasantly. "My hands are falling off. Nothing to replace them with."

The trucks come out of their covers. We hitch the mortars. And again we hear the snorting of the Vanyusha and the whistle of the shells overhead and their screech, somewhere behind us. Missed. Missed again. How sickening your own helplessness can be. Am I a rabbit? Do I have to wait until I'm hit? Why doesn't anything depend on me? I stand on a flat piece of land, and suddenly . . . you've had it — it's better in the infantry, really . . . at least there you can go into attack screaming . . . and then it's each man for himself . . . and there's no fear, the enemy is right there. But here, you're fired at, and you cross yourself: maybe, maybe . . . There it is again. Vanyusha keeps snorting more and more persistently, stubbornly. The shells keep landing more and more frequently, more accurately. Our trucks screech heartrendingly as they get out of the line of fire . . . Hurry up, damn it!

And there's that snorting again. It seems so peaceful. Again and again. And the whistling . . .

"Get down!"

Behind us, Shongin keeps turning round and round.

"What are you doing, picking mushrooms?" screams Karpov.

"My leggings . . ."

And he keeps turning and turning. He catches his leggings like a kitten playing with a ball of string.

Something hits me in the side. The end? . . . I hear running. It's to me. No, they go by. I'm alive. My dearest mother . . . alive . . . alive again . . . I live . . . I'm still alive . . . my mouth's full of earth, but I'm alive . . . It wasn't me they killed . . .

They all run past me. I get up. I'm okay. My dearest mother . . . I'm okay. Shongin lies not far from me. And Sashka stands over him. He holds his chin in his hand, and his hand shakes. It's not Shongin lying there, just remnants of his coat . . . Where is Shongin? Can't figure out anything . . . There's his tin, sub-machine gun, spoon! Better not look, better not.

"Direct hit," says someone.

Kolya takes me by the shoulder and leads me away. I follow him.

"Spit out the earth," he says, "you'll choke."

We walk towards the trucks. They're already moving. Several people remain beside Shongin.

"Come on, come on," says Kolya as he sits me down.

"Everyone okay?" asks Karpov.

"The rest are," says Kolya.

. . . Towards evening we arrive at some kind of village. We stop. Is it really over? Are we really going to get some sleep? The kitchen comes up. My stomach is empty, but I don't want to eat.

The three of us are sitting on a log. I drink my soup straight from the tin.

"The Krauts are putting up a fight," says Sashka.

"It's all over now," says Kolya.

"Now we're even flying in the daytime," I say.

"Is your head all right?" asks Kolya.

"He's got a head like a rock. It can take anything," says Sashka. He laughs. Quietly. To himself.

"It's tough about Shongin," I say. We finish eating our soup in silence.

"It's easier for you without a spoon," says Kolya, "you take a couple of gulps, and it's done. But this way, by the time you get in the spoon and bring it up to your mouth, you've spilled half of it . . ."

"I saw some German spoons here," says Sashka, "new ones. They're all over the place. I should bring you some."

And he gets up and goes off to look for the spoons. I'll have a spoon too. Of course, it'll be German. But what's the difference? How long I've gone without a spoon. Now I'll have one at last.

The spoons are really good ones. A whole bunch of them.

"They're washed," says Sashka. "The Krauts love cleanliness. Pick any one of them."

The spoons are in my hand.

"They've been washed," says Sashka.

There are a lot of them. Pick any one you want. After eating you diligently lick it and put it deep down in your pocket. But a German has also licked it. He probably had big, wet lips. And when he licked his spoon clean, his eyes probably bulged.

"They're washed," says Sashka.

. . . And then he put it in his boot top. His leggings were probably soaked with sweat. And then he dipped it in porridge again and then licked it clean again . . . On one of the spoons there is a dried piece of food.

"Well, what's the matter?" says Kolya.

I return the spoons to Zolotaryov. I can't eat with them, I don't know why . . .

We sit and smoke.

"That *Heinkel* is having a ball for himself," says Kolya, and he looks up.

A German reconnaissance plane is flying above us. Our boys shoot at it lazily. But he's high. And it's already twilight. He also shoots at us from time to time. You can just barely hear the machine-gun fire.

"He's getting mad," says Kolya. "That Fascist was probably walking up and down this street yesterday."

And Sashka flips away one spoon after another. He draws back his arm and throws. And suddenly one spoon hits me in the leg. I can't understand how it happened.

"That hurts," I say. "Why are you throwing those spoons around?"

"I'm not aiming at you," says Sashka. And the leg hurts more and more. I want to get up but my left leg won't straighten.

"What's the matter?" asks Kolya.

"My leg won't straighten for some reason," I say. "It hurts very much."

He looks at the leg.

"Take down your trousers," he orders.

"What's the matter?" I say. "Why?"

I'm not wounded. It didn't even scratch me . . . But I'm already scared. Somewhere inside, just below the heart, I have a strange, sick feeling.

"Take 'em down, I say, you bastard."

I take down my padded trousers. My left leg is all bloody. There's a small black hole in my white underpants, and blood is pouring out of it . . . my blood . . . and the pain is getting duller . . . and my head is swimming, and I feel slightly sick.

"It wasn't the spoon, was it?" asks Sashka in alarm. "What happened?"

"The *Heinkel*," says Kolya, "it's a good thing you didn't get it in the head."

I'm wounded! . . . How could it have happened? In battle, nothing. In the still of the evening. I didn't rush any enemy bunker. It wasn't a bayonet charge. Kolya goes off somewhere, comes back and goes off again. The leg won't straighten.

"It hit a vein," says Sashka.

"Why isn't anyone coming?" I say. "I'll bleed to death."

"It's all right, you have enough blood. Lean against this. Lie down for a while."

Kolya comes back. He brings a medic with him. The medic gives me an injection.

"That's so you won't get tetanus."

He bandages me. They put me on someone's coat. Someone comes and goes away. How uninteresting it all is now. I lie there for a long time. I don't feel the cold. I hear Kolya shout, "The man'll freeze to death. He must be sent to the dressing station, but that bastard of a sergeant won't give us a truck."

To whom is he saying this? Oh, that's the battery commander who's coming over to me. He doesn't say anything. He looks at me. Perhaps I ought to tell him to order them to give me a pair of boots? But on the other hand, why do I need them now? . . . The one-and-a-half-tonner drives up. It's carrying empty gasoline barrels.

"You'll have to put him among the barrels," I hear the voice of the battery commander say.

What's the difference where.

They shove some papers into my pocket. I can't figure out who is doing it . . . anyway, what's the difference?

"These are documents," says Kolya. "Hand them over at the dressing station."

They put me in the back of the truck. The empty barrels stand around me like guards.

"Goodbye," says Kolya, "it's not far."

"Goodbye, Kolya."

"Goodbye," says Sashka Zolotaryov, "see you soon."

"Goodbye," I say, "of course, I will!"

And the truck drives off. That's all. While we're traveling the same road we went north on, I sleep. I sleep. Without dreams. It's soft, and I'm warm. The barrels surround me.

I wake up for a few minutes when they carry me into the barrack of the dressing station. They put me on the floor, and I fall asleep again.

. . . It's a large, nice room. And there are windowpanes in the windows. And it's warm. The stove is going. Someone is pulling at me. It's a nurse in a padded jacket worn over her white uniform.

"Let's have the papers, dear," says the nurse. "We have to check you in for the hospital train. They're taking you to the rear."

I take the papers out of my pocket. The spoon falls out. Spoon? . . .

"Don't lose your spoon," says the nurse.

Spoon? . . . Where did I get a spoon? . . . I'll hold it up to my eyes. An old worn-out aluminum spoon, and on the handle is scratched the name "Shongin" . . . When did I have time to pick it up? Shongin, Shongin . . . something to remember you by. Nothing's left except a spoon. Only a spoon. How many battles he had seen, and this was the last one. There's always a last one. And his wife doesn't know anything. Only I know . . . I'll hide this spoon even farther down. I'll always carry it with me . . . Forgive me, Shongin, old soldier . . .

The nurse gives me back my papers.

"Sleep," she says, "sleep. Why are your lips trembling? No need to be afraid now."

No need to be afraid now. What is now? Now I don't need anything. Now I'm completely alone. Supposing Kolya comes in and says: "We're attacking now. Now we'll have some fun, boys. Now we'll drink some cognac . . ." Or supposing Sashka Zolotaryov suddenly comes in: "My hands are falling off from all this work, and there's nothing to replace them with . . ." And Shongin will say: "You talk too much, you're a bunch of animals . . ." But Shongin won't say anything now. Nothing. What kind of a soldier am I? I didn't even fire my submachine gun once. I didn't even see any live Fascists. What kind of a soldier am I? I don't have a single ribbon or medal . . . And other soldiers are lying near me. I hear groans. They're real soldiers. They've gone through everything.

New wounded are brought into the barrack. They put one next to me. He looks at me. The bandage has slipped off his forehead. He puts it on again. He swears.

"Be with you in a minute," the nurse says.

"I'm plenty sick without you," he says. And he looks at me. He has large, malevolent eyes.

"You with the mortar?" he asks.

"Yes," I say, "mortar. Do you know any of our boys?"

"Yes, I know 'em," he says. "I know everybody."

"When did you get it?"

"This morning. Just now. When did you think?"

"And Kolya Grinchenko?"

"Yes, he got it, too . . ."

"And Sashka?"

"Sashka, too. Everybody. Wiped out. I'm the only one left."

"And the battery commander?"

He screams at me, "Everybody, I say, everybody!"

And I scream, "You're lying!"

"He's lying," someone says. "Don't you see his eyes."

"Don't listen to him," says the nurse. "He's not himself."

"He talks too much," I say. "We're going forward."

And I want to cry. And not because of what he said . . . But because you can cry for something else besides grief . . . Just cry, cry . . . Your wound's not dangerous, kid. You've got a long way to go yet. You'll still be around for a long time, kid . . .

translated by ROBERT SZULKIN

The River Oka

LEV KRIVENKO

❈ ❈ ❈ ❈

> . . . *nature:*
> *Is neither shell nor soulless image —*
> *It has a soul, it is unfettered,*
> *It has a love and, too, a language . . .*

F. I. Tiutchev

I

IN 1942, in the last days of September, our division set out. They said that we were being transported to the front. During the night the freight train was hauled along a single-track railroad up to an impasse of some sort. At dawn we got out and were counted.

I remember: no traces of the advanced detachment were to be seen anywhere. The road we walked along wasn't even made smooth, trampled down. It sprouted grass, was strewn with leaves, and was guessed at rather than seen.

Storm clouds, squeezing toward the slippery earth, were thickening and mingling with the mist. The early dawn, with its biting frost, had settled where the mist was smoking. But in the ravines, night was still whole. The peak of the forest glowed in the sun, screened from us by the half-cloud, half-mist.

I suddenly wanted to be alone with this glowing mist which, like hoarfrost, had splashed on my heavy overcoat, with this orange-colored forest. And when you know that you may be drinking in all this for the last time, the forest and the road and the brightening sky appear somehow in a special light; you examine a rusty leaf gnawed through by snails, a little spider's web sagging under a string of dewdrops, now flashing out, now dying down, with the feeling that you are really seeing all this for the first time in your life.

"Why have you lagged behind?"

I shook off my languor and caught sight of the commander of the regiment's supply unit, Kozlov, leaning from his horse.

I couldn't explain to him why I had lagged behind and so remained silent.

"Company? Name?" he shouted, and narrowed his eyes.

I gave him my name.

"Report to the company commander! Let him set a penalty on my orders."

The distant forest seemed to move farther away and glowed as before in the sun.

I caught up with my own company while they were shouting to a halt. I didn't venture to address the company commander, Leushin, right away. He was sitting at the edge of a precipice, his legs dangling, and was gazing at the river below with fixed, absent eyes, thinking his own thoughts. His hands, with fingers yellow from cheap tobacco, lay limply on his knees. His slightly bent, hilly back, with a deep groove down the center, seemed drawn taut. I didn't want to disturb his concentration, to grieve or anger him.

I knew that Kozlov would make inquiries; he checked everything, checked everyone. I cleared my throat. Leushin didn't move.

"Comrade captain, allow me . . ."

The groove in his back, moving, disappeared. He turned around. A grimace wrinkled his drawn face.

"Well, what now? What do you want? Out with it!" he said in vexation.

I reported Kozlov's orders.

Leushin waved his hand and swore, "To hell with him. Look. The Oka."

The bank was invisible from the precipice. The lingering mist lay below. Detached from everything, the splash of the advancing and retreating waves reached us. This was the river's breathing. A little farther away the mist was already moving slowly and, in the alternating breaks, a buoy, lying on its side, first appeared, then disappeared. Still farther on, the open water was rippling.

The flat bank opposite looked far away. Sandbars were whitening. A field with haystacks, inundated by the sun, was growing yellow. I longed to become saturated with this sun (perhaps the parting smile of summer) and, no matter what might happen in life, to carry in myself the warmth, the caress, the smile of the Oka sun to the end of my days.

"Have you written a letter to your mother?" asked Leushin.

I answered that I had written.

"A letter for the unit commander has arrived from your mother," Leushin observed. "She asks why she hasn't had any letters from you."

"But there are no events worth writing about."

"For a mother a letter is an event in itself. She'll find out about the international situation from the newspapers. Write again, do you understand?"

"I understand."

Leushin turned toward the Oka.

II

MORE and more often during recent years I have wanted to visit those places where I chanced to fight during the war. Having left the army long before, I suddenly discovered years later, that there, in the entrenchments, in the scorched forest or on the roads, by some inexplicable forgetfulness, I had dropped and left behind a part of myself.

Having set aside a free week, I decided to go out beyond Tarusa to the Oka, to the remembered place. That's where our division had passed, moving toward the front.

My brother Volod'ka, a pupil of the ninth form, nicknamed "the student" in the neighborhood, came with me.

We took groceries, fishhooks, floats. We made up our minds to live only in a mud hut which we would dig by the river.

. . . We arrived in Serpukhov in the evening; the lights were already being lit when we reached the pier. It turned out that the steamer wouldn't cast off until late at night. Volod'ka sat down on a log and dozed off.

I couldn't sleep. I began to smoke. The noise from the city was gradually dying down. Darkness was thickening. Nearby a boat was bobbing up and down. The water made a champing sound, striking against the piling. The city, finally, became a dark wall. Several lanterns hung, separating this wall from the sky.

How solitary those lanterns were, how pallid their light, not giving warmth, intended for all and for no one in particular.

I looked at the glassy water, wrinkled in circles by the splash of a big fish, at the distant lights of the buoys, feeling how, involuntarily, my chest expanded to the full, trying to take in as much as possible of the Oka air.

They began to let people on the illumined steamer. We didn't go inside but chose a bench on the bow deck. The steamer finally cast off from the pier, making the water foam up and rocking the pier.

When we got out onto the open water, the wall of the city retreated and blended with the darkness. The lanterns seemed to be dying out. They didn't separate the wall of the city from the sky anymore. A turning point in the river — and the lanterns went out. The wind began to blow sharply from all sides; at once it became fresher, lighter.

Forward! If only it were possible, just like that, at a turning point, to tear oneself away from one's past life!

Volod'ka lay down on the bench and, having pulled his padded jacket over his head, began breathing regularly. I, too, began to make myself comfortable: I moved the knapsack under my head, lay down, stretched way out, but I couldn't fall asleep. He sleeps well who isn't afraid of sleeping through anything, who has everything before him. I cannot fall asleep at once, as if I were afraid of sleeping through a blow from the corner, or some unique event, or simply of yawning my life through yet another sunrise or sunset or dashing wave, not like the one moving now from the steamer to the shore, but another kind . . .

From behind the clouds, which had become illuminated, then drifted apart, the moon came out, at first not the whole of it, then, after another turning point, all of it. In one segment the water glittered, making the far-off places still darker, still more impenetrable. I began to smoke and to examine my past life, abstractly somehow, without regrets for the unfulfilled, without joy for the successes. And when the moon again became covered by a micaceous cloud, then the river and the distant forests and the shrubs stealing up towards the bank mixed together into one mass. It seemed to unite all these separate existences, to fasten them together in something common.

If you ask yourself what you are thinking about here on the expanse of the Oka at night, you won't find an answer. You are just aware with your whole being of thinking about everything at once, about some unanalyzable and still undiscovered unity of experience.

The moon grew completely overcast. The banks were obliterated. It seemed that the Oka had overflowed. Having washed everything away, it closed in upon the sky.

And when you don't see anything around you, those things which you had set aside in your memory as urgent questions demanding an answer emerge from the darkness.

III

ON your approach close to the advanced line, you realize right away that it is an especially rotten sort of place, and everyone walks on with relief, cheered up, when this place remains off his path. When you haven't taken part in a battle, you feel as if you had escaped unharmed from a battle the likes of which you hadn't hoped to scramble out of. No one feels like falling into a hole, knowing in advance that he won't get out. Sometimes such holes are already forming during an attack.

I remember: our unit advanced on an attack and entrenched itself at the foot of a hill. With a running start, we tried dashing up the hill, but fell back. A white rocket goes up — the artillery barrage, a green — the tanks crawl out, a red — the infantry. And so events unwound in such regular succession. But all the same we had to fall back. The infantry was cut off from the tanks and was laid low.

The top of the hill grew bald, became black, and gave out smoke for a long time.

We prepared a second attack. Again the rockets: white, green, red. Again the infantry was squeezed off from the tanks. Six times we went up the hill, never with success.

The rumor spread that this was a special hill, with some kind of underground trenches for trucks.

I have never felt so wrung out, so crushed to bits as when we crawled out to the line of departure. Even our company commander, Leushin, who had never before raised his voice, suddenly began to scream out the simplest orders.

It was barely becoming light. The hill lay like a grave. Pressing into the ground, we waited for the white rocket — the artillery barrage, then the green . . . There were still some minutes ahead of us, to fit our whole lives into. And then — the red — our sign.

The hill seemed to move in the smoky air, which undulated in the sunlight. At such moments of expectation you can even see with your back. The sky, the sun, the brittle grass, seemed disconnected. Everything had been splintered up, partitioned off by trenches, wire entanglements, shell holes, ditches.

And suddenly everyone turned cold; taking our last minutes away from us, the red rocket leaped forward. No escort at all, neither artillery nor tanks.

Leushin, lying nearby, stared at me in bewilderment, as if he didn't recognize me. I looked at him, trying to guess what was going on. Perhaps he knew. Someone began shouting "hurra-a-ah" and immediately stopped short. The red rocket! There was no point in waiting. We got up and moved forward, as if on tiptoe. We wait, and in no time at all the mincing machine will begin its work. We passed the place where the infantry had been cut off from the tanks, bowing down mechanically. And here we felt that this hill, which had seemed to be under a spell, now lost its power. Things got hot right away. We ran forward. Several shots rang out to greet us, but we put a halt to them immediately. Getting to their trenches was like rolling downhill.

The sky and the sun and life returned once more to harmonious oneness and wholeness.

They brought out one smiling, whitish-looking first lieutenant. He seemed to be satisfied with what had happened. We asked him what he was so happy about. He slapped his brow, "Oh, Russ, you were sly! The artillery was alerting us. On the double, to our places. Bang! Bang! — and Ivan had to start all over again . . . Oh, you were sly!"

Apparently this German was giving us our due for our resourcefulness, our quickwittedness.

We were surprised ourselves at how adroitly we had captured the hill.

When we met one another, each time, again and again, we were carried away, going over the details, and we added more and more enraptured evaluations.

"Wow! Terrific! They know what they're doing at headquarters, and that's that!"

Only on the following day did we learn the real details. The man who had thrown out the red rocket had almost been shot on the spot. He was a signalman who had mixed up the rockets.

IV

THE village where Volod'ka and I stayed for a reconnaissance of the area clung to the high bank of the Oka.

The precipitous, slippery bank was overgrown with nettles, wormwood, sweetbriar. If you stand by the fence, you can see the aspens and birches growing below. The Oka isn't visible. But a little to the side, both banks are spread out before your eyes: the one opposite, with its sandy shoal slipping underwater and, a little farther away, peeping out again from the water; and the bank on this side — hilly. And still farther, in the bluish-gray distance, both banks have merged. The river has taken a turn there.

A little way off, beyond the village, there is a rye field with a road, beaten to dust, going out to the forest.

The forest rises in a half circle, a birch forest, growing lilac-colored at its depths. At the point where the half circle abruptly breaks off, the birch forest turns to aspen, growing silver as the wind stirs its leaves.

Going through the forest, dry and resonant, you come out to a winding stream, jumping among the stones, which empties into the Oka nearby.

A mud hut, hardened in the sun. Dust-covered blackberries, raspberries in a copse right by the road. Mushrooms, perusing one another. Butterflies, fluttering from one swaying flower to another. A pair of dragonflies on the wing, scurrying in all directions.

And beyond one distance, new distances, beyond the new distances, infinite new distances living in each of us. And — the Oka.

v

We decided to dig a mud hut, military style, all by itself, removed from road and village, alongside the Oka.

Not wanting to lose any time, I went to the village for an axe and spades. By a locked shop with an iron door I saw a local woman in felt boots, with a kerchief tied up to her eyes. I told her what I needed. She led me to her house. When we entered the hall, I noticed a stove bed, covered with sheepskin, a smoke-blackened icon in the corner, and a door, leading to a room, with a shiny, new padlock. Clearly someone was living in there. While handing over a rusty axe and bent spades, my hostess muttered a curse and pulled the kerchief from her face. I saw a face which seemed crumpled up into fine wrinkles, with lips puckered like an accordion. I asked her what her name was. It turned out to be Dar'ya.

"Aunt Dasha," I said, "don't you worry. I'll come back soon."

She didn't answer. I went. She shouted, "And will you sharpen the axe for me?"

I nodded. Little did I know that they would skin us fifteen rubles for this sharpening.

. . . We didn't succeed in digging a foundation for the mud hut. Having cut away the turf, having cleared the site, we could dig down only a couple of feet. We began to hit rocks which even the two of us couldn't roll away. We were just wasting our time. We decided to put up a hovel in the forest itself, slightly above the bank, in a remote, unfrequented place.

We began to live as we had never lived. We bathed; turning over in the water, we cried out in delight. We drank steaming tea, seasoned for tartness and aroma with the leaf and berry of a stone bramble. We cooked buckwheat groats, double portions of fish soup, and the rest of the time we simply slept right out in the blazing sun, keeping ourselves warm from the north wind.

At first, at night, it's true, we weren't used to it: it seemed as if someone was coming, somewhere twigs were snapping, someone was crawling, rustling the leaves and grass. But afterwards this snapping of twigs and rustling of grass stopped bringing precautions to mind. We began to think it laughable that we, who hadn't encroached either upon anyone's property or anyone's life, who hadn't harmed anyone, were nonetheless in constant fear of something.

Once, at night, I struck a match and caught sight of a fleeing mouse. Let it run. Once, in the morning, a goldfinch flew into the hovel and, not noticing us holding our breath, he turned his neck, making himself a bit more comfortable, to peck up a crumb. Then he took wing and, continuing to chirp beckoningly, flew off. Let him fly where he likes, he's not doing anyone any harm.

In the morning, chilled through, we would crawl out of the hovel and, moving the wet branches aside, would go down to the Oka.

The Oka is cloaked in mist. Only the shore reeds are seen, emerging in the smoke. The dew is so thick, dense, that you walk on the grass as upon the first fresh snow, fallen during the night; only you leave dark green traces — footprints. The traces fill up right away with spring water. You cautiously move the reeds aside, push apart water plants with crayfish clinging to them. After clearing a passage, wincing, you dash into the burning water.

And in the evenings we built big bonfires. Steamers, barges, would be floating past. The sky would be fading. And I, gazing at the lights, at the moths jumping in the smoke, as once they did when I was marching to the advanced line, would become so lost in thought that I would almost dissolve into my surroundings.

VI

I CAN never remember either a single number or a single figure or a single fact by itself. I only remember in connection with something or someone. That may be why I don't forget anything. That may be why, even when I am walking in a forest or field, where everything distracts me, I do not cut myself off from the past, I cannot run away from the past. It stands before me in a whole row of obligations which have to be fulfilled, no matter what. Not to fulfill them would mean to be broken.

Today the sun is so bright that at times you don't see anything, or, for an instant, everything looks red.

I was going to the town of Tarusa for cigarettes. The whole way I walked along the bank of the Oka.

When you look at the Oka, remaining constant in its flow, at the forests, dissolving in the distance and never disappearing, at the clouds, creeping away and ever returning, in the sun's blaze, before the gleaming water, before every birch bending in a thicket to keep from dying off, you see the ineffaceability of the earth and, above all, you begin to hate everything that wishes to smash up the indestructible — life.

I must be a happy man if, in the society of trees, of the river, I am never bored. I can drink in the clouds, floating and dissolving in the shining blue flood, for hours. I may be thinking of something far away from the clouds, the trees, from the river sounding on the shoal; but there is some inner tie between these clouds and my thoughts, far away from the clouds.

Volod'ka arrived with a shining face. I saw at once that he wanted to surprise me with something. And so it was. It turned out that he had swum across the Oka and, while investigating some distant marshes where, we supposed, ducks were fattening, he came out in an old river bed and, clambering about the sandy bottom, hardened to stone, he came across the tip of an arrow — a green, moldy arrowhead. For a long time I sniffed at this piece of metal, tasted it.

"Well, what is it?" Volod'ka asked.

"Not bad. A Scythian arrowhead."

"These people," said Volod'ka, "did a lot of harm, if all that's left of them are rusty arrowheads."

Once we woke up earlier than usual. A few drops seeped through into the hut. Suddenly it grew much darker. Leaning out, we saw that a bluish-violet cloud had moved above us. Thunder cracked, shattering into fine splinters all over the forest. The rain poured down in a wall. The hovel caved in at once and settled on its sides. Having undressed and tied our underwear up in a bundle, we ran towards the road. We ran up to Aunt Dasha's house and stood under the awning. As I later found out for certain, Aunt

Dasha has an acute sense of hearing. Let there be a scraping somewhere, and her ears immediately prick up.

The door opened slightly. Aunt Dasha looked out and asked us
in to get dry. I hesitated. I knew what kind of hospitality this was,
just as with the axe and spades: we would have to pay at the
regular restaurant rate. But Volod'ka had already entered the house.

We told her that we were living in the woods, in a hut.

She led us to a shed, mumbling that, anyway, it was better here
with people than in the woods with wolves. We kept quiet.

Soon it cleared up. Small clouds crept about the blue, cleansed
sky. Shadows were moving on the roofs, the doors, the trees, the
field, the river.

The hovel had become lopsided, had worn down. But it survived
three days in all, as we noted. We decided to enter into negotia-
tions with Aunt Dasha; maybe she would let us stay there at night
and, from the morning on, we would go out to our own place. She
asked the outrageous price of fifty rubles. I glanced at the icon,
darkening in the corner.

She suddenly became infuriated and shouted, "God has nothing
to do with this!"

"All right, all right," I immediately agreed, feeling that we all
have corns that it's better not to step on.

In the early morning, its nighttime freshness not yet scattered,
steeped in the autumnal odors of rotting leaves and in old, sopping
wet mushrooms which had swollen up during the night, we would
go to our hovel.

We would return when the Oka was growing dim, weary, but
with that weariness after which, when you pop your eyes open in
the morning, you feel still stronger, still more resilient.

VII

ONE time Volod'ka tried to prove to Aunt Dasha, scientifically
you understand, that God does not exist. With all his arguments,
he didn't produce any turnabout. Volod'ka didn't know that each
believer sees in God his own God, modeled from his own unfulfilled desires. Aunt Dasha's God was, so far as I could tell, of a
special sort. The commandment, "Love thy neighbor as thyself,"
she evidently didn't remember. Most readily of all she would go

on and on about God's punishing of sinners with a vengeful force, the embodiment of retribution.

But all Aunt Dasha had to do was to hear a stirring in the room with the gleaming lock forever hung on the door, sometimes locked, sometimes unlocked, and she would immediately shrink into herself and, lifting her brows, would whisper, her whole aspect beckoning us to conduct ourselves more quietly, "The chief!" and her brows would crawl still higher, wrinkling her forehead.

Why this lingering servility? As if "the chief," a visitor, by the way, whom she didn't know personally, and to whom she rented a room during the summer season, could snatch away her kitchen garden, dug up long before by her husband, killed in the war, dug up again more than once by her son, also killed in the war.

Man cannot live without spilling out the stuff that settles like rust, like soot on his soul. To pour out one's soul to someone (and if there isn't another person on hand ready to listen without indifference, without a smirk, without a self-satisfied air, then, if you like, to a tree, to a hen, to a stray dog) is to inject oneself with an antidote against cancer of the soul. And sometimes Aunt Dasha would agree with Volod'ka that God doesn't exist, just so she could share with us memories of her husband, of her son, Pyotr.

We spent the whole of our last night in a boat, taking turns at the oars.

In the morning we left on the first steamer. Aunt Dasha accompanied us all the way to the pier and was so moved that she burst into sobs. She had already accompanied so many people who didn't return.

We stood on the deck and waved our arms as long as the pier was in view. Somehow Aunt Dasha had become so close to us, so kindred, in her denlike solitude.

The steamer turned; the village moved backwards; new distances opened up before us.

VIII

Two years passed from the time we tore ourselves away from the Oka.

But sometimes, in a flash, we would remember the hovel, the village, Aunt Dasha, snatching separate details out from our memory.

I remember: Volod'ka was sitting over his schoolbooks, frowning, with an air of a person who had decided to prove, no matter what, that he could "mop up" the mathematics teacher himself, when suddenly he slapped his forehead.

"He's solved it," I thought.

And he jumped up and said, "The funniest thing is that in the village they took us for real, live fishermen. There we were, walking through the village, suddenly a 'beard,' bending out of the window down to his waist, shouts all the way down the street, 'Hey, boys, what are the fish biting today?'"

"Another funny thing," I added readily, "is that we didn't catch much ourselves. If we scrounged together enough for fish soup we were doing well. But we would meet that same bearded fellow and he would praise us — 'Good boys! That was fine advice: we caught five kilos in one morning. If there were a few more experienced people like you around, life would be more jolly.'"

"I think I'm going to have to pack up . . ."

"Certainly," agreed Volod'ka. He always agrees with me.

. . . In the city everyone is rushing somewhere, afraid of being late; all are scurrying, colliding with one another like blind men, moving from place to place, and you have the sensation that you are as old as mankind, beginning the chronology from the first Neanderthal man who accidentally struck a fire. In the city, it seems, everyone is occupied only with the rearrangement of numbers in an addition column.

On the Oka, where movement is apparent only in the change of light and shadow, in the change of the weather and the seasons, you come out of the water, of the forest, as if you were eighteen years old again. Again there are no barriers, either to human aspirations or opportunities.

I felt this anew when I caught sight of the Oka again.

IX

EVERYTHING seemed to be as before: the old pier, the same lights as before. The river was sleeping peacefully; barely audible, it flowed onto the bank and settled down again. At the same time, everything was different, revised, but, most of all, not unstable, not secretive. Even the distant lights weren't smoldering in solitude, as they had been on my first arrival, but were shining amiably. Although it was late, quite a few people gathered on the pier. They were outshouting one another, laughing loudly, as one never laughs in the city. I even caught myself laughing, while gazing after a man carrying a bundle of fishing rods and an enormous leather bag which hid his whole body.

The steamer went out onto the open waters.

Familiar places passed. The sky was overladen with storm clouds. Only from rents in the clouds did paths of light stream out. Then a wind blew up — everything began to stir. The circle of the sun began to show through the clouds.

I kept looking out for the boulder: we had placed our hovel about thirty paces from it. But there are the cottages over there . . .

I confess, I didn't think that Aunt Dasha would greet me so warmly.

" 'Leksandrych!" she clapped her hands. "You haven't forgotten. Ah!"

Slapping my back, she kept repeating, "You haven't forgotten, you haven't forgotten, ah!?"

"I see you haven't forgotten; have you gotten any younger, or what?" she asked, looking me over and nudging against the door which had no padlock.

"You really haven't rented it?" I asked.

"Out with them! At least in my old age I'll live by myself."

"So, we're still alive, Aunt Dasha!"

"Seems our time hasn't come yet," she said, and she began to laugh.

Never before had I seen her laughing. She used to just grumble.

She wouldn't think of letting me go off to the Oka before she had given me some tea with sugar.

"Lie down, 'Leksandrych, after your trip, you see," she fussed.

I lay down and fell asleep. While she was in the room I must have slept soundly, but, when she went out, that peculiar Oka silence set in, so unusual for a city person that I was awakened by the buzzing of a fly beating on the closed window. The teapot, grown cold, stood on the table. I upbraided myself. It was probably already past noon. I ran out. I went out along the edge of the village toward the precipice, toward the river.

One could smell that special freshness which a rising wind, promising rain, brings. Rain was already falling, but it was a little way off, over the darkening forest. The rain couldn't be seen, but above the Oka a blue cloud with lilac edges was visible, and one could see how the boiling river was bubbling under the cloud, how the forest had grown thicker, denser, and how, on the far bank, everything was smoking.

And to the right lay the blue sky with its immeasurable depth. Here the Oka was gleaming under the sun. The land could be seen far, far into the distance.

On the opposite side, where it was raining, the earth was steaming. My native land: understood and at the same time inscrutable.

translated by EDYTHE HABER

II

Poetry

Naum Korzhavin

✻ ✻ ✻ ✻

They have taken my loved one away:
The cunning ones call her their own.
Duty has dressed her in chains,
Piety chews at the bone.

I weep, not because she is changed,
But because she was born to endure.
Does tenderness need to be chained?
Is piety meant for the pure?

translated by STANLEY KUNITZ

✻ ✻

PREAMBLE

Vanity
  Vanity
    Vanity — those midnight monologues.
Why put the blame on others?
  The fault is to be traced
    elsewhere.

Time?
  Time is granted.
    This is not a matter for discussion.
You yourself
  are the topic
    on the agenda.

Don't believe
   posterity will care enough
     to spot you for applause,
as if to say, "Poor chap,
   he couldn't stand his age,
     he simply withered up."

No century is easy.
   Earth has no use or honors
     in reserve except for him
who carries to the grave
   the burden of his time
     on mortal shoulders.

                        translated by STANLEY KUNITZ

✠ ✠

LIGHTNESS

That's the way it goes:
     Lies
     Evil
     Oblivion . . .
The passing of friends
         (his passing)
And the darkness packed in joyless hearts
Aware that we endure
       a little hour.
He knocked against it time and time again:
Flared,
   fought,
     and understood . . .
And he was — light,
        his touch was light,
Not from philosophies he'd figured out,
But simple things he knew:
That winter glitters on a windowpane,
The storm-wolf howls,
        a girl lies fast asleep,

And midway in her dream
        the weather veers;
That men are born to grieve
        and still be passionate;
That luck means poems
        and certain friends that stay;
And that he kept the hope of happiness,
Though not for you or me
        and surely not today.
Say it! Life that for a moment rages
        must serve
           forever.
It will flow into the ages:
        each of us will die,
Given one chance to live
For all eternity
        as well as time.
He drank wine and saw
        a far-off light.
How clear! how clear!
        Though the night was coming on,
He turned his face
        to distance and bright air.
Lightly, so lightly:
        That Pushkin lightness
Outsoaring time and space.

translated by STANLEY KUNITZ

⌘ ⌘

Not by planning and not by choosing
I learned the mastery:
What a damnable trade
Where winning is like losing!
The wheel keeps spinning,
The thread gets broken,
I can't even tell
My work from my loafing.

This life isn't tragic,
Just a hell of a pickle;
In age as in youth
I don't have a nickel.
And nothing shall save me
From meanness and sinning
But more of the same,
More losing like winning.

translated by STANLEY KUNITZ

✼ ✼

From foolishness or wiseness
We lived together laughing
And would not give our fondness
The name of love.

Though the war had scarcely ended
And everyone had troubles,
Spring taught us to move surely,
Light shimmered on the sea.

Yes, I know. Love is grievous,
Fugitive, exalted,
But I had what I wanted:
To live simply and to write.

Not to move mountains,
Not to dig to China,
But as Pushkin did it,
Easy and serene.

translated by STANLEY KUNITZ

✼ ✼

How difficult to live without you!
You tease and trouble me all day . . .
I know you can't replace the world
For me: it only seems that way.

This life of mine is adequate
To serve for better or for worse;
But lacking you, my dear, it fails
To add up to a universe.

How difficult to live without you!
My heart is always in a stew.
What if you can't replace the world?
It couldn't take the place of you.

translated by STANLEY KUNITZ

✄ ✄

THE THOUSAND-YEAR-OLD SONG

"It's an old song
That is forever new."
HEINE

An old song
A thousand years old.
He worships her
But she is cold.

History flows
And fashions change;
Familiar customs
Yield to strange;

But still through this
Incessant stir,
She loves him less
Than he loves her.

Horseman or poet
Though he be,
Her light is his
Necessity.

She seems perfection
In his eyes,

And must be so —
Since she agrees.

A thousand years
Like one unfold;
He worships her
But she is cold.

Who is this other
She finds fair?
No devil rides him,
He's Mister Square.

If such an ass
Can be preferred,
The point is plain:
She likes being bored.

She wants to eat
Her chicken fried,
And not to glow
As a luminous bride.

Maybe her suitor
Will cry: "Enough!
I'm sick of yearning!"
And shuffle off.

Maybe he'll turn,
Like his rival, fair;
Get rid of his devil,
Become Mr. Square;

Maybe she'll play him
Another tune.
How should I know?
The song lets me down.

To hell with the song!
My choice is not free;
Already both fates
Have happened to me.

And that's why my hurt
Is a thousand years old:
He worships her
But she is cold.

translated by STANLEY KUNITZ

Evgeny Vinokurov

❋ ❋ ❋ ❋

THE WOMAN

The woman, in truth, was bony.
Her shoulders jutted like two right-angles,
She was that bony.
Her dress hung limp like a net,
Her earrings fish-weights,
Her hair seemed glued to her scalp.
Shrewd as a lioness,
She cunningly perched her head
On the shelf of her collarbone.
Mysteriously, she smiled
A smile that might have scared you,
Save for her redeeming glory.
Warm green eyes,
Wise with compassion,
Fruit of a lived-out life.

translated by MELVILLE CANE

❋ ❋

HOTELS

I fear hotels.
The very thought of filling lungs
With poison from unbeaten rugs,
The stale bedroom reek,
Disgusts me.

I fear hotels,
The cruel cold from windows.
Curtains, a lamp, a sofa,
Fake hospitable warmth,
Make a wretched shelter.

But most, I fear hotels
For that unpredictable hour
When, all alone,
Entrapped within four walls,
I'll face the fact
There'll be no checking out.

translated by MELVILLE CANE

✖ ✖

FOOLS

The world is full of fools;
In fact,
You'll find choice specimens
Right here in this neighborhood.
Crazy ones! Dreamers!
Never a haircut,
Eyeglasses spliced with string.
Always dreaming!
Bed-covers pulled up over their ears,
Scared of a noise in a pipe.
Poor fools!
And yet, I wonder
How much I may have missed,
Never having risked
Their eccentricity.

translated by MELVILLE CANE

❈ ❈

Old sins return to plague us,
To exact their pound of payment.
Is this just?

We were young, rebellious, tough,
But, remember, we were young,
And youth runs headlong,
Heedless of consequences.

Now I'm ready to pay,
But only for what I owe today,
Not for the folly
Of the lad I was.

translated by MELVILLE CANE

❈ ❈

BATHING THE CHILDREN

Thursday's the bath-day at our place.
How the children love to race
Around the rooms, naked and free!
My wife presides over the weekly dunking;
Skirt securely tucked up,
Arms bare to the elbows,
She's set, and gets to work.
They squeal over her scrubbing,
Squirm under the steam,
(Hair over their eyes),
Squeeze their eyes to keep the soap out,
Shrink, as a basin of water
Plops and shocks and overflows the tub.
My wife drops to her knees and mops the floor.
"No stalling! Wash behind the ears! Out you go!"
They're back in bed, now, naked,
Sheets pulled up over their heads,
Snug.

translated by MELVILLE CANE

❋ ❋

THIS POETRY BUSINESS

Would you care to know
How it feels and what it means
Being a poetry editor?

Then listen, and I'll spill the beans.
I'm an authority.
I've had it good and plenty.

These birds move in
With a sly, feminine
Gambit; they court you,
They actually woo you,
But when that fails
They assail you.

Each day, from one to five,
This poor slob,
Meaning me,
Stuck to the job,
Multiplying enemies,
Just hoping he'd survive.

All my paltry salary went
Toward the reinstatement
Of friends whom I'd offended.
They'd pass me on the street
And turn their heads
And cut me dead.
I made an odd discovery at last:
That what they wanted most,
Yes, even more than publication,
Was praise,
And then, more praise!
What egos!

And so,
Whenever I turned a manuscript down,
I gave a sedative,
A pill of flattery,
To ease the pain.

They gloried in rejection,
Not dejection.
They'd leave with faces shining
And tears of gratitude.
That was the general attitude.

Acceptance of a poem was never final.
I'd pass it on to an editorial board.
Their comments fell
Like a burst of artillery shells
On a practice target,
But, by and large, it
Would be voted in.

What characters!
A youth. Writes staircase verse
Like a sectional bookcase.
An old has-been.
Sat across from me,
Gasping, a signet ring
On his beefy hand.

A construction worker,
Tall as a beanpole,
Overalls caked with paint and lime.
Put down his cap —
It stuck to the desk.
Leaving, he had to yank it free.

Then the story
Of the corpulent lady:
"My children have the whooping cough,
My husband has no sensitivity.
I write in bursts!

How else, when there's cooking
To do and shopping,
And no help?
Alone, alone."

And that oddball;
With a wild gleam
In his piercing eyes,
He crazily demanded:
"Appoint me Poet-Laureate
Of the Soviet Union!"

They kept crowding in.
They all wrote poems,
The whole cockeyed world writes poems.
I've grown more and more suspicious.
The odd look of that embassy guard!
And when the high executive
Locks himself in his office
Announcing that he's not to be disturbed?
Is he composing an ode?

Authors come and authors go.
Tons of verse forever flow.
In the sultry, humid weather
Words and phrases melt together —
Sticky fruit-drops in a bag,
All of Russia's on a jag!

I was poisoned by them
And, like a supersaturated solution,
Crystallization began to set in.
And then
The muse emerged in strange seductive guises
Of rhomboids
And octahedrons of assorted sizes.
I might have hated poetry all my life
But for that happy, unexpected time
I came across one line . . .

translated by MELVILLE CANE

Boris Slutsky

✤ ✤ ✤ ✤

SNOW

White snow . . . not white . . . light . . .
Not light . . . lights! Lights coruscate,
Lifting the night up out of its darkness,
Drifting on warm May winds although
It's dead winter and there's no sun.
Strange — a sudden happiness
Has just begun
To lift me up as though I had no weight.

translated by ANNE STEVENSON

✤ ✤

THE ADVANTAGES OF OLD AGE

It's easy to tell a greenhorn of twenty,
"Come back in a year or two, son!"
Even the middle-aged, pots full, heads empty,
Can usually be forgiven
For believing the stuff they say.
Only for old men danger is day after day.
No waiting, no watching, no choosing another way,
An old man knows what he can't afford to do.
No second chance for his bones. His few
Brittle hours are
                very close
                        to the frontier.

Beyond that no man goes.
Notice
    how often
        an old man shows
Grandeur,
Simplicity.

translated by ANNE STEVENSON

✣ ✣

OLD WOMEN WITHOUT THEIR MEN

There were many old women, not many old men;
What bent the old women broke the old men;
They died with their fingers clenched hard on their ribs
As their wives, like hurt animals, fussed over the funerals,
Jerked open closets, brushed out old dresses,
Spent too much money for the solid oak coffins
Where they laid out their husbands, alone, for the last time,
Resting big hands like stones on their lapels.
— Soon there were tenements full of old women,
Whole blocks full of widows who prayed by themselves,
Heard thieves in small noises, gabbed about death
As if death were a person, a friend they had tea with.
Gaunt Anna Petrovna, sad Mar'ya Andrevna!
They got up like sailors, early in the morning
To comb out their long slats of Hindu-black hair.
To roll their old beads in their stiff, blunt fingers.
They undressed early, too, punctual as soldiers,
But lay without sleeping, lay thinking and sifting,
Turning over old lovers, old duties, old habits,
As if nothing could waken them out of their sleeplessness,
And all the dead mouths of their lives, of their years
Chattered in a streetcar's
              empty rattle.

translated by ANNE STEVENSON

✖ ✖

It's not too bad, living twenty floors high
With all of Moscow stretched at my feet,
Fading into its suburbs.
Up here where the windows are pale blue squares
There's cleanness, quiet, perennial brightness.
Too high for mice
— Mice can't stand heights —
Clouds keep me company, purring
And rubbing their sides against my balcony.
After spring storms, in May, for instance,
The puddles light up like coins in the streets.
Look up from below and my floor is a birdhouse
Swaying four hundred fifty feet nearer to the sun,
Four hundred fifty feet nearer to heaven,
Where I live on a level with the moon.
Yes, it's a good life up here, I think,
(Especially when the lift's not on the blink).

translated by ANNE STEVENSON

Andrei Dostal'

❋ ❋ ❋ ❋

Thank you
For the pain.
For the bliss
Thank you again.
(For the lines made fast
And the still sails.)
For having
Become mine
So long ago now,
As though a century.
Thank you
For it all.
For these sleepy embraces,
For this beautiful dress
You've thrown off
Light-handedly.
And thank you for the light
That grows in my heart
At midnight,
For my hands full
Of sadness,
         of warmth,
              of you.

translated by ANDREW FIELD

✖ ✖

I touch your hair
With my lips . . .
Your submissive
Downy lashes flash
As though you dreamed
A wonderful dream.
I feel
How your heart beats,
With my lips
I feel
How your heart beats!
And trains go by.
Quietly.
In a string.
Like camels
On the level steppe.

translated by ANDREW FIELD

✖ ✖

What will the owl convey
In this dark stand?
One ought thrust one's hand
In the hollow
Of such a centurian tree
More frequently!

There's nothing to fleece
From this old fellow,
He's disheveled all his feathers.
His eyes move blindly,
Quite unkindly.

Slowly
A mole burrows.
I hear him, too.
While he,

I think,
Takes me
To be a canopy.

Thus I lie on the ground,
Heard by all.
In the mist
A star weeps.
Time drips down
By drops . . .

translated by ANDREW FIELD

✖ ✖

A cold dock
In autumn.
The sensuous mouth
Of a river.
Somewhere before
I've known
Eyes
As doleful.
Somewhere before
I've known
Hands
As thin.
A cold dock
In autumn.
And parting,
 and parting
  and parting

translated by ANDREW FIELD

✖ ✖

In a field wires are
Droning.
Somewhere trains are
Flying.

Someone's star
Descends.
That's how it always
Ends.

translated by ANDREW FIELD

The Driver

a narrative poem

VLADIMIR KORNILOV

The very first talk of the Virgin Lands
Began in March, quite early . . .
"Where's that? Yes, where?" came rapid demands.
I pointed it out on the wall map.
I remember the sergeant who winked and teased,
"Hey, driver, let's go there together!"
Beating me to it, someone replied:
"Good lord! Is he off his rocker?"

I remember, before the grass appeared,
When the river was still breaking up,
How Moscow, almost at dawn, embarked
On its Virgin Lands exhortations.
I won't forget, either, how all spring long
We learned of the Virgin Lands from
Politicals giving our gang
Their mountains of information.
"You go," they told me,
"The people must be served . . ."

Political talks on the Virgin Lands
Divided Company opinion.
"Let's go," my neighbor whispered one night,
"Let's go! The epoch summons . . ."
I woke and gave my grumbling reply:
"But I'm quite okay in Moscow."
(That's where I used to drive a cab.)
I told my neighbor: "Now go to sleep.

I'm no girl, so you're wasting your breath.
Say what you will — I'm not going."

The summer arrived. Camps and heat.
Marches. Trenches. Shooting.
I ripped off the calendar's pages and kept
Whispering: "Faster! Faster!"

Autumn. Lazy dance of leaves.
One damp, misty morning,
I remember, they ordered us out to the square,
Each man carrying his suitcase.
The officer shouted:
"Lengthen the step!"
So we said goodbye to the army.
Discarding my topcoat for a jacket,
I climbed back into my taxi.

Some people are deeply in love with the past.
They remember years now distant:
"Before the war we really lived!"
But I say:
"Before the army!"
That's when things were swell.
When life
Was understandable, simpler.

Our ancient house, with its dovecote beside it,
Was far away from the city.
At twenty I scrambled all over the roofs,
Pursuing our white-feathered flock, and
I never read what the newspapers said:
I believed them without even reading.

Four days the accordions
Wept and wailed.
But not for a wedding.
They were
Sending me off to the army. First
I was shoved in a train — like a sheep!

Taken out at Ivanovo, they gave
Me boots and a uniform, and
Shaved my hair off to the scalp.

The town had little to please me.
The whole place seemed stupid and dull.
Every morning the women
Rushed out to line up for bread. They'd wail:
"No butter, no meat, and now no sugar . . ."
And every day the papers paid
Thankful praise to Stalin.

. . . Beside a restaurant near the Kremlin wall,
I'm smoking again in my taxi.
Where have you gone to, faith of my youth?
You're lost beyond trace or recall.

But look around you — life is fine!
You won't remember it better.
You leave the garage, to Kursky Station fast,
Then back to the restaurants at midnight.
You take on a cool-looking passenger, drunk.
He is — let's suppose — an airman.
Agreed on a fare, you take him along,
Without even turning the meter.

Well-fed and shod, healthy and clothed,
I drove and knew no sorrow.
Trucks were few: their drivers had all
Been dispatched to the Virgin Lands!
I'd carry the good-time girls around
And listen to their endless chatter.
No one, in fact, to boss me about!
Only the traffic lights changing . . .

A taxi-driver's free as a bird!
Not in the least like a soldier . . .
"Are you content, then?" I was sometimes asked.
"No," I'd say. "Discontented."
I drove and drove, but my soul rebelled,

You can't really call that working!
And to live on tips at twenty-four
Is not my idea of joking.
It's absolute hell on a taxi-stand,
The constant fight for a place . . .

Suddenly I find my mind returning
To the Company, where life was honest,
Where I ate my bread with soul at ease,
And my soup and the main dish that followed . . .
Where I was silly and young and a tease,
But still always yearned for home.
I yearned . . .
And earned it.
I'm in Moscow now.
Rain. The approach of winter.
And deep in my soul a strange desire,
Desire for life in the army.

2.

You could hardly call the apartment posh.
The table rocked and the bed was quite
Narrow. Four hours once a month —
That's the leave the lieutenant gave us.
And I used to sit, my chest bare,
At the table — it scarcely stayed upright! —
And drink my fill of homemade beer
Brewed by a friendly widow.
I'd down each glass in a toss till drunk!
I was one of the hottest drinkers!
It even seemed there was freedom, or a spark,
In kissing kindhearted widows.
How I longed for those hours! Sometimes
They were cruelly canceled.

But now I'm walking on Avenue Tver
As if there had never been sometimes.
Fall's at an end, so thaws have stopped.
The wind drops as midnight draws near.

And snowflakes settle softly on top
Of my beautiful goat's fur collar.
What's that to me?
Sad, without sleep,
As if I'd just fought with my
Best friend, I roam down a Moscow street.
A voice says: "Your time is up.
Quit loafing and drinking.
There are roads before you."

"Well, choose one!"
But which would be best?
I'd memorized the notion,
In school I'd been made to learn it by heart,
That before me lie goals in the thousands,
Goals in numbers you can't even count.
But now, though you won't believe it,
Life had arranged things so that
Two paths, no more, lay before me:
To take to drink or find a wife . . .
I stood at the legendary crossing:
To the right lies sorrow, to the left lies grief.
You scratch your head a bit, puzzling,
Can't decide which of the turnings to take . . .
The girls who've rushed into marriage
Fade away in the flower of life,
While behind — you can well imagine —
Remain only those forsaken by luck.

The children who yesterday fitted
Beneath the table have now grown up,
Their bearing quite different from that of
Their unsophisticated sisters in the past.
I'd meet them on Sverdlov Square, where
They walked in the glow of the ads
In unbelted, well-cut overcoats,
In new suede shoes and felt hats . . .
So will you get married?
No desire.

But it's also hard without it.
In three years something important and quite
Incomprehensible had happened.
A tiny light, unextinguished by drink,
Had started flashing in my brain-cells:
"What! Are you clinging to Moscow as if
To some new sort of apron-strings?"

I whispered this to my innermost self
(I knew the mistake I'd been making),
And I ran through the coldness of Gor'ky Street,
My overcoat billowing behind me.
Beside the entrance, discarding reserve,
With all my decisions taken,
I flew like a madman under the globe
Hanging over the Telegraph Office.

Consumed by a restless courage —
Like in cards when you're breaking the bank! —
I seized not a sheet of paper
But, in my fever, a telegram blank.
More drink or the marriage office —
A similar paradise both!
Blotching the ink and panting,
I scribbled:
"I ASK TO BE SENT . . ."
And out on the sleepy sidewalk,
Where the snow had dispersed the crowd,
A little green light was winking
On a cab looking cold and sad.
As I sank on the seat like a gentleman,
I shouted: "Where's the Komsomol boss?"
Deafening the drowsy cabby.
(The guy was from our garage.)

To Kievsky, Kazansky and finally
To Kursky Station. As we drove
Life seemed happy to me
On the lonely midnight roads.

Snow was veiling the windows,
The guy was on the verge of sleep,
And I was constantly repeating:
"Let's go to the Virgin Lands!"
I urged him on: "You stupid idiot!
Chuck Moscow, we'll go to the steppe.
Isn't the bread shortage urgent?
Okay, then, we'll help with the bread!"
That's how I put my ideas,
And I glorified life on the land.
It seemed as if the whole planet
Was no bigger than a billiard ball.
But the driver shrugged his shoulders,
"The Virgin Lands?" he said.
He didn't believe they could dissipate
All sorrows in a single day.

At dawn just opposite Moscow Trade,
With the guy now swearing freely,
At last we found the Komsomol boss.
Slumped on his wheel, he was nodding.
He started, wiped his lips,
And barked: "What's eating you?"

He hated me, I didn't like him.
At meetings he'd spew out his anger,
Denounce us for drinking all the time.
But far more slyly than we did,
He had his various deals on the side.
It was only me who worried him.
I'd call out:
"You're a fine one to talk!
You loyally lie about Communism, sure,
But why aren't you above taking bribes?"

The form was mucky — blotches galore!
"Read this!" I handed it over.
"And please, I beg you, don't be afraid:
I'm not going to change my mind."

3.

Talk about the Virgin Lands
Begins after Saratov.
But I can't place any trust
In ecstatic train orators.
I gaze through the window at the fields:
I daren't interrupt the talking:
Anyway, they'd tell me ruble lies
And give me no change . . .
What are my thoughts on the Virgin Lands?
Whatever will happen — will happen.
Mostly I gaze through the window at the fields,
But I feel a need to glance at a girl,
Resting in her bunk, turned on one side,
Installed above the gathering,
She lies with her back towards my bunk,
Ignoring everyone's arguing.
But now they've switched to a poker game
And serious concentration.
They bang down their cards without malice.
They swear, but in moderation.

When she entered our coach
She had looked at everyone wearily,
Asked to be given a light,
Begun to smoke, then, taking
Out a letter, read
It not from the start, but from halfway.
I had noticed — my eyes were good! —
The first word: ANTONINA.
For a moment I hadn't thought: then
I suddenly said, quite casually:
"They must call you Tonya for short.
Let's get acquainted, Tonya!" . . .
I shut up and realized at once:
With her not a thing will come of it.
I lowered my head and blushed,
And lay on my bunk in silence.

As if from afar, in the night,
I suddenly heard someone shouting:
"Which stop is this one? Wake up
That guy or he'll miss his station!"
Waking, I wiped my eyes.
The smoke in the coach was stifling.
I took all my stuff outside,
Caught sight of her on the platform.
"Come on," I told her. "Let's go.
You'll get lost alone in this wilderness.
And somehow it's better with two.
I'll help by taking your cases."

It was night — no stars, no light.
The platform squeaked a little.
In front of me Tonya walked
Obediently, without her suitcase.
My head was going round and round,
I forgot myself in happiness.
There was no discordant sound,
Nothing I couldn't do!

The soles of my feet were inflamed,
My overcoat inflated,
And my soul had never been fired
So fiercely by Muscovite vodka.

And so we proceeded.
We came to a house.
The shutters glowed weakly.
"So long as the landlord doesn't snore,
We should succeed in sleeping."
The bolt scraped at last,
A young girl appeared.
"Hey! Are you the landlady?"
"No, I'm not, but we've got no room!"
"Tonya," I barked, "push right past her!
We don't intend to freeze on the street.

They'll make room enough on the floor."
I gave my commands like a brother-in-law:
"Get inside and take off your coat, Tonya."

4.

The room was certainly cramped.
A floor of people sleeping.
Spreading out my coat, we camped
In a corner no one was keeping.
I watched how she lay, all curled up,
How she covered herself with the greatcoat,
And waves of pity arose
In me, sweeping up through my body.
I felt strongly for her, a stranger
Lost on her way through the steppe . . .
"Hey, Tonya. I'll be the watchman
And guard our things. Now you sleep."

Still I dreamed of achieving wonders,
Still I expected great feats — how absurd!
God knows, love wasn't my intention,
God knows, that's what occurred.
I was stroking and stroking her hair,
Until at last fatigue overtook me.
At dawn I couldn't stay asleep
And woke to find the day quite light.

A kettle whistled away on the stove,
And a man, oh, about fifty,
(He looked like some sort of local boss)
Was already making up to Tonya.
In a thick Ukrainian accent he asked:
"Where you from?"
"From Leningrad."
"Your profission?"
"I'm a pharmacist."
The more I listened the worse it got.
"What brought you out to our steppeland?"
"Oh, nothing. I left my husband, that's all."

A weary sigh.
"What was that for?"
His slyness revealed itself in his glance . . .
Extracting my head from the greatcoat,
I got to my feet and shouted out:
"Hey, you, lay off!
Leave other men's wives alone!"

She simply bit her lips.
I probably sounded silly . . .
I was thinking:
Heads or tails!?
And decided:
Death or glory!?
"Let's go!"
"What's the rush? . . ."
"Pick up the suitcase," I said.
Tense and hunched and threatening,
I waited, my head held low.
Was it folly or maybe pride that
Kept me there in the hut?

No! I liked her figure!
From head to toes
The whole was carefully sculptured,
As if from a single piece.
Her makeup lacked any excesses,
She was dressed first-class!
I loved her urchin hairdo:
In Russia the style was new.
"Let's go! There's no time for joking."
She rose from the bench with a yawn,
Reluctantly took from a hook her
Waist-length, stiff leather coat.

The boss was sitting on the counter,
Twirling his pale, corn-colored mustache.
Whoever he'd have been in a ministry,
Here he reigned like the ace of trumps.

. . . At last the silence oppressed him.
"D'you drive?" he asked.
I nodded.
"Perhaps."
"Well, you see, I need a driver."
Not half a syllable more.
He winked his eye with a flicker,
As if he were asking a waiter for drinks:
"Two beers and a pint of vodka!"
In fact he didn't speak like that at all.
He was really quite reserved.
But what struck like a sock in the puss
Were those words of his: "*I* need . . ."
I tensed myself at once, like a spring,
My sleepless nerves were edgy:
"*You* need? Well, then, whose is the machine?"
"Whose? Mine. I'm Plyushch, the director."
He certainly wasn't a low-level boss:
A state farm's as big as a regiment!
But even he found himself without defense
When faced with my cabbie's impudence.
"Think it over a bit," he urged.
"No," I said. "It won't wash."
"Why not, then?"
"I haven't been trained in a personal cult,
My work lies in serving the people."

Preserving my pose as a tough guy,
I stuck to my battle; but she
Was silent and sat, for some reason,
Trapped in a world of the deaf.
Changing our pronouns we had already turned to
The intimate form of speech.
The landlady was now removing
The dumplings she had warmed on the stove;
And people were flooding into the cottage.
It became impossible to talk.
"Okay," I said, "give me
A mobile repair-shop, and I'm yours."

5.

The Virgin Lands with their noble name
Are a kind of newborn planet.
Not many people live there, for sure,
Though its praises are sung with passion.
The railway doesn't reach very far,
But in every kind of weather
State-farm tractors ply to the trains,
Their single wagon behind them.
A tractor's like a steamboat, hauling its blood-
Red wagon without a schedule.
The wagon lies on a sledge
Instead of wheels.

Our tractor is moving . . .
What more,
It would seem, could you want? . . .
But you swear because in the compartment
It's boring, congested and dark.
Thoroughly drowsy and huddled
Beside the wrought-iron stove,
The boss and I weakly marshal
Our pawns for the umpteenth time.
We each say checkmate to the other
At least some fifty times . . .
Against the wall the driver
And his mate take turns sleeping.
Both of them swear at the snowstorm
And crawl towards us for warmth.
I open the door for them, feeling
Sympathy rise in my heart.
Instead of moving this bishop,
I should leap on the tractor myself!
But duty didn't permit my
Abandoning Tonya to them.

Beside the window, rolled in a ball,
My loved one lies — she's smoking.
How could I suddenly believe in a love

Which lasts right up to the grave?!
Who had instilled in me nonsense like that?
And how had I meekly swallowed it?
Maybe by going to movies too much?
Or by reading cheap novels?
The Virgin Lands for days on end
Passed by outside the window.
Pure white. White as the moon itself.
Even our eyes began aching.
The tractor got overheated, but arrived.
Its guts had delivered us safely!
"Is this the whole state farm, Pavel Kuz'mich?"
"That's it. There are twenty-two barracks."
(My darling was asking simple things
Concerning their life here.
They told her conditions were cramped
But, nonetheless, quite cheerful.
Among all those men her tiny voice
Somehow sounded pitiful . . .)
I looked around and spat in the snow:
"Your life's pretty boring, director."

No corners, of course, to hide in!
The steppe lacked beginning and end . . .
Brazen guys swaggered up to us,
Simply to say, "What a piece!"
The eyes of my Tonya would widen,
Apparently filled with fear.
I knew any monkey business
Would lead straight away to a fight.
Restraining my temper for the time,
I said to them gruffly: "Keep off!"
But then a guy started something,
And I belted him one on the ear . . .
Plyushch parted us.
He was strong, that Plyushch.
It would have been bad for me otherwise.
Plyushch began:

"You, my lad, are bad-tempered —
And you'll pay not a little for that.
And, brother, I don't much envy you:
Where beauty is — trouble's there too.
Tomorrow you'll get a compartment,
For tonight the office'll do" . . .

The frost had stuck to the panes,
The electricity wavered.
The storesman knocked on the door,
And brought a mattress and blanket . . .
With the mattress against the wall,
And encasing the pillows in covers,
I turned and said:
"Come here!"
And took her in my arms.
It doesn't take long to lose your head.
But she simply smiled:
"You silly one!"
And pulled herself up to my face
To kiss me on the lips unaided.
I thought I'd go mad
Fiddling in a maze of buttons.
But the Mongol khan, Mamai, grabbed my hand,
And I ripped off her hooks in a blaze . . .

Yesterday I'd never have dared to think of it.
I thought I'd lack the courage for a long time.
But I wasn't very happy that things had gone
So simply for the two of us together . . .
No, a fear was growing in my soul.
Till dawn I kissed her
In the empty office, held her in my arms,
My Tonya, my joy, my sorrow.

I washed in the morning in haste,
And straight off went to eat . . .
My shoulders were thumped by the lads:
"Well, how did you sleep last night, eh?"

The girls were smiling:
"Go home, friend,
Eat at home!
Won't your chemist
Cook you some *kasha?*"

I started overhauling engines —
They gave me the help of some girls.
Milka was so stupid that allusions
To her mother were frequently heard.
Tan'ka was a beanpole, but still, she
At least had brains in her head.
The third girl was beanpole's sister,
One Zhen'ka Vorotnikova. This
Zhen'ka was dressed like the others,
In tunic and ski pants.
Maybe that's why the bow in her braid
Seemed so out of place.
I pitied poor Zhen'ka the most;
She ought to be still playing with dolls.
I'd tell them all:
"Put on your coats,"
Then chase them off to the office.
They didn't provide much help,
Only lots of laughter:
"Come on, girls, let's throw
Snow down the driver's collar!"
"He's okay by us, girls!"
"Big news, Milka!"
"Is he better in full face or profile?"
"He's best of all from behind!"
That's how they talked, day in, day out,
They sang and seemed to get prettier.
"You know," the men in the workshop said,
"You ought to get rid of those menaces."
But all their laughing, truth to tell,
Kept me in very good spirits.
If people laugh on the Virgin Lands,

It means things can't be too bad there.
If you're fooling around all day,
You must enjoy life a bit.

I only wished, with the others so gay,
That Tonya would laugh a little.

6.

The snow had subsided more and more
Without completely melting.
Now it resembled the mealy core
Of an unripe melon.
Beside the railway coaches and tents,
And next to each of the barracks,
There raged in greenish puddles and pools
The flustered quacking of ducks.
The sowing of corn had already begun —
Dispensed from narrow baskets —
And the people now were being moved
From their coach-quarters in the meadows.
Rows over blankets and pillows and pots
Blazed from the crack of dawn.
The women lamented, but all the same
Their coaches were fastened to tractors.
. . . We found ourselves in a family which
Had five unpleasant children.
Behind the stove we cleared some space
To squeeze in a bed and a table.
We lived in poverty, in an awful mess.
The father wore nothing but tatters . . .
It completely mystified us what he did,
On what, precisely, he existed.
From early morning he swore at his wife,
Then wandered about the settlement,
Deranged, with a straggly, rye-colored beard,
As bald as the moon on his noggin.
I heard that for ten long years at a stretch
He'd kept on the move without stopping.
A dozen times he'd changed his job,

And two dozen times his dwelling.
Well, what of it? —
People like him walk around in rags
And wear dilapidated trousers.
They say, during the thirties,
They called them "fliers."

He boasted to me,
"I used to live well!"
His bragging really sickened me.
The children would howl all through the night,
While the hungry bedbugs devoured them.
The fool — he'll not get bread
For breeding only bedbugs.

My Tonya went off to the pharmacy
And I began to sleep in the attic.

The snow disappeared. Motion began.
The puddles dried in the breezes.
I drove Tat'yana to join a brigade,
And also her sister Zhenya.
Beside me sat Tan'ka. She gave me hell.
She pressed me:
"Well, driver, what's up?"
"Are you going to get married? That's great!
But what were you doing till now?"
Again I remembered the city.
There, if things are bad in your house,
You close the doors and windows
And nobody guesses the truth.
"But why d'you want Antonina?"
The girl who drove tractors all day
Relentlessly hammered the question,
Opposing my instinct to act.
"The whole thing would tangle," she said.
"It's better to spit and forget."
Her sister, however, kept silent,
Ignoring us all the way.
Well, what could I say for an answer?

I blushed and gritted my teeth
At questions like,
"Will there be children?"
"And will they be born in your name?"

I had sipped from glasses at weddings,
At christenings I'd sometimes drunk,
But I'd hardly considered children,
And I disliked people who married.
I haven't seen many good marriages . . .
In a month or perhaps a year,
Despite the adjustments, all love turns
To ashes in a terrifying way.
The girl shakes her fist in anger,
The guy spits: a rotten business . . .
I hoped for something so different,
I thought things would turn out well.

At top speed the sowing continued,
At night people worked with lights,
And I was dispatched to the state farm
To shouts of,
"Get on! Get on!"
The steppe sky towered above us,
Especially clear that year,
And it promised harvest,
And it concealed woe.

7.

Director Plyushch ascended the platform,
The meeting settled down on logs.
A two-minute question touched on
The results of the sowing campaign.
Said Plyushch:
"The winter's approaching"
(The summer had scarcely begun!)
"And so we must mix adobe.
It's the only stuff we've got."
Three hundred and seventy people

At once raised a terrible din.
It rose in a wave to the sky,
Never returned to the logs.
My neighbor cried,
"Give us water,
And give us some straw and clay;
If not, my norms are beyond me,
I'll collapse from hunger at once."
The patient Plyushch reassured him:
"There's *going* to be clay and straw.
We'll pay you for piecework and add on
The per cent for the Virgin Lands labor."

The following morning the peasants,
The lads and even the girls
Discarded their shoes and sneakers
And tap-danced down in the clay pits.
All were wild to get working —
If only the straw could be cut!
But Tonya looked at them playing,
Detached, secluded in her hut.
The laughing, the din and the heat
Had startled the sleepy kingdom
Where bottles of alcohol in rows
Displayed on their labels — MEDICINE;
And where, making herself safe
From the bedbugs infesting our place,
For a month now my love at night
Had put up her camp cot.

I'd loiter beneath her window:
"D'you love me, Tonya, or don't you?
We'll build a house and move in.
You'll build it with me — or won't you?"
Then I would play the orator,
Though always losing my courage . . .
"I detest," she'd say,
"Petty seekers of private property."
Rejecting every tenderness,

She worked me into a temper:
Why had she yielded at first,
And never again thereafter?

But life without women is hell!
And despite my neighbors' mocking,
I decided to build a dwelling
Of adobe and take her captive.
I hewed the stones from the stream,
While the women all cackled: "Quarryman!"

By dinner I'd got the foundations dug,
And the seams of my shirt were in pieces.
At the office I bought adobe in bulk
By loading the hands of the storesman
With almost the whole of three weeks' pay
For dust all dirty and yellow.
My suit was traded in exchange for boards . . .

Dispersing my goods to the breezes,
For a month I was scarcely clothed or shod.
Like my neighbor Filipp Matveich

The sun above the steppe consumed;
The corn that appeared was sickly.
No showers arrived. Time passed.
Already disaster impended.
"What hopes d'we have for a crop?"
Was the central conversation.
Wives said to husbands:
"Decide!"
The husbands toiled to the office.
"Permission to leave!"
"Sign here!"
"Please, a favor!"
"Release me, if only to hell!"
Plyushch now yelled:
"How much more of this crap?"
And swept the forms from the table.
My neighbor replied by drawing his knife.

"I'll cut all your throats!" he exploded.
"Then you'll go to court,"
Came the answer from sunken-cheeked Plyushch, the
   giant.
He continued: "Get a grip on things, bearded guy.
Are you a man or a sniveling skunk?
The best sort of virtue is
Discipline.
With your reckless behavior you'll soon
Be rolling around Russia again.
Should our women in Oryol or Syzran
Have to jostle each other in breadlines?
I won't let you go.
The Virgin Lands are
Both your hope and mine.
Nothing will grow here
If I'm soft with you."

Now the lads were ploughing not
For this year, but really for the next . . . They
Weren't — one can scarcely allot any blame! —
Experts on the droughts of the region.
The tractor-drivers — unlike me! —
Accepted the hardships with laughter.
Of course, there's nothing to compare
With the beauty of midnight ploughing.
Once Tonya came to the place where we worked
On some pharmaceutical mission.
The tractor, just then, broke down in the field,
So she had to spend the night there.
She couldn't sleep. Her ears were glued
To the endless roar of the engines.
Throwing my jacket around her for warmth,
She clambered out of the wagon.
For nearly a mile the light was as strong
As the light round railway stations.
The tractors were crawling, thick on the ground,
Devouring the difficult surface.

Black, pure black, blacker than ink,
The gloom was slashed by light-shafts,
And it seemed as though
On every side there was — nothing,
And the only real town was where we were.
I now grew warmer and warmer in my chest,
But words still came rather awkwardly . . .
I exclaimed: "Oh, look! Just look at it all."
She answered by blocking her ears up.
I could live thousands of years and die,
And the place where I'm buried could be razed,
And still I'll never know why,
How she was lured to this desert.

Anyway, my first house was now begun,
I hung the doors, the windows,
Took to spending the nights inside,
Rising at dawn with a shiver.
At this point my mind was quite unaware,
And saw nothing strange in the fact that
Around my house so frequently walked
Our Zhen'ka Vorotnikova . . .
The ancient mailman at his post-office chores
Would sympathize,
"Life's not kind to you.
They all write reams not to you,
But to Antonina Pavlovna."
I mumbled something by way of reply,
And sadly walked to the pharmacy.
I was carrying a letter for Tonya. I
Handed it over unopened.
She tore herself free from other concerns,
And, opening it up, she read it;
I just kept silent in the corner of the room,
Devoured with curiosity.

8.

For a month I worked as hard as an ox,
I thought: perhaps I'll get ruptured.

I'd hung the doors and put up the walls —
That left the roof to cope with.
I chatted with Plyushch, who said: "You're doing fine!
How I hate that crowd of asses
Who beg me to let them desert us!
But you're a good sort of guy,
And now would you cart that rubber?
Try not to get bitter," he urged,
"The future is right behind us!"
He smiled. But his words appeared
To contain a good deal of sadness.
It was clear that he felt for the crop
Exactly as I did for Tonya . . .
"We've chatted too long. Now get going!"
I clambered aboard my three-tonner.

Again the road.
The dust and heat.
The truck was stuffy and airless.
But though on occasions it's tough,
In fact the road's terrific!
You swing your wheel with skill,
Press on over meadows and rivers.
A trying way.
But without a way
The life of mankind withers.

I pulled my cap down over my eyes,
Remembered my earlier boldness,
Stepped hard on the gas and sang to the skies!
It was long since I'd sung from such happiness.
I sang as if fate were spoiling me fast,
My grief was reduced to nothing . . .
I sang as if the corn grew high where I passed
Through fields that were only rotting;
As if my abundance of joy and verve
Would bring an abundance of harvest.
And Antonina was only waiting
For us to go off and get married . . .

Like a madman I dashed the whole day long,
Arrived precisely at midnight.
At the station I had thousands of things to do
Which weeks wouldn't see completed.
For days I attended to endless chores,
Some roofing, or fuel for the diesels.
And midnight would come before I returned
To my home — we called it the clearinghouse.
Today it was twilight inside the room.
The furniture seemed to have vanished!
Alone on the bed sat a naval guy,
His jacket hung over a sofa.
I remember my thoughts: Sub-captain, that's it.
A kind of lieutenant-colonel . . .
What brought a guy like him to this place?
Too little to do in the navy?

His looks were not only handsome but tough,
He can't have been much over thirty.
"Maybe I woke you?" I asked him straight.
"No, I've not slept for a long time."
And so he sat, propped up by the wall,
Not even removing his footgear.
Clearly what had made him so content
Was the company of a couple of bottles.
"D'you drink?" he threw me a glance.
"I can."
"You won't go to sleep while driving?"
He handed me over some brandy in a glass.
"Our very good health!" he suggested.
It's good that in summer the nights are short:
We left as dawn was breaking.
For days on end I'd taken no sleep,
So the brandy had made me dreamy.
The captain continually urged me on:
"You're going too slowly, old man!"
Cursing hard, I breathed in his face
A powerful whiff of the brandy.

For that really irked me a lot —
That he played the smart guy on top of it!
"What's your hurry? Meeting your wife?"
"No," he replied. "My mother-in-law."

The stars had begun to pale,
The sun was coming up.
Reluctant to ransack another man's soul,
I kept my mind on the driving.
The Zis would pant as we mounted a slope,
But the great truck fought its way over!
The state farm lay, as if on a plate,
With its twenty-two little barracks.
The steppe wind and a breeze from the stream
Collided forehead to forehead,
And marmots romped in the fragile stems
Of the cornfields that we divided.
The captain here, surveying the steppe,
Turned his gaze from the cabin.
He whistled casually: "Hey, the corn's thin."
"Are you really that indifferent?
Is it all the same to you," I said,
"If the harvest is great or little?
For a long time only the bosses here
Have not been virtually starving."
"Okay," he said. "You can drop me here."
I put him out at the road fork.
Before he left he gave me half
A bottle of excellent cognac.
"Perhaps you'll be driving back to town?"
"My respects to you, but I won't be.
I've got to find the brigade to sleep."
"Well sleep, then," he said. "And soundly."

At first I was lulled by the deepest sleep,
As if I were lying with Tonya,
And Tonya were gently kissing my lips,
And my lips didn't smell of tobacco . . .
I woke and lazily stretched myself out.

As I wiped my eyes with my fist, my
Neighbor came bursting into the tent:
"Your girl's been taken, driver!"
He flew straight in, unwashed and unshaved,
And black with dirt and suntan,
And now he blurted with rude delight:
"D'you hear? Antonina's been taken."
Filipp Matveich was smirking with joy,
He hobbled around in my footsteps:
"Your wife's been taken. Don't you believe?
Her husband arrived, a captain."

9.

The machine flew off like a bullet,
And leaped away across the fields.
I looked in the mirror: a furrow
Divided my forehead in equal parts.
My teeth were bared, my mouth was
Aslant like a wheel bashed in by a crash.
Because of it, my face seemed
Strange to me, almost totally new.

And so I tore on, swallowing
My tears and sending up dust to the skies.
Sometimes my wheels ran over
Poor marmots not guilty of anything wrong.
What a chase!
But the pleasure was bitter
In such a useless merry-go-round!
(In one of Lermontov's tales, when
An exiled officer chased a girl,
His faithful horse collapsed and
Expired, lifeless on the side of the road.)

The windows were rattling so badly
That it seemed the three-tonner would fall apart.
But still I pressed the accelerator,
Stoking the hate that burned in my heart . . .
Some devil inside me whispered,

Advised me:
"Stop the engine at once!
You're wasting time on a wild-goose chase!
Go home, my friend, and put up with life.
You're no more than a driver,
And beauty's not born for you to have!"

Six months sooner I'd probably
Have paid no attention to beautiful girls.
I had driven them around in Moscow,
Their escorts decked out in gaberdine coats.
They would look at me condescendingly:
I turned away to attend my wheel.
I also rewarded them with: "Thank you,"
On receiving an extra ruble tip . . .

On the bumps the three-tonner was shaking,
But my mind was more concerned with
Catching up to Tonya
And not for a trip to Moscow.
Our vast inhospitable planet,
Which still had little to keep us warm,
Which still lacked housing and lighting,
Was better in tune with the note of my soul.
And any really hard worker,
Who's covered with grease and full of fight,
Who's been hot as hell since breakfast,
Is idolized there like Plyushch.

However long any drought may last,
I still remain firm in believing
That the strictest social justice precedes
Even bread as man's first requirement.
On distant travels I've often thought
The populace lives pretty poorly,
And the bosses are the ones who must answer first
Wherever the populace suffers . . .
And life would be very much better if
The bosses were firmly lectured:

"Now listen, my friends! You'll get your deserts,
But first you'll provide for others.
When once you've provided, take what you've earned.
If you fail, there's no harm in waiting.
The soup is ladled out last of all
To soldiers sent to the guardroom."
I've long been firmly convinced of this,
And I've dreamed on many occasions,
That if Lenin rose from the dead today
He'd promulgate such an instruction.

But meanwhile I worked away at my wheel,
Swallowing thick yellow dust. I
Looked forward to giving the captain a taste
Of my fist in his ugly kisser.
My mouth became dry. Then bitter too.
My T-shirt was soaked, goddamnit!
I flew up a hillock.
The hillock's view
Revealed nothing whatever!
O! Pursuit's such a pointless affair!
Like a windmill grinding water.
The sun was down; through the twilight air
The night flew forward to meet me.

I saw them both in the station-yard.
They were eating — wife and husband.
If earlier someone had told me the truth
I'd not have believed such rubbish!
But there they sat on top of their bags,
Wrapped in an army blanket —
A husband and wife for all the world to see . . .
And there was I — all for nothing.
Like a hungry wolf in front of a fire,
I gazed down at them from my cab.
My feelings of anger and insult kept
Me from moving a single muscle.
As if I were bound or shackled by chains,
I didn't dare spit or curse them.

I caught the sound of guttural tones
And Tonya's rippling laughter.
Throughout the journey I'd gaily dreamed:
I'll catch him and give him my fist . . .

But now these thoughts were completely smashed,
They simply counted for nothing . . .

10.

A year's gone by — what's just brought
These details of the past to mind?
. . . My fate was being rent from my grasp,
Like my wheel when I drove too quickly.
The year had been heavy going, been bad.
For fear of a meager harvest,
And spitting at bonuses, people had
Assembled their things and departed.
And then,
I mean in the very same year,
And right at the height of summer,
I thought my poor little song was sung,
And life seemed beyond endurance.
I scarcely found courage to move at all.
For two days I crawled from the station,
And my leaden head would continually fall
On the wheel in tired desperation.

By chance I ran into Plyushch:
"Ah! Come to run off like a rabbit?!
Don't think of that, I won't let you go!"
"I don't even wish to think of it."
He returned my stare, as if in rebuke.
But I wasn't lying an atom.
And he himself changed the line of talk,
As if he were lowering a pistol.
"Okay, I was wrong. So forget your hate.
We all make mistakes pretty often.
You've fought for a hundred miles to arrive,
And all the way you were happy . . .

But here there's someone who's crazy on you,
This Zhen'ka Vorotnikova . . ."
"To me," I said, "she's as useful as
A horseshoe to a drowning man . . ."
In this way I took my leave of him,
And went off to sulk in the settlement
Where I'd found a place for my private home,
Unfinished and not really lived-in.
I ended by staying in my house.
For the sake of the house?
Why was it occupied?!
It's really beyond my powers to explain,
Why I didn't leave, but persisted.
The rains descended.
And then the snow.
And then the puddles grew smaller.
And melancholy seized me tight by the throat,
Pressing me harder and harder.
I was young, it's true, but also inept,
In Moscow I thought quite wrongly
That I had only to go to the steppe
And the whole of life would run smoothly.
But once you've started — stick to your guns . . .
I lived in a home unlived-in.
Life likes to break a man so that he can
Grow strong in the place that was broken.

. . . A year has gone by — and now I'm not sad
That I didn't go scurrying elsewhere.
The outsize harvest we've had
Is known to you through the papers.

For a month not once have I closed my eyes,
I sometimes forget to breakfast.
It's I who keeps the great railway line
So busy with convoys of wagons.
The Virgin Lands had failed to observe
How they'd packed the barns and storerooms.

Such mountains of grain
And with them heaps of problems.

Beside the station, where, twelve months back,
The captain had nestled with Tonya,
A soldier was standing alone by the track —
Clearly the train had just dumped him.
I called to him:
"Climb aboard, my friend!
If you're bound my way, I'll take you."
He quickly inquired:
"But where and how?"
I answered,
"It's swell just anywhere" . . .

Towards us the grain rolled by.
We passed some hundred-odd trucks.
He gazed at each of them:
"That's just great!"
"No," I said, "only the usual."
The stars had begun to pale,
The midnight hours were dwindling.
Reluctant to ransack another man's soul,
I kept my mind on the driving.

translated by PETER REDDAWAY

III

❧ ❧ ❧ ❧

Tarusa's Past
and Present

The Poetry of Marina Tsvetaeva
VSEVOLOD IVANOV

❌ ❌ ❌ ❌

I HAVE LONG been familiar with Marina Tsvetaeva's poetry. In my youth, we read her often and avidly. We were particularly attracted to the verse of new poets and even wrote a few lines ourselves — who has not so sinned in his youth? We felt that the new poets were responses to our dreams. The youthful verses of Tsvetaeva seemed to me as complicated then as they seem simple now. Even then you had in her verse a foretaste of the sad and bitter life she was condemned to endure.

Nevertheless a sense of life's joy was there — hardly perceptible, it seemed, and, because of that, even more highly prized. These small notes of life's happiness, of the love of one's native region rang forth in a hymn to the motherland — a motherland far off and yet every second near, insulted yet magical, simple yet heroic. It is a motherland expressed in two words: Soviet Russia.

Now I read Marina Tsvetaeva's verses over and over. Not a few of them are printed in *Pages from Tarusa*, and they bespeak a highly gifted and original poet. Yes, and her prose too. *The Kirillovnas*, for example, is very characteristic of her, and I must add that it is marvelous prose.

Here is something that has dawned on me: is not Marina Tsvetaeva very close to Nekrasov? Not in meter or intonation, no. But in this: with his very being Nekrasov had understood and sung, as no other Russian poet, the sufferings and tortures of the unhappy Russian woman, from the simple peasant woman to the wife of a noble Decembrist.

A different century means different joys. The twentieth century brought the Russian woman an easing, and, in time, a freedom from many past sufferings. The October Revolution brought the happiness of communal life, with its creative and poetic sense, within the reach of the Russian woman. These are well-known truths, forgive me if I repeat them. I wanted only to stress how unhappy is man when he is removed from these joys, from this creation, this communal creation. For Marina Tsvetaeva, owing to complicated circumstances, lived for a long time outside her motherland, in emigration.

The poetic gift is varied. In this, poetry is remarkable. A given poet will express his, and at times not his, thoughts with the greatest of ease, astonished at how all is effortless and simple. This is, so to speak, the first story in poetry's edifice. On the second story, where the poet tries to express his thoughts and feelings more profoundly and, at the same time, more clearly and openly, matters are already more complicated. The more you want to be open, the harder it is, the more effort is demanded of you in expressing yourself. The higher the story, the greater the slice of life seen by the rising poet, and the harder it is for him to express himself with all the strength and beauty he would like.

Marina Tsvetaeva lived on the tenth, perhaps even on the fifteenth story of the edifice of poetry.

She loved Russian life, she loved the poetry of its spaces, the wide span of creation with which the Russian people lived, and this love, combined with the bitter days of her life, impeded her song and made it at times severe and sad. Look how in *The Kirillovnas* she describes nature, the provincial town of Tarusa, the secretiveness of childhood; look how much joy and happiness there is, and yet with what a sad, joyless wailing the story ends.

It seems to me that our readers will read Tsvetaeva's verses and prose with great attention and respect. Amid the wide and firm tracks left by our poets and prose writers on the great path of Soviet literature, the narrow but ineradicable track of Marina Tsvetaeva cannot go unnoticed, for she is profound and shines not with a reflected light but with one of her own. Her verses are distinguished by their splendid craftsmanship; her vocabulary is rich and passionate; she chooses words not for their outward beauty but for their inner ring. And when you have finished reading her verse, you will love and understand it; lines, at first incomprehensible, will suddenly become quite clear. Love explains everything, just as it forgives much, if not all.

translated by PHILLIPE RADLEY

Marina Tsvetaeva

✠ ✠ ✠ ✠

A LETTER

So they don't expect
letters. So they wait for —
letters.

A ragged scrap
circled by
sticky tape. Inside —

a scribble,
and happiness.
And that's all.

So they don't expect
happiness. So they expect —
the end.

A soldierly
salute, and
three slugs of lead in the breast.

Their eyes are red,
and just that.
That's all.

It's not happiness, old girl!
The wildflower color —
the wind blew it away.

A square courtyard
and black thoughts.
Of a square letter,

ink, sorcery.
When it comes to
death, the

last dream, no one's
old.
A square letter.

translated *by* DENISE LEVERTOV

⌘ ⌘

Someone sweeps on towards
                    mortal victory.
The trees —
            gesticulations of triumph:
Judas
        in sacrificial dance.
The trees —
            a shudder before the
                            mysteries.
Conspiracy
            against life, weight, measure,
            against fraction and fission.
The trees — a
            tattered curtain.
The trees —
            gestures of
                    entombment.
Someone sweeps on
                away.
The sky —
        a portal.
The trees —
            gesticulations of
                        triumphal rites.

translated *by* DENISE LEVERTOV

✠ ✠

AUTUMN IN TARUSA

A clear morning, the air is
cool. Lightly you cross
the meadow. And there
on the Oka, a barge
slowly draws by.
Unwilled, a word is
speaking itself, over and over, and
others follow. A bell can be heard
somewhere, faintly
rung in a field.
A wheatfield? A field of hay?
Are they going to be threshing?
My eyes looked away
for an instant, straight into
someone's fate,
between pine trees the deep
rifts of blue, the voices
across the noise and the heaps of
chaff and grain . . . And Autumn
smiles at our Springtime.
Life has thrown open its coat
and yet —
oh golden days, how remote,
how remote they are, Lord,
oh God, how far-off.

translated by DENISE LEVERTOV

✠ ✠

No need for talk:
my lips are for you to
drink from

the thick of my hair
hangs heavy for you to
stroke. Please.

And my hands.
For you to kiss.
Or let me

go down into
black sleep.

translated by DENISE LEVERTOV

✖ ✖

DIALOGUE OF HAMLET AND
HIS CONSCIENCE

— She's on the bottom, where the slime is
And the slippery weeds . . . She went away
To sleep, and yet there's no sleep
                                  there!
— But I loved her like a brother,
No, like a thousand brothers!
                          — Hamlet!
She's on the bottom, where the slime is,
The slime! — And the last funereal reed
Has slid onto the shore . . .
— But I loved her like
A thousand . . .
                    — Less,
Really, than one lover.
She's on the bottom, where the slime is.
— But I —
          (unsurely)
                    — loved her?

translated by ANDREW FIELD

The Kirillovnas

MARINA TSVETAEVA

❊ ❊ ❊ ❊

THEY EXISTED only in the plural, because they never went out alone, but always two at a time, even with one colander full of berries they came two at a time, a younger one and an older one — the one just a bit younger and the other just a bit older; and all of them were of a certain collective age, between thirty and forty (the age of a proper number), and they all had the same face, amber and tanned, and from underneath an identical kerchief-white and eyebrow-black border one was scorched by an identical, collective eye, and a good-sized brown eyelid was lowered to the ground with a collective whisk of eyelashes. And they all bore the same name, a collective one, and it was not even their first name, but their second, or patronymic: Kirillovna. Behind their backs though, they were called flagellants.

Why Kirillovna when there was no mention of any such man named Kirill? And who was this Kirill? Was he really their father? And why did he have quite so many — thirty, forty, or more — daughters and nary a son? Why, that red-haired Christ was obviously not his son, since he wasn't a brother of the Kirillovnas. I would now say that this many-daughtered Kirill existed only as a patronymic for daughters. At that time, however, I didn't give it any consideration, just as I didn't stop to consider why the steamship was called *Catherine*. It was *Catherine*, and that was that.

I had explained away the sharply resounding word "flagellants," which might be startling in its incongruity with their sedateness and propriety, as due to the willows under which and behind which they lived like a flock of white-headed birds, white-headed because of the kerchiefs and birds because of my nurse's eternal

commentary as she led me by: "And there's the nest of those flagellants." It was said without condemnation, just a simple comment on
that particular stage of our walk from the summer house at
Pesochnoe back to Tarusa, "There, we've passed the chapel . . .
There you can see the well, halfway . . . And there's the
nest . . ."

The nest of those flagellants was, actually, the exit of the town
of Tarusa. The last — after how many? — descent, full darkness
after so much light (immediately full, right away green), a sudden
freshness after that heat, after the dryness — dampness, and by the
forked post, which had grown deeply into the ground just as if it
were growing out of it, across the cold, black, loud and swift
stream, behind the first willow hedge on the left-hand side, invisible behind the willows and elders was "the nest of those flagellants." It was a nest, not a house, because the house was completely
invisible behind all the undergrowth, and, even if the gate opened
a tiny crack once in a while, the eye, overwhelmed by all that
beauty and color, especially currant red, by that gray overhang
somewhere in there, did not even notice it, did not take it in, like
the part of one's own forehead above the eyebrows. There was
never anything said about the Kirillovna house, just the garden.
The garden consumed the house. If someone had asked me then
what the flagellants did, I would have said without thinking, "They
take walks in the garden and eat berries."

But more about the entrance. It was an entrance into another
realm, this entrance itself was another realm which extended over
the whole street, if it can be called that, but it can't be called that,
because, on the left, except for their endless hedge, there was
nothing, and on the right there was burdock, sand, and that same
Catherine . . . This wasn't an entrance, but a crossing: from our
place (a lonely house in lonely nature) to over there (to people,
to the post office, to the market, to the wharf, to Natkin's shop,
and, later on, to the municipal boulevard) — it was a halfway state,
a middle kingdom, an intermediate zone. And suddenly enlightenment: it wasn't an entrance or a crossing, but an *exit!* (The first
house, you know, is always the last house!) And it was an exit
not only out of the town of Tarusa, but out of all towns! Out of all

the Tarusas, walls, bonds, out of one's own name, out of one's own skin — an exit! Out of all flesh — into spaciousness!

Of all of Tarusa or, more exactly, of all the "treats," that is sweets and other children . . . I loved most of all that sudden drop, entrance, descent into the green, cold, streamlike darkness; I loved passing by the gray, endless willow-elder hedge behind which — so it remained in my memory — all the berries ripened at once: strawberries, for example, and ashberries; behind which there was always summer, the whole of summer at once, with everything it offers that is red and sweet, where all you have to do is enter (but we never went in!) and everything is right at your fingertips: strawberries and cherries and currants and, especially, elderberries!

But apples I don't remember. I remember only the berries. And as for apples, strange as it may seem, in such a town as Tarusa where during a bumper-crop year — and every year was a bumper-crop there! — they were carried off to the market in clothes baskets and even the pigs would no longer eat them, the Kirillovnas didn't have any apples because they used to come to our place for them, to our "old garden," that is, the garden which we had aged and worn out, and which had the most costly varieties, gone wild, half-edible and used only for drying. But "they" did not come for the apples, not the sedate Kirillovnas with their downcast eyes; it was rather THEY who came, their Virgin and Christ, who was red-haired and thin, with a forked beard and eyes which I would now call waterlogged — he was a very raggedly dressed and barefoot Christ — and their Virgin, who was old, no longer amber-colored but rather leathery and tanned, and, although not exactly ragged, nevertheless still somewhat frightening. The attitude of my parents toward these forays was . . . that it was destined. "Again Christ has come for apples . . ." or "Again the Virgin and Christ are walking close at hand . . ." They did not ask, and my parents did not forbid. The Virgin and Christ were a sort of household calamity, a prescribed misfortune, fate, inherited together with the house, because the Kirillovnas were in Tarusa before we were, before anyone, perhaps even before the Tatars themselves, whose rusty ammunition we used to find in the stream. This was not a foray, but rather an extortion. It's necessary, however, to add that whenever we children caught them at this business, they (especially Christ) nevertheless sort of sidled away, buried themselves, isolated themselves behind a different apple tree where the Virgin would already be hurriedly stuffing a large gunnysack full. They did not say anything to each other during such moments, and it would never have entered our heads to give a vocal affirmation of our presence. We sort of silently agreed that they were doing nothing and that we saw nothing and that no one, whether they, or we, or anyone else, for that matter, was there, and that everything was as it should be . . .

"Papa! We saw Christ!"

"Did he come again?"

"Yes."

"Well, Christ be with him! . . ."

Our parents did not inquire about the missing apples, and we did not inform them. Once in a while we came across the red-headed Christ asleep right there in a haystack. The old Virgin would be sitting beside him and shooing the flies off of him. At such a time, without saying a word, on tiptoe, raising our eye-brows high and indicating our "find" to each other with move-ments of our eyes, we would leave and go to our "hole" where we would sit, dangling our legs and peeking at them as he continued to sleep and she continued to shoo. Once in a while our nurse would say to the governess, not to us, but in our presence, that this Christ was a bitter old drunk and that he had been hauled out of the ditch again, but, since we ourselves were always sitting in the ditch, this did not amaze us, while the word "bitter" to us explained drunk, calling to mind the taste of wormwood (we all constantly ate everything), after which you could drink a whole bucketful of water.

Once in a while Christ would sing, and the Virgin would harmonize in, and it did not surprise us at all that her voice was the more masculine and his was quite feminine and thin; it did not surprise us, first of all, because nothing surprised the Tsvetaev children, and, secondly, because she was dark-skinned and strong, while he was light-skinned and weak, and the result was that each of them had a particular singing voice corresponding to the size and strength of each, like a mosquito, for example, or a bumblebee.

And from our green ditch we could hear a song about certain green gardens coming from the apple-green summer house . . . We did not even ever think about (even now I don't know) whether they were mother and son, just as we never asked either our parents or our nurse, whom we were afraid of, why they were the *Virgin* and *Christ*; and not because we believed that it was they, we could tell from the icon (they were on the icon, and besides that, too, there were the apples . . .) — they were not they, but also it wasn't exactly that it wasn't they. Perhaps even the names themselves inspired trepidation — after all, everyone can't be called the Virgin and Christ! — and established a certain unquestionableness and authority about them. Our attitude at that time was rationalized in approximately the following manner: Since they steal apples, they aren't exactly Christ and the Virgin, but since they are, nonetheless, Christ and the Virgin, it means that they don't exactly steal. And they didn't steal — they took, and they hid, I see now, not from us (children themselves are beggars and thieves), but from eyes. Neither wild animals nor children (and not only children and wild animals, believe me!) can stand it when people stare at them. In a word, to us this vagrant pair were not merely people, and, if not the real *they*, then, still, sort of *also* they. Christ and the Virgin lived (that is they walked: I don't know anything about their life) apart from others and always together, never separately, and I often thought while looking at them: That's the way it should be: the Virgin followed the Christ, because she really followed him, right at his feet, lingering behind just enough so as not to step on his heels (which were bare). She followed and seemed to support him with her body — he was entirely enfeebled, entirely distracted, as if he were going where he himself didn't want to go, but where his feet wanted to go, and even his feet were uncertain where to go: first in a rut, then against a stone, then onto a mound, and then, without any sense whatsoever, diagonally. That's the way people would come across them in the market place and on the roads and in the burdock fields by the Oka . . . But — just as they, the sisters, never came for apples, neither did mother and son ever bring berries; it would be absurd even to think that suddenly — Christ has brought Victoria berries! And no matter how low the Kirillovnas bowed in greeting someone, the Virgin never exchanged a greeting, not to speak even about Christ — he not only stared right by, but his whole body stared right by!

"Mistress! The Kirillovnas have brought Victoria berries . . . Shall I take them?"

We were standing in the entranceway, Mother in front, we, out of cowardice, so as not to show the sudden greediness on our faces (Mother got after us for our unconscious reactions most of all!) behind her, just ever so slightly craning our necks out from behind her side. We would finally tear ourselves away from the strawberry pouring and suddenly meet the flagellants' eyes only just *barely* raised from the ground (we were so small!) and give them an understanding grin. And while they poured the berries from the colander into a basin, Kirillovna (which one? they were all alike! all thirty faces the same, under all thirty kerchiefs!), with her eyes still lowered, but not letting Mother's departing back out of sight, calmly and unhurriedly fed berry after berry into the nearest, most daring and hungriest mouth (most often mine!), like a bottomless pit. How did she know that Mother wouldn't allow us to eat that way, before dinner, a whole bunch at once, and, in general make pigs of ourselves? The same way we did — Mother never forbade us anything in words. Her eyes said everything.

The Kirillovnas, and I affirm this with delight, loved me most of all, perhaps just because of my greediness, blooming health, strength — Andryusha was tall and thin, Asya was small and thin — because they, having no children, would have wanted just such a daughter, just one — for them all!

"But the flagellants love me the most!" With this thought in mind I used to fall asleep, offended. Asya was loved best by Mama, Avgusta Ivanovna, and our nurse (Papa, out of kindness, loved all of us "the most"), and, on the other hand, I was loved by grandfather and the flagellants! The sedate Baltic gentleman would thank me for such a unification!

Of all my visions of the heavenly garden of Tarusa there is one which is most heavenly, because it is unique. The flagellants invited our whole family to a haymaking, and, oh, surprise, amazement (Mother couldn't stand family outings, or, in general anything in a group, especially her own children out in public), oh, complete shock — they took us. Father, of course, insisted.

"That one will get nauseated," objected my mother over my already guilty head. "The horses will shake her up without fail, and it will make her sick to her stomach. She always gets nauseated, everywhere nausea, I simply don't understand whom she takes after. Papasha (that's what she called that grandfather) doesn't get nauseated, I don't get nauseated, and, after all, neither Lera nor Andryusha nor Asya get nauseated, but just one look even at the buggy wheels, and she's sick to her stomach."

"Well, she'll be sick . . ." Father meekly agreed. "She'll get sick, and that's it . . ." (and apparently thinking about something else already) "she'll be sick — marvelous . . ." (and, recollecting himself) "but maybe she won't be — in the fresh air . . ."

"What's fresh air got to do with it?" said Mother getting excited and feeling embarrassed ahead of time over the roadside spectacle. "Whether it's a train, a cart, a boat, a landau with or without springs, a ferry or an ascensor — it doesn't make any difference, she's always nauseated, everywhere she's nauseated . . . and they call it *sea*sickness!"

"I don't get sick to my stomach when I walk," I inserted in a timid outburst, having acquired courage from Father's presence.

"She can sit facing the horses. We can take some mints with us," said Father convincingly, "and another dress too, for changing . . ."

"Only *I* don't want to sit next to her! Not next to nor in front of her!" burst out Andryusha whose face had long since turned sullen. "Every time I have to sit next to her, like the time in the train, you remember, Mama, when. . . ."

"We'll take some eau de cologne," continued Father, "and I — will sit next to her." ("Only you be sure and tell us, please," he said confidentially to me, "when you feel dizzy — just say so, and we'll stop the horses, and you can get down and rest a bit. We're not going to a fire, you know . . . But, really, it's strange, why you always get nauseated!" And, to make things as smooth as possible, he added, "Nature, nature, there's nothing you can do about it. You could even say it like this, 'Papa, I want to pick that

poppy over the-ere!' And you hop out quickly and run off quite a
ways — so you don't upset Mama").

In short, we went, and, with that very poppy in my hand, we
arrived at the flagellants' haymaking, far beyond Tarusa in some of
their extensive meadows.

"Ay, Marina my dear, why do you look so green? Did you get
up too early, my dove? Didn't you sleep enough, my beauty?"
said the Kirillovnas, surrounding me, weaving around me, enticing
me away, passing me along from one to the other as if drawing me
into a circle dance, all of them immediately taking possession of me
at once as if I were a sort of flagellant treasure common to them
all. I don't remember anyone from our family in that paradise;
neither Papa, nor Mama, nor the governess, nor the nurse, nor
Lera, nor Andryusha, nor Asya. I was theirs. I raked with them
and scattered the hay in the midst of them as they moved, I lay
down to rest with them, plunged down with them and again re-
appeared, like the pup in the immortal verses ("all a flurry!"), I
went to the spring with them, made a fire with them, drank tea
with them out of a huge, colored cup, biting off bits of sugar like
they did, with them I would have . . .

"Marina, dear, my beauty, stay with us, you'll be our daughter
and live with us in our garden and sing our songs . . ."

"Mama won't let me."

"But would you stay otherwise?" Silence. "Well, of course you
wouldn't stay — you'd miss your mama. She probably loves you a
great deal, doesn't she?" Silence. "Probably, she wouldn't give you
away for money either, would she?"

"But we won't even ask her mama — we'll just take her ourselves!" said one of the younger ones. "We'll take her away and
lock her up in our garden, and we won't let anyone in. Then she'll
live with us behind the hedge. (A wild, burning, unfulfillable hope
began to glow inside me: would it be soon?) Cherries you will
pick with us, Masha you'll be known to us . . ." said the same
one in a singsong voice.

"Don't be frightened, dove," said an older one who took my
enthusiasm for fright, "No one will take you away, but you will
come visit us with your papa and mama or with your nurse — it's
every Sunday you walk by, we all watch you, though you don't

see us, but we see e-everything, everyone . . . In a white dress you will come, a piqué one, all dressed up, in slippers with buttons on them . . ."

"But we'll dress you *our* way," chimed in the same singsongy one, who couldn't keep still, "in a black ca-assock, in a white ke-erchief, and we'll let your hair grow so you'll have a braid . . ."

"What are you frightening her for, little sister! She'll really believe it! Everyone has his own fate. She will be ours as she is — our envisioned guest, our imaginary daughter . . ."

And they hugged me, squeezed me, lifted me up and pushed me — oof! onto the load, onto a mountain, into a sea, under the sky, to where everything was visible at once: Papa in his tussore jacket, and Mama in her red kerchief, and Avgusta Ivanovna in her Tyrolean hat, and the yellow bonfire, and the most distant sandbars on the Oka . . .

I would like to come to rest in the flagellants' graveyard in Tarusa, under an elderberry bush, in one of those graves with a silver dove on it, where the reddest and largest strawberries in those parts grow.

But if that can't be done, if not only will I not come to rest there, but if perhaps the graveyard won't even be there anymore, then, on one of those hills where the Kirillovnas walked on their way to our place in Pesochnoe and we to see them in Tarusa, I would like a stone placed from the quarry at Tarusa:

Here would rest
MARINA TSVETAEVA

Paris
May 1934

translated by COLLYER BOWEN

Empty Eyes and Magic Eyes

from a Tarusa sketchbook

FRIDA VIGDOROVA

❆ ❆ ❆ ❆

COMING OUT onto the square by the railroad station in Serpukh-ov, I looked for the bus to Tarusa. Outside, there was a line. A good many people had collected; evidently there had been no bus for a long time. I got a ticket at the window and stood last in line.

The people were not standing in a chain, singly, as is supposed to be the case in a line, but in twos and threes, and were conversing among themselves. Rain drizzled down, the wind was cold, the bus didn't come and didn't come. And the main thing was that there was no assurance that you would get on it; the machine certainly wouldn't take everyone.

Before me stood an old woman in a tidily belted blue dress and a clean, gray, quilted jacket. Her high, calf-length black rubber boots were also clean and nice. Her faded blue eyes gazed without the tired sadness usual in old people. She smiled as she spoke, the faded blue eyes watched good-naturedly, and the little turned-up nose lent something childish to her face.

"I'm watching to see which driver comes. There's one here who never takes everybody."

"How's that?"

"He's sorry. The bus isn't strong enough for very many people, and he's just taking care of it." She said this approvingly, and again explained, "He's sorry, you understand. He's sorry about the transportation."

"But why be sorry about the transportation?" said a gray little old man who was next in line. "He ought to be sorry about us, not the transportation. A machine, what's that? They'll put it under a press and melt it down into something else. And they'll melt you and me down into horseradish, understand?"

"What's not to understand? I understand. Only the transportation, too . . ."

"It's coming," someone said.

And it was true; the bus was coming up to the stop. For the moment all conversations stopped. Everyone was absorbed in how to crawl into the bus as quickly as possible. But once they had sat down, they began immediately to talk again. The driver was the same one who was sorry about the transportation, but this time he took everyone. The bus wasn't fast, but it stubbornly conquered the road, jumping on the pits and bumps.

"We made it, we made it!" said the old woman, arranging her skirt on her knees.

"It was me who brought you luck," said the old man who had just arrived. "I'm lucky. Here it is the third day after Victory Day, and I keep walking and walking. My kin were every one of them front-line soldiers. The first day, the ninth, I was at my son's in Serpukhov, the second, at my nephew's in Tarusa, the third, back here again, just the same, at my son-in-law the soldier's. I tied on a good one. Some schoolboys came to give their congratulations to my son. You were in the war, they said, and we are very glad that you have returned alive and unharmed. It was very solemn. An honor!"

"Schoolchildren came to me, too," said my neighbor, a man of forty. His face was tanned even from the winter sun, his hands brown, with short, thickened fingers. He was wearing a short jacket, which appeared to be much used, and dark trousers, torn at the knees.

"Yes, they came to me, too. I hadn't been in Tarusa long, but they found out that I'd been at the front, and they came to congratulate me. Only there wasn't any kind of honor in it."

"Why was that?"

"Well, you judge. Three little girls come in. They're neatly dressed, with flowers in their hands. My wife says to me, 'Kolya, some Pioneers to see you.' Well, I put on my dignity, invite them in, ask them to have a seat. But they don't sit down. One takes out a piece of paper and reads: 'We congratulate a defender of our native land, we wish him success in a peaceful life and in his labor activities,' and then they left. Defender of our native land!"

"Well, aren't you a defender? You are, too, a defender. What are you upset for?" wondered the old woman.

"Oh, I can't explain. They spoke badly. Painfully beautiful."

"That's how they had to," said the old man who had been walking around for three holidays. "There you sit now, your pants patched and your jacket not so nice and new. But on the holiday you most likely dressed up, right? Don't you have a dress suit? And here the words were dress, for a solemn occasion. That's how it should be."

"I do have a suit to go out in. But if it bound me under the arms, and was too tight on the shoulders, and didn't meet over the stomach, and if the collar squeezed around my neck like a button-hole, I wouldn't wear a suit like that. Let the words be solemn, I don't object. But let them be . . . well, alive, sort of. Here they sprinkle words on a paper and read them. And my mother was lying there sick, and they didn't even look. You know, they scatter their words, 'progress in labor,' 'labor activity,' they poke their flowers at you, and go out. It's true that one held back at the door, the littlest of all. She looked at my mother and said, 'Get well soon, now.' I'm not against solemn words. By all means, let them be solemn. But here, you know, there aren't solemn words, but wooden words, understand? Sort of like balls — they hit and bounce off, hit and bounce off."

"But look, they spoke from the heart. They wanted to make you happy."

"No," my neighbor answered stubbornly, "people don't speak like that from the heart. If it's from the heart, the words aren't that kind . . ."

But where do they come from, these words not from the heart? Why do words of congratulation seem empty and rounded to a man, expressing nothing? Where has the color of these words disappeared to, their incandescence, their penetration?

These words were sprinkled on as the ashes of other words, not their own, others'; not matured, not prompted from within. They cost nothing, and this is why even the better of them lost their heat, their color and fragrance.

. . . Once, when I came to the home-museum of Polenov, the artist's daughter, Ol'ga Vasil'evna, said to me: "When children come to the museum on an excursion, I understand from the first glance what sort of teacher they have. I know by their eyes. Sometimes they come happy and heated, and in their eyes is curiosity: 'And now show us what you have here!' But sometimes they come . . . well, how to tell you? Empty-eyed, in a way. I understand by those empty eyes that their teacher, too, is empty-eyed. Children like that walk after me lazily, sluggishly. And they themselves ask about nothing, and they answer my questions yawning. They're bored. It's very difficult to stir up such children. But there are . . . oh, what children there *are!*"

And Ol'ga Vasil'evna told how she had once brought a group of third graders up to Korovin's picture, *At the Tea Table.*

"Oh, look how he's put them!" one boy joyfully exclaimed. "In a wheel!"

Why did he say "in a wheel"? There, you see, is a table, at which people are sitting in Korovin's picture, square. But he said it exactly as he saw it: in a wheel!

Korovin's picture is a festivity in white; all the tints of white whirl in it: a cream-white tablecloth, yellow-white milk, a white blouse diffuses blue, a blue-white picture, a white ray of sun on the samovar, a white plate on a blue cloth, a white highlight on the side of a wooden chair, a white cap, a white bow in the hair. The white is dazzling. The white is cautious. The white is radiant. The white is strict. A white brilliance, a white whirl — and the little boy saw this, felt it, and exclaimed, "In a wheel!"

And the artist's daughter — she was leading the excursion — was not astonished; she heard and evaluated, and was happy together with the boy. She knew that the apt word is not engendered in an empty place; it always reflects thought, feeling. On the contrary, the empty eyes never make you a gift of a burning word. The empty fish-eyes want each word to be empty as a nut: there is a shell, but there is no kernel.

Once I was present at the discussion of a play which had been put on by the Moscow Children's Theater. A girl of thirteen came out on the stage and said: "The exposition here is somewhat drawn out . . . The climax is artificially sustained . . . The urbanistic motifs which permeate the play seem to me not to be justified . . ."

On one side of me sat the president of one of the Moscow city councils. He nodded his approval and was very much satisfied with the girl's performance.

"Cultured . . . She's well-read . . ." he kept repeating.

My neighbor on the right was Aleksandra Yakovlevna Brushtein. She listened, putting her hearing aid to her ear, and her face expressed suffering.

"When children swear like troopers," she said suddenly, "that's very bad. But it's not so terrible; they'll grow up, come to their senses, and stop it. But 'exposition' and 'climax' — that's more terrible, much more terrible. It's like the mange, there's no way you can get rid of it."

It's true; it is more terrible. And why? Because the appearance of inexpressive, empty words is deceptive. They are not words, but masks. They teach children not to express their thoughts, but to freeze them. Or simply to conceal them. They teach untruths.

Once a teacher told her students: "Now you will write a composition about the May Day demonstration."

"But what if I wasn't there?" asked one little girl. "It was raining, and my galoshes were worn through."

"You're fibbing," answered the teacher. "You live in a refined family, and it's not possible that they didn't take you to the demonstration. Sit down and write a composition with everyone else on 'How I went to the May Day demonstration.'"

The little girl obediently took her pen, and bending over her copybook, she rather quickly wrote this:

The morning was sunny. The workers went to the demonstration in orderly lines. In the blue sky we heard the roar of airplanes. The people carried posters, slogans, and portraits. Everyone was happy and joyful. I went with Mama and held a little red flag.

All of this was untrue; it rained on the first of May. The sky was covered with clouds. The little girl had stayed home.

"But you *weren't* at the demonstration. Why did you lie?" her family asked her at home.

"But how did I lie? I only wrote a composition. You know that's not the truth. It's a composition."

A particular case? Not typical? Uncharacteristic? No, such legalized untruth is encountered not infrequently.

"I wish," said Ol'ga Vasil'evna, "that people would always have magic eyes. Magic eyes see everything as if for the first time; fresh, clear-cut, and right straight through. You will understand this well if you look at children's drawings. If only this would remain through life; if the eyes wouldn't become empty, if they didn't lose this freshness, if they didn't get accustomed to spring, winter, fall, if they always saw as if for the first time. You understand: not getting accustomed! Everything for the first time!"

Ol'ga Vasil'evna knows by their eyes what kind of a teacher children have. I think that it is also good to find this out by children's compositions.

On the eighth of March, the sixth grade was given the composition topic, "My Mama." Borya B. wrote: "I love my mama very much. She is happy and good and never scolds. Our neighbor scolds her son and calls him all kinds of things. But Mama says to her, 'Now why are you at him? Don't you remember yourself when you were little? You did the same things and worse.' "

The teacher wrote in the margin: "You didn't describe your mother's qualities of character, such as industry and principles."

Next to these words was written in Borya's hand: "My mama doesn't have any principles, but I love her just the same."

Under the scribble of the teacher, there was a "D." All the same, I think that in this duel, Borya remained the victor.

In the Tarusa school, I also read compositions about mamas. Volodya Z. wrote: "I came home and started to think. I don't know *why* I love Mama. I love her, that's all."

The teacher be thanked; he appreciated Volodya's restraint and did not give him a "D."

There are many good compositions in the Tarusa school. Here is one, "The First Snow":

The first cold weather began. In the evening you do not go out without mittens, for the frost begins to nip at your fingers and fumble along your cheeks. And suddenly the first snow fell. It fell like rain, in a slant. And people said, "Look, winter has come."

Short, expressive. These eyes have not lost the ability to see, and, for that reason, words were found which are not empty. And the teacher's red pencil did not underline the words "fumble along," did not find them unliterary or out of place.

Here are a few lines from the composition, "My Character":

I sometimes tell lies. For instance, when I spilled a can of sunflower oil, I dumped the blame on the cat. I know I did wrong, but I couldn't do a thing with myself.

And this composition is convincing; the teacher is not expecting a standard response, and the children write what they feel like writing.

There are better compositions, and there are worse. But there is no standard in them, these compositions. In this, they are most attractive of all. A standard breaks one of thinking, reflecting, searching. A standard commands one to go by the beaten path, and declares everything that is unusual to be incorrect and harmful.

The unusual word, the fresh insight, the unexpected turn of thought are inimical to it, always, everywhere.

"Draw a forest in winter!" said the teacher. The pages of the drawing books began to rustle. A little girl with a thickly plaited braid dipped a brush into yellow paint, and, first thing, drew a big, round sun. Her neighbor, with a decisive sweep of a green pencil, depicted something that, without especial difficulty, could have been taken for a fir tree.

The beginnings were made. For ten minutes everyone drew. Everyone except a little boy who was sitting right by the window. Pressing his cheeks with the palms of his hands, he pensively gazed before him.

"Tikhomirov, Kolya!" called the teacher. "Why aren't you drawing?"

Kolya Tikhomirov stood up. He was shorter than the rest of the third graders, and very thin. His dark face with its large forehead and button nose was sprinkled with brown freckles.

"Why aren't you drawing?" The teacher's voice sounded impatient. Sighing deeply, Kolya answered, "If I had a sheet of black paper . . ."

"Black? Everlasting notions! Please don't talk back! Sit down!"

The boy sat down and opened a box of colored pencils. And the teacher, walking past the young journalist who was present at the lesson, bent down and said to him, "That's a very backward boy. Something foolish is always getting into his head."

Kolya began to draw. He took a green pencil and drew an even row of little green fir trees. Then, looking aslant, he glanced at the drawing of the little girl who was sitting close by and added a yellow sun next to a little fir tree. Then he took a white pencil and tried to draw snow. He drew long white stripes across the green firs. He sighed and laid his pencil to one side.

After the lessons, the journalist saw Kolya go out of the school. He quickened his pace, and when he caught up with the boy, he asked, "Why did you need black paper?"

Kolya raised his eyes to him and said, "I thought up a picture: it's snowing, and it's night in the forest. Everything is black — the sky and everything, you know? And the snow is white. With chalk! So if I had a sheet of black paper, I'd draw — is that all right? Or not?"

"It is all right!" said his interlocutor. He said it perfectly sincerely. Because he saw it all: the blindingly black sky, and the blindingly white snowy haze, the white earth in the black night. Yes, a sheet of black paper would have come in handy there. What can you say? . . .

In the paper *Literature and Life*, not long ago, an article by Vsevolod Kochetov was printed under the title, "The Face of the Writer." It said:

At present, a group of dandies is hanging around in literature. They write about what . . . they have seen from the window of a trolley-bus on the Moscow sidewalks, about how downy the snow is on Nikitsky Boulevard; they twitter, and go out with their twittering onto the stages of "creative evenings"; they take the applause of girls

with average education as a sign of universal recognition, and, drunk
with cheap success, they become farther and farther removed from the
great life of the people.

If you don't know what this is all about, you can neither quarrel
nor agree about whether the writers with whom the article is concerned are correctly called dandies. One thing is impossible to
understand: if the writer does not see how downy the snow is on
Nikitsky Boulevard, then what kind of a writer is he? If he does
not know how to see anything interesting from the window of a
bus, he is also not a writer. And the real writer, not the empty-eyed
one — in everything, always, constantly, no matter where he is —
in a forest, in the Virgin Lands, by a river, in a factory, in a bus,
on Gor'ky Street or in Bratsk, will catch sight of life, its color, its
shades, its people. Who has established what the artist, whether
writer or painter, really ought to see and what he ought not to see?
He ought to hear and see everything, both the snow on Nikitsky
Boulevard and the Moscow sidewalks. The teacher should also hear
and see. And think. If he hears that a little boy needs a sheet of
black paper, let him not be in a hurry to declare him mentally
backward . . . Let him try to understand that there is something
behind it. Let him not establish how fixed the answer should be to
the question which is put to children, because as soon as children
grasp (and they think things out quickly) what is fixed and what
is not fixed, then immediately a standard springs up. They leave
their true thoughts for themselves and for each other, and teachers
assign "compositions": "The morning was sunny. In the blue sky
we heard the roar of airplanes . . ."

translated by KAREN BLACK

Meyerhol'd Speaks

Notes on some of V. E. Meyerhol'd's utterances
at rehearsals and in conversation,
as recorded by Aleksandr Gladkov.

✻ ✻ ✻ ✻

T HE THEATER was the chief interest of my life from the age of
seven. Even when I was seven, my elders put me in front of
a mirror, where I made my childish mug transform itself. Later
there were still stronger enthusiasms for music (the violin), literature, politics; but the attraction for the theater proved to be the
strongest of all.

What influenced me most in my life? There were many influences: first, the greatness of Russian literature, in particular Chekhov and Stanislavsky; the remarkable masters of the old Maly
Theater, Blok, Maeterlinck, Hauptmann; a study of the old eras of
the theater; a study of the Eastern theater; a return to the creative
works of the great Russian artists — Pushkin, Lermontov, Gogol —
the storm of the October Revolution and its stern beauty; the new
young art of cinematography; Mayakovsky; again, Pushkin; and
all with an increasing power . . . Can you sort all of this out?
The artist should be attracted to many things, come back to something different, throw something out, leave something in himself . . .

In my life, there was one crossroads where I almost became a
musician and violinist. At Moscow University in the mid-nineties,
there was an excellent student orchestra which did entire great
concerti. I was studying in the law school, but I loved music passionately, perhaps even more than the theater. I was mad about the

violin. And then a competition was announced for a vacancy in that orchestra, for the chair of second violin. I dreamed about that position. I practiced stubbornly, abandoned Roman law . . . and failed at the competition. From grief, I decided to give myself up to acting. They accepted me. But now I think: if I had become second violin, I would have worked in theater orchestration under the leadership of Bendersky or Ravensky; people would rail at them as they do at me now, but I would scrape away to myself and chuckle . . .

I began as a director with a slavish imitation of Stanislavsky. Theoretically, I no longer accepted many of his directing methods of an earlier period; I regarded them critically; but practically, having undertaken the business, I at first timidly followed in his footsteps. I don't regret it, because this period was not prolonged. I quickly and intensely passed through it, and it was all the same an excellent school in practical directing. The imitativeness of a young artist is not dangerous. It is almost an inevitable stage. Moreover, in youth it is useful to imitate a good model; it refines one's own internal self-dependence, and stimulates its appearance. Formerly, people were by no means ashamed of the word "imitation." You recall Pushkin: "An Imitation of Parny," "An Imitation of Chénier," "An Imitation of the Koran." Mayakovsky, in his words, began with an imitation of Bal'mont, then imitated Whitman and Sasha Chyorny, but this did not interfere with his standing on his own. Even more explicitly, the imitation of an artist whom you feel to be close to yourself permits you ultimately to determine yourself.

Do you know who first engendered in me the doubt that all paths of the Art Theater are the true ones? Anton Pavlovich Chekhov . . . His friendship with Stanislavsky and Nemirovich – Danchenko was by no means as idyllic and cloudless as they describe it in the tear-off calendars. He did not agree with many people in the theater, and there was much he criticized directly. But he did not approve of my leaving the MAT. He wrote me that I ought to stay and quarrel with what I did not agree with in the theater.

The art of the theater does not progress, but only changes its means of expression in relation to the character of an era, its ideas, its psychology, its technics, its architecture, its fashions. I think that to the audiences of Euripides and Aristophanes, our best actors would appear lacking in talent, as Karatygin would probably surprise us if we were fated to see him. Each epoch has its own codex of conventions, which must be observed if one is to be understandable, but it must not be forgotten that the conventions change. When I see another kind of performance in the Maly Theater, it seems to me that I see a little old Bolshevik woman dropping a curtsey, or a hero of the civil war kissing the hand of a girl in a man's leather jacket. In life, we easily feel the falsity of antiquated conventions, but in the theater we often applaud them out of habit.

I love to re-do my old works. People often tell me that I spoil them in the process. Perhaps, but I have never once been able to watch a performance which I have done without a desire to change something.

If it appears to you that some scene or other turned out for me all at once at a rehearsal, then be aware that I have already set it up many times in many variants, in my imagination. Properly, experience consists not in the fact that you try and reject less, but that you gradually learn to do an ever greater part of that work privately with yourself.

The director ought always to work with assurance. It is better to make mistakes, erring boldly, than to crawl towards the truth uncertainly. It is always possible to refute mistakes the next morning, but it is completely impossible to repair the loss of the actor's faith in a doubting and wavering director.

If today I tell an actor, "Fine!" that does not at all mean that I will be satisfied with him when he repeats that place exactly the same way the next day.

Now I would be able to put on Blok's *The Puppet Show* as a *sui generis* theatrical Chapliniad. Read *The Puppet Show,* and you will see in it all the elements of Chaplinesque plots, only the wrappings of everyday life are different. Heine is also akin to Chaplin and *The Puppet Show*. In great art, there *is* such a complex kinship.

If you like, I'll tell you what it was that divided artists with a sharp line when the Revolution came. It is naïve and superficial to think that all the émigré writers, musicians, and artists thought only about their lost bank accounts or their requisitioned villas, for most of them didn't have any. Shalyapin had self-interests. Everyone knows that, but even for him this was not the main thing. The main thing is that Gor'ky, Mayakovsky, Bryusov, and many others (and I among them) at once grasped that the Revolution was not only destruction, but also rebuilding. Those who thought it was only destruction, cursed it. Mayakovsky and I belong to different generations, but for both of us the Revolution was a second birth.

A bitter admission: we theatrical people live in Moscow so apart, in such separate cloisters, that we often feed on legends in our intelligence about each other. It is easier for me to communicate with Gordon Craig, who is in Italy, than with Stanislavsky, who lives on the next street . . .

In tragedy, the voice ought to be dry. Tears are intolerable.

The actor should rivet his role down tight, as a bridge builder does his metal structure. He must leave slots for bits of acting *ex improviso*, for improvisation. Molchalov played the same scene in a play in various ways, but he did not change the motives of the acting; he found new variations depending on his own feelings of the day, the number of people in the hall, and even the weather.

If the viewer is bored, it means that the actors have lost the content and are playing a dead form.

No matter what you do on the stage, observe moderation in everything, both in voice and in motion. The viewer always notices the strain and tension of the actor who is trying too hard.

More than anything else, I hate it in the theater when the text of the role is cluttered with various unappetizing interjections and prepositions: "Oh," "Well, well," "Yessir," "There you are," and so on. Usually actors of less skill are devoted to this.

Even in the pauses, you have to know how to hold the tempo of the dialogue.

A phrase said distinctly will penetrate a wall of any thickness.

Creativity is always joy. The actor playing the dying Hamlet or Boris Godunov ought to tremble with joy. His artistic enthusiasm gives him that internal voltage, that tension, which causes all his colors to glow.

Speaking of the skill of self-restraint in acting, I usually give the example of Varlamov's acting in some play, now forgotten, in which he acted for about twenty minutes lying on a bed. I recall an even more vivid example: the remarkable French actress Réjane played an entire first act lying on a divan. At the end of the act, in the course of the action, she had to stand up and walk to the door, and she stood up . . . but how she stood up! And there the curtain came down.

In a dress coat, there should be a half-motion: the elbows must be held closer to the body, the strokes of the gestures short, the motions lighter. When Dalmatov entered the stage in a dress coat, that alone was already the whole show; it was worth paying your money just for that. I remember, Stanislavsky once walked before us in silence for two hours in a cloak, turned, sat, lay down, and after that I couldn't get to sleep all night. And one has to love this in the theater!

Nearer to the door before you exit! Nearer still! This is an axiom! The closer you stand to the door, the more effective the exit. In climaxes, everything is decided by seconds of scene time and centimeters of stage floor. Neither Ermolov, nor Komis-

sarzhevskaya, nor Lensky, nor Mamont Dal'sky held this algebra of
scenometry in disdain.

An object in the hand is an extension of the hand.

You must try at rehearsal to make this playing with things your
reflex, and not every time a passively performed stunt.

Don't deprive drunk scenes of internal logic! The conduct of
drunks is notable only in that all of their bits are, as it were, unfinished. A motion begins and is suddenly broken off. Or in the
motion, more effort is expended than necessary. Or less. In this
lies their comicality. But he ought to go easy — the more easily, the
more refined. I would check an actor's taste by how he plays a
drunk.

The problem of the intermission in the theater is not so much a
question of breaks for the audience's rest, as it is a question of the
compositional divisions of the play. A play in one enormous unin-
terrupted act is hardly possible, like a speech without pauses or
caesurae, or a symphony consisting of one movement. It is not
desirable that breaks between acts or scenes be no longer than the
pauses between the movements of a symphony; this, however, is
no longer the task of drama technique, but of theater technique.
From my point of view, the play ought to be constructed so that
the viewer rests sitting right there in his chair (ideally, if only it
were possible to change the angle of the back or the pitch of the
shoulders — I am trying without success to get this from the
builders of my new building), rests in a quiet scene from a loud
one; in a peaceful one, from full action. You know, psychologists
long ago arrived at the fact that rest is any change . . . The
change of various strains on the viewer's attention is one of the
director's serious tasks. Max Reinhardt in Germany often made one
long intermission, which he put not precisely in the middle of the
play, but nearer the end, since he considered that at the beginning
the less fatigued viewer could take in a larger part of the play
without a break. Reinhardt's intermission came after approximately
two thirds of the play. When you produce Shakespeare or *Boris*

Godunov, where the acts are not designated, the finding of a place where it is possible to put an intermission is a technical and creative problem; it is as important as it is for a good orator to know when to inhale and when to exhale.

Shakespearization is by no means the restoration of the technique of the theater of Shakespeare's era, but is an adaptation to new material of his use of many levels, his sweep, and his monumental greatness.

In our *The Forest* [by Ostrovsky] at first there were thirty-three episodes, but since, when the performance was over, it was very late and the audience was missing its streetcars, I heeded the requests of the managers and shortened it to twenty-six episodes. The play, which had run more than four hours, began to run three hours and twenty minutes. Some time passed, and the managers informed me that it was again going for four hours. I decided that the actors had, on their own, replaced some of the scenes which I had cut. I went and looked — nothing of the sort! It was simply that they were warming up to the remaining twenty-six episodes. I make them a suggestion. It doesn't help. I set a rehearsal, and with pain in my heart I cut the play to sixteen episodes. For a while, it runs two and a half hours, but then again it stretches out to four. Ultimately the show was rather a flop, and we had to rehearse it again, determining all the rhythms and proportional timing within the play. Once I had to post an order that if the scene with Pyotr and Aksyusha, which should last two minutes, went one minute longer, I would impose a penalty on the performers. Actors must be trained to feel time on the stage as musicians feel it. The musically organized play is not one in which something is always being played or sung behind the scenes, but one with an exact rhythmical score, with exactly organized *time.*

One of the most necessary qualities of a director is that he feel keenly the dramatic climaxes of the play. I sometimes have had to correct and re-do plays produced by other directors, when there was already little time left, and theatrical production demanded the issue of a premiere. I always did thus: I determined for myself alone two climactic scenes (how often they are incorrectly found — the greatest of mistakes!); I worked on them and, lo and behold, the play went out, and everything at once fell into place.

In art, the important thing is not to know, but to surmise.

The faster paced the text, the more clearly marked the divisions should be — the transitions from one bit to another, from one rhythm to another. In the contrary situation, motivation is lost, and the living breath of the thought vanishes.

To some people, the image of an abyss calls forth the thoughts of a chasm; to others, the thought of a bridge. I belong to the second group.

The most terrible enemy of beauty is prettiness.

It is hardest of all to produce bad, empty plays. For the doing of bad plays, I would pay directors twice as much as usual. But for the opportunity to do *Hamlet* or *The Inspector General,* I would take money from them.

People have reproached me that our *Inspector General* is not gay; but you know, Gogol himself criticized the first portrayer of Khlestakov, Nikolai Dyur, for trying too hard to make the audience laugh. The focus of Gogol's stage style is in this transformation of the funny into the sad.

In the good director, there potentially sits a dramatist. You see, once these were one profession; only afterwards did they separate, as sciences do gradually divide and differentiate. This is not a division in principle, but it is technically necessary, for the art of the theater has become complicated, and one would have to be a second Leonardo da Vinci in order both to write dialogue with sparkle, and to cope with the world (I am, of course, simplifying a bit). But nature is universal! For this reason, the director's art is the author's art, and not the performer's. But you must have a right to it . . .

I have often been reproached to the effect that I do not develop my own finds and discoveries, I always hurry on to new labors: after one play, I do another, completely different as to style. But in the first place, human life is short, and in repeating yourself, there are many things you won't have time to do; in the second place, where a superficial glance sees a chaos of different manners and styles, my colleagues and I see the application of the same general principles to a different material, a variant treatment of it in relation to the style of the author and the problems of the present day . . . And more! . . . "In a style heretofore unknown . . ." Doesn't that phrase stir you? Isn't the highest honor for the artist to execute a work "in a style heretofore unknown . . ."?

When I was almost simultaneously rehearsing the two plays of Lermontov, *The Masquerade* and *Two Brothers*, I crept so deeply into the 1830's that once, in response to an insult in the press, I quite seriously tried to call out my offender to a duel. It isn't surprising that these plays went over well for me.

Salvini had two sons, and both became actors. They were as alike as twins, but one inherited his talent, and the other did not. Identical education, almost identical endowments — and nothing in common. I often think about the secret of talent, and it has sometimes seemed to me that the story of Salvini's children might be an excellent subject for a novel.

The director ought to believe in his actors just as Pavlov believed in his dogs. He himself told me that, getting carried away, he sometimes overestimated their capabilities so that it would begin to seem to him that they played tricks on him.

For Pavlov's jubilee, I sent him a telegram, in which I wrote, somewhat lightly, that in his person I greeted a man who, at last, was done with such a dark and secret thing as "soul." In answer, I received a letter from Pavlov in which he courteously thanked me for my greetings, but remarked, "As concerns the soul, we shan't be in a hurry and shall wait a little before we confirm anything . . ." I would like to say the same to anyone who thinks that all the truths about the secrets of the actor's creative work are known to Stanislavsky and me. Observe Stanislavsky's work, and you will see that he is constantly amending his "system." I once asserted that man is a "chemico-physical laboratory." Of course, this is very primitive. In my biomechanics, I was able to determine altogether twelve or thirteen rules for the training of an actor, but when I polish it, I leave perhaps no more than eight.

You say "the science of the theater," and I don't know what sort of thing that is. Scholars quarrel among themselves about the remote, final conclusions of science, but everyone is agreed that water boils at 100° C. In our field, similar alphabetical truths are not yet established. There is complete lack of accord in everything! The first task of a so-called "theater science" is the establishment of a unity of terminology and the formulation of "alphabetical truths." Only then can it have pretensions to being called a science. But I am afraid that it is a long way to that point . . . You expect from me a thick volume on my directing experience, but I dream of a thin little book, almost a pamphlet, in which I shall try to set forth some of these alphabetical truths. And all my "enormous" experience will prove useful for that. Only I don't know if I'll have time to be brief, as someone wisely said.

I consider that a *sui generis* "claque" in the theater is permissible, if it helps the performance to be correctly apprehended. You of course have noticed how a small group in the audience sometimes meets a favorite actor appearing on the stage with applause, and how the entire hall at once joins this small group. The audience's emotion is a very infectious thing. When people are laughing around you, you involuntarily laugh, too; when they yawn, you, too, begin to yawn. For this reason, we always try to fill the theater with a friendly humored audience for the "surrender" of a play. But considering the infectiousness of the audience's emotions, why on earth should we exclude the device of active arousal in the hall of the emotions we require? Let this shock the puritans of the theater, but I confess that in [Vsevold Vyshnevsky's] *The Last and*

Decisive (1931), I seated an actress in the hall who, in the place where I needed it, began to sob. And at once, as if at a command, everyone around her reached for his handkerchief. Into this came Bogolyubov's cue: "Who is weeping there?" . . . All means are good if they lead to the necessary result!

In a piano concerto, Chaikovsky used the melody of a French music-hall song which, as his brother told me, his uncle had often sung. The artist has the right to draw his material from anywhere; the question is what he does with it.

I consider that Chaikovsky's opera *Eugene Onegin* should be called "Tat'yana." Listen attentively to the music, and you will see that the composer is almost indifferent to the internal peace of his hero, but is, on the other hand, in love with the heroine.

The strength of Shalyapin was not in the resources of his voice or the beauty of his timbre (there were some stronger and more beautiful), but in the fact that he was the first to sing not only notes, but text. He succeeded in this because he was so musical that he could allow himself not to think about the notes at all; for that reason, he sang more naturally than many people say.

Shalyapin's quick-temperedness, scandals, outbursts at rehearsals and in performances, and his quarrels with directors and co-actors were very easily explainable: he was so extremely musical that a barely perceptible falseness wounded his ear, as the scraping of brick against glass grates on you. Try to sit quietly while a mischievous little boy takes a piece of brick to glass. Shalyapin heard everything in the orchestra, even the smallest squeak which you and I don't notice; it tormented him like the rack. This wounded sensitivity is a characteristic not only psychological, but also psychophysical, as is the vulnerability of lyric poets, who must be protected from suicide as we protect the worker in unhealthful industry, giving him milk antidotes. The death of Mayakovsky violates the rules of the protection of labor in the most dangerous of industries: poetry.

Komissarzhevskaya had a strange style: she always spoke the first phrases of a role somewhat sharply, as if in a strange voice. Only after that did her voice heat up as it were; the tone grew warm, and not a single false note would jar you. She had a weak and fragile lower register, especially in conversational speech, but in singing, it was suddenly revealed. Her variety in modulation and intonation was staggering. She was not beautiful, and never tried to pretty herself with the aid of grease paint, but a more feminine actress I have never met (not excluding even the great Eleonora Duse). With all this, an absolute lack of vulgarity. A small, slightly assymetrical face, a stooped figure, drooping shoulders, and a striking smile from which, it seemed, footlights lit up. They say that she was not at all successful in the role of Ophelia (I didn't see her in this role), but it isn't surprising; she was not a tragic actress, but she was the magnificent dramatic actress of her age. The time in which she lived did not demand from her all the color which she possessed. There was no high romantic comedy in her repertoire, but she had all the gifts for it: great resources of a playful joy of living and an internal buoyance.

When I have to read obituaries and various commemorative memoirs concerning distinguished people whom I was fortunate enough to know personally, I always wonder: is it he or isn't it? Who would say, reading the elegaic pages on Chekhov, Komissarzhevskaya, Blok, or Vakhtangov that they were very happy people in life? But I remember that well, because I laughed a great deal together with them. I remember one day on tour in Poland, when Komissarzhevskaya and I roared with laughter at every trifle all day long — such was the mood. I remember Chekhov almost always laughing. And Vakhtangov and I, when we met, cracked jokes and were witty more than we conversed penetratingly about something significant. Or perhaps it was I who was such a frivolous and carefree person that they acted so with me? I think not. If, after my death, you have to read memoirs in which I am portrayed as a priest, puffed up with my own importance and uttering eternal truths, I charge you to declare that this is all libel, that I was always a very happy person: in the first place, because I greatly love to work, and when you work, you are always happy; but in the second place, because I know for a fact that what is said in jest is often more serious than what is said seriously.

translated by KAREN BLACK

Zabolotsky in Tarusa

NIKOLAI STEPANOV

❉   ❉   ❉   ❉

Nikolai Alekseevich Zabolotsky spent the last two years of his life (1957-1958) in Tarusa.

This quiet little town on the bank of the river Oka, surrounded by forests and far from the railroad, has preserved the rural tranquility lost to the area around Moscow. The full-flowing Oka, the broad fields spreading up against the high bank where Tarusa is set — all this attracted Zabolotsky, and he fell in love with this little corner.

In Tarusa, Zabolotsky took two rooms with a porch, almost at the top of a hill, on Karl Liebknecht Street, which was unpaved and grown over with grass as in the country. The little single-storied wooden houses with their green fences and their shingles were surrounded by closely planted gardens, where, in the spring, the apple and cherry trees and lilacs blossomed wildly, and in the summer, bright flowers peeped out from behind the fences — pink, red, yellow, light blue.

On the streets and in the courtyards, roosters, hens, geese, and baby chickens scurried about, feeling themselves lords over the whole territory. From early morning on one could hear everywhere the chickens' scolding, the cackling of geese, the ringing high-spirited cries of roosters. The house where Zabolotsky lived was usually quiet and unfrequented.

The entire building consisted of two rooms: a dining room and an adjoining bedroom. Zabolotsky spent most of the day on the porch, where there was a cot with a mattress, and a dinner table, or, in good weather, he was in the garden.

Zabolotsky settled in Tarusa after his first heart attack, owing to which he now led a sedentary form of life.

Here, in Tarusa, were born Zabolotsky's verses on nature, infused with the panoramic views near the Oka, with the ranging woods and fields, with the restrained beauty of the Russian landscape. Although Zabolotsky was enthusiastic about the majestic country in the Caucasus, the mountains of Georgia, the flowering of Crimean parks, the marine panorama of Gurzuf, yet more than anything he loved the modest Russian countryside. He told me that mountains and a broken horizon strike you without giving the same feeling of space that a level landscape of Russian fields and woods gives. In one of his Tarusa poems, "Evening on the Oka," he depicted this Oka landscape with characteristic accuracy and lyric intensity.

The classical balance and philosophical depth of this landscape remind one of Tiutchev, whose poetry Zabolotsky especially loved and treasured.

Zabolotsky worked a great deal — he translated Serbian epics, or wrote or considered new verses. The long poem, "Tumbruk," was written in Tarusa. Zabolotsky told me several times that his work had never gone so well as in Tarusa. He worked for the most part from early morning until dinner. After dinner he would rest, chat with friends, or take a walk. Sitting on the porch or under the apple trees, he could think, or observe the country-world around him, for hours at a time. Such poems as "Bird Court," "The Laundry-washing," "Summer Evening," "Evening on the Oka," "A Storm is Coming," "Small Town," "Moscow Groves," "At Sunset," were not only written in Tarusa, but were infused with its nature, with the quiet life of the little town, and with the distances in the landscapes on the Oka.

Zabolotsky was already grievously ill and experiencing an agonizing personal drama. And all the same there was such spiritual fortitude in him, such true understanding of his surroundings, such deep love toward people and nature, such interest in life, that I forgot about the deadly threat hanging over him. He did not like to talk about his disease — to complain. He tried only to accomplish as much as possible, to finish directly what he had begun. He liked immaculate order in everything, and he tried, even in his difficult position, to follow this order.

On his open porch, Zabolotsky would sit for a long time watching the hens bustle about in the yard, or good-humoredly chuckling at the handsome gay blade of a rooster, who would appear from a new cockfight with a much-reduced tail and a lacerated and bloodied comb. More than anything he was attached to a rather small, somewhat shaggy little dog with a sort of beard, whose appearance vaguely suggested descent from some Scotch terrier forebears. This little dog would sit patiently for whole days on the stoop and look at Zabolotsky touchingly. The little dog was quick, and would bark piercingly at unfamiliar visitors. It was about this very dog that he wrote in the poem, "Small Town":

> *All day the wash-girl scrubs —*
> *Her husband is off to get a shot.*
> *On the stoop sits a little mutt*
> *From whose chin some hairs jut.*
> *All day, with comprehension*
> *The little dog just stares . . .*
> *And should there be tension,*
> *To the side, she begins to whimper, too.*

The dog's name was Druzhok ("little friend"). Zabolotsky loved to chat with her.

One morning he read me these verses, squinting at them a bit nearsightedly, with the sly good-natured smile which made his face especially hearty looking, almost peasantlike.

He loved a joke like no one else, but usually he joked with the most serious look, putting on a show of uncomprehending simple-mindedness.

From the little garden could be seen the roofs of houses descending to the Oka, and a sea of greenery. It was quiet. Only now and then, somewhere in the distance, could be heard the whistle of some little steamboat, reminding one that Tarusa was not on the edge of the world, but three hours' ride from Moscow.

translated by HUGH OLMSTED

Nikolai Zabolotsky

❆ ❆ ❆ ❆

AN OLD FAIRY TALE

Here in this world where our person
Plays a very uncertain role,
You and I will grow old together
Like the king in a fairy tale.

Shining patiently, guttering, life
Burns out on our preserve
And without saying a word here we wive
Ourselves to what we deserve.

But when silvery locks will shimmer
On your soft and lovely brow,
I'll tear my notebooks to pieces
And take leave of my final poem.

Let the soul like a lake keep quivering
At the sill of the underworld gates
And the crimson leaves keep shivering
Without touching the waters' face.

translated by F. D. REEVE

❆ ❆

ART

A tree grows, bringing to mind
a natural wooden column.
Parts come out from it
dressed in round leaves.
A gathering of such trees

makes a wood, a leafy forest.
But the definition of a forest fails
if you discuss only the formal structure.

The fat figure of a cow
set on four endings,
crowned with a temple-form head
and two horns (like the moon in the first
quarter), will be just as obscure,
will be just as incomprehensible,
if we forget its significance
on the chart of the world's living things.

A house, a wooden building,
knocked together like a cemetery of trees,
composed with a hovel of corpses,
like a pergola of carcasses —
can a mortal make sense of it,
can a living thing get it,
if we forget the man
who cut down the wood and built it?

Man, lord of the planet,
sovereign of the wooded forest,
emperor of bovine flesh,
Sabaoth of the two-storied house —
he runs the planet,
he chops down the forest,
he cuts up the cattle,
but he can't get a word out.

But I, just an average man,
put a long shining flute to my lips,
blew hard, and, called forth by my blowing,
words flew into the world, became things.
The cow cooked me porridge,
the tree told me a story,
and the dead little houses of the world
started jumping around like the living.

translated by F. D. REEVE

❄ ❄

A MEMORY

The months of languor have settled in . . .
Maybe life is really over and gone,
Or maybe, having done its things,
Like a late arrival it's come sat down.

It wants to drink, won't touch a glass;
It wants to eat, lacks appetite.
It listens to the whispering ash
And to the goldfinch singing just outside.

The bird is singing of that distant land
Where through a snowstorm you can see
The little mound of a lonely grave
In white and crystal symmetry.

There no response comes from the birch,
A giant ice-root in the ground.
There overhead in its ring of frost
The blood-stained moon swims on.

translated by F. D. REEVE

❄ ❄

A POEM OF SPRING

You even came along with a fiddle
and made me start playing a reed;
with your arm on my shoulder you led me
out across the April-blue fields.
You slapped the pessimist lightly,
threw the windows everywhere wide,
picked an old man up in the hallway,
sent him dancing along down the road.
Driven out of his wits by your beauty,
a tightwad pulled out his bills,

and they turned to leaves of acacia
shining in the sun on the hills.
Bureaucrats, minor officials,
priests, joiners, painters, and glass-blowers,
like little birds out of their shells,
opened their beaks up joyously.
Even those who sit back in chairs
weighed down with medals and rank
started smiling and, as they say,
for a moment were full of thanks.
It's you, you extravagant spring!
I've caught onto your tricks, you rascal!
From my window I've watched everything,
seen your smile and your know-how: the minstrel
beetle hopping over the field,
the butterfly dallying on tiptoe.
Sprawled out over books the April moon
pinned cornflower aiguillettes on.
It knows that forest and field
are one of my regular themes
and that spring, that extravagant fool,
is a friend of mine, is a poem.

translated by F. D. REEVE

Chapters from "The Golden Rose"

KONSTANTIN PAUSTOVSKY

✖ ✖ ✖ ✖

I.   IVAN BUNIN

No matter how unhappy
this incomprehensible world may be, it
nevertheless is beautiful . . .

I. BUNIN

I T was as far back as high school that I became infatuated with
Bunin. At that time I knew little about him. I learned a few
things from the autobiographical notes he had written for Ven-
gerov's *Dictionary of Writers*. There it was said that Bunin had
passed his childhood in a village somewhere between Elets and the
town of Efremov (in the then province of Tula) and later had
attended Elets high school.

In the cold April of 1916 I went for the first time to Efremov to
visit a relative of mine, a lonely old woman. She asked me to come
to stay with her and to rest for a while after wandering about the
South.

The old woman was a teacher in the Efremov city school. Like
all schoolteachers, she often came down with a sore throat. She
treated it in all kinds of ways and even tried "Bunin's miracle cure."

"Which Bunin?" I asked, surprised.

"Evgeny Alekseevich. The writer's brother. He works in the
excise tax office here in Efremov. He discovered a way to treat
sore throats. He rubs your throat with a dry squirrel skin and the
sore throat disappears at once. I was the only one this skin didn't
help. Evgeny Bunin is a businesslike and rather dryish gentleman. They say his brother, the writer, is a delightful and remarkable person. He sometimes comes here."

Although in general Efremov was a rather depressing town, from the minute I learned that Bunin often came here, it was immediately transformed for me. I think of it now as the embodiment of Russian provincial comfort.

Almost all our out-of-the-way cities were alike. In the words of Chekhov, they all were "typical Efremovs" — with run-down monastery hostels, with the earthy faces of saints over the stone gates of the churches, with the play of the bells on the troika of the local chief of police, with the jail on the common, with the district council building — the only building where an incandescent light burned at the entrance, with the lime trees in the cemetery, and with deep ravines. In the summer dead nettle stood like walls in the ravines, and in the winter onto the snow, gray from ashes, coals were thrown out of stoves, and samovars gave off a blue-gray smoke.

Elets was close by. I decided to go there in order to see this city of Bunin's.

Since early youth I had had an irradicable passion for visiting places connected with the lives of my favorite writers and poets. I considered (and consider to this day) the best place on earth to be the hill under the wall of the Svyatogorsky Monastery in the region of Pskov where Pushkin is buried. The views which are revealed from this hill are more distant and pure than any others anywhere in Russia.

A work train, the so-called "Maksim Gor'ky," used to go from Efremov to Elets. I left for Elets on it.

A cold dawn found me in a jarring old railway car. I sat under a flickering candle and read Bunin's story "Elijah the Prophet" in a tattered old issue of the journal *Contemporary World*. Because of its poignant grief, this story is one of the best in Russian literature. Each detail and each feature of this story (even the "sheep, pale as a shroud") touched my heart with a presentiment of the inescapable misfortune, poverty, and loneliness which had become the lot of Russia of that time.

At times one felt like escaping from this Russia without ever looking back. But rarely did anyone decide on this. That is because, even in her bitter humiliation, a beggar-mother is loved.

Bunin left the only country he loved. But he left only outwardly. An unusually proud and severe man, to the end of his days he longed very much for Russia and spilled many hidden tears over her in the alien nights of Paris and Grasse, the tears of a man who had voluntarily exiled himself from his homeland.

I was on my way to Elets. Outside the windows stretched fields of stunted grain shoots. The wind whistled in the tin ventilators and drove on the low clouds. I reread "Elijah the Prophet," and reread the mournful story of Ivan Novikov, the peasant of the Predtechen region of the Elets district. And I tried to understand: how, by what words, and by what magic had this genuine miracle been achieved? The miracle of the creation of a short and powerful, sad and magnificent story.

In Elets I didn't stay at the hotel. I was too poor for that then. All day until late evening, when the return train left for Efremov, I wandered about the city, and, of course, I became very tired.

It was a high, gray day. An unexpected, late, light snow started falling. The wind blew it off the pavement laying bare white flagstones worn down by hoofs.

The city was all stone. I seemed to see something fortresslike in its stone appearance. It was felt both in the desertedness of the streets and in their silence. I had heard that Elets was a busy trade city, and I was surprised by this quietness, until I understood that the silence and small number of people were a consequence of the war.

Elets really was a fortress. Bunin, in *The Life of Arsen'ev*, says about it: ". . . the city was proud of its antiquity and had a right to this: it indeed was one of the most ancient Russian cities and lay among the great black-earth fields of the Podstep'e, on that fateful boundary beyond which once extended 'wild and unknown lands,' and during the time of the Suzdal' and Vladimir principalities it belonged to the most important strongholds of Russia, which, according to the word of the chroniclers, first breathed the wind, dust, and cold from under the threatening Asiatic horde . . ."

In this excerpt almost each word, with its simplicity, exactness, and colorfulness, gives enjoyment. How priceless can be mere words about these ancient cities breathing the wind and dust of Asiatic attacks! These words revive the anxious whistle of the sentries, the all's-well banging of wooden mallets on sheets of iron, and the summoning of all to the city ramparts.

For a long time I stood by the boys' high school and its stone courtyard. Bunin had studied in this school. Inside it was quiet; behind the windows the classes were going on.

Then I crossed the square where the market was, and I was surprised at the abundance of smells. It smelled of fennel, horse manure, old herring barrels, skins, incense from the open doors of a church where a funeral mass was being sung over someone, and from the gardens behind high gray fences it smelled of fallen and already rotten leaves.

I drank my fill of tea at the inn. It was empty and rather cold there. From the inn I went to the outskirts of the city. Much time remained before the train departed.

On the edge of the city — in a long, bare pasture leading down to a hollow — dark blacksmith shops smoked and rang from anvil blows. Above the pasture was a white sky. Alongside stretched the cemetery wall.

I entered the cemetery. Broken porcelain roses and rusted tin leaves on funeral wreathes lightly rustled and creaked in the wind from time to time.

Here and there on ornate iron crosses with peeled paint could be seen framed photographs which had been defaced by the rains.

Toward evening, I arrived at the station. I have often been alone in my life, but rarely have I experienced such a bitter feeling of desolation as on that evening in Elets.

Somewhere nearby, behind the walls of the houses and in warm rooms, life, perhaps happy and bright, and perhaps poor and silent, went on. But I was outside these warm walls. I was sitting in the dimly lighted third-class waiting room where it stank of kerosene and where a cold draught blew across my feet.

Everyone has strong, at times pleasant, and at times sad coincidences in life. I also have them. But the most surprising coincidence happened that evening in the Elets station.

I bought a damp copy of *The Russian Word* at the newspaper stand. Because of the darkness it was difficult to read in the third-class waiting room. I recounted my money. There was enough to drink some tea in the brightly lighted station buffet and even enough to give a half-drunk waiter a tip.

In the buffet I sat down at a table near an empty, nickel-plated champagne bucket and unfolded my newspaper . . .

I came to only an hour later when the station's doorman, shaking a bell, shouted in an intentionally nasal voice, "The second bell for Efremov, Volovo, and Tula!"

I jumped up, rushed into a car, hid in the corner by the dark window, and sat there all the way to Efremov.

Everything inside me trembled from sorrow and love. For whom? For a wonderful girl, for the high-school student Olya Meshcherskaya, who was killed here in this station. Bunin's story, "Light Breathing," had been printed in the newspaper.

I don't know if this work can be called a story. It's not a story, but an illumination, life itself with its emotions and love, a writer's sad and calm meditation, and the epitaph on a young woman's beauty.

I was certain that I had walked past Olya Meshcherskaya's grave at the cemetery, and that the wind had timidly rung in the old wreath as though calling me to stop.

But I had walked by, knowing nothing. If I had only known! And if I could have known, I would have strewn this grave with all the flowers that grow on the earth. I already loved this girl. I shuddered from the irreparableness of her fate.

Beyond the windows the sparse and pitiful lights of the villages quivered and went out. I looked at them and naïvely calmed myself with the fact that Olya Meshcherskaya was Bunin's invention and that only my inclination toward a romantic acceptance of the world compelled me to suffer because of sudden love for this girl who had perished.

Probably during this night in the cold train, on the black and gray steppes of Russia, and among the bare birch groves which rustled from the night wind, I completely understood for the first time what art and its elevating and eternal power are.

Several times I opened the paper and in a candle's dying light and, later, in the watery light of a lonely dawn I read the same words over and over about the light breathing of Olya Meshcherskaya, and about the fact that now "this light breathing again has been scattered in the world, in this cloudy sky, and in this cold spring wind."

The second congress of Soviet writers met with an ovation the words that Bunin was to be returned to Russian literature.

And he was returned. Bunin's most precious works, among them the story *The Life of Arsen'ev*, were returned to his homeland.

It is just as difficult and almost as impossible to write about this story as about Bunin himself. It is so rich, so generous, so varied, and it so mercilessly and precisely sees every person from the gentleman from San Francisco to the carpenter Averky, sees each slightest gesture and each change of thought so astonishingly clearly, simultaneously harshly and tenderly, speaks about nature inseparable from the course of human days, that, as they say, it is useless and almost absurd to write about it "secondhand."

You have to read Bunin and give up forever pitiful attempts to tell in everyday non-Bunin words what he wrote with classical strength and clarity.

It is impossible to retell in one's own words Pushkin's "The rainy day was extinguished," Levitan's "Over Eternal Peace," or Lermontov's "Along the blue waves of the sea." This is just as vain as verifying Mozart and all the great composers from the sixteenth century to Stravinsky with the dry algebra of harmony. For this reason I won't make any attempts (doomed in advance to failure) to paraphrase Bunin and to interpret his works from the viewpoint of "issues of the time."

"Issues of the time," in other words, the idea of contemporary life, cannot exist without a very close bond with everything that has preceded our time and that, to some degree, has determined it.

Bunin's books are remarkable in that they are entirely in their time and are simultaneously connected by a living bond with the past of our people.

In Bunin's prose and poetry the feeling that life is a lengthy and, at its basis, beautiful path from man's birth to his death is clearly present. This feeling of life is particularly strongly expressed in *The Life of Arsen'ev.*

This story is not only a glorification of Russia, not only the summing up of Bunin's life, and not only the expression of his very deep and poetic love for his country, the expression of sorrow and enthusiasm for it, which from time to time flashes from the pages of the book like grudging tears resembling the rare early stars in the sky; it is something else, too.

It is not simply a procession of Russian people — peasants, children, beggars, ruined landowners, cattle dealers, students, holy fools, artists, and people who happened to be on all the roads and crossroads of the author and who were painted with a sharp and at times stunning power.

In some parts *The Life of Arsen'ev* recalls the picture *Holy Russia* by the painter Nesterov. In the understanding of the artist this picture is the best expression of its country and people.

Along a wide road among thickets and low hills, past clear streams and blackened log churches, measuredly dropping the peal of their bells into the quiet of a fall day, past forgotten graveyards, and small villages, walks a large crowd under a bright northern sky.

Who isn't in this crowd! Here walks all Russia! Here walks an ancient tsar in heavy brocade and pressed gold, here walk prisoners lightly clanking their chains, shy peasants wearing clothes made of coarse homemade gray cloth, young herdsmen with long whips, pilgrims in skullcaps, and girls with lowered, seemingly blackened eyelashes that throw a soft shadow on pale faces illuminated by a chaste inner light. Here walk holy fools, wandering beggars, fervent old women, carpenters, reapers, menacing old men with staffs, and apprentices, and here walk quiet towheaded children looking up at the sun glistening on cranes yearning for the south.

Here walks Leo Tolstoy in the crowd, and not far from him — Dostoevsky. They walk in the dust of the road with all their truth-seeking people, they all walk together into the clear but, for the present, still far-off distances, which they never grew tired of talking about throughout their whole lives.

Bunin's books have something in common with this picture. With the difference, however, that Bunin's people are completely real and familiar to everyone, and the country is much simpler and poorer than in Nesterov.

In Bunin, Central Russia rises before us in the charm of its short, gray days, in the peace of its fields, rains and fogs, and at times in a pale radiance with wide, smoldering sunsets.

Here it is appropriate to say that Bunin had a rare and unerring feeling for colors and lighting.

The world consists of a great number of combinations of colors and light. And the person who easily and exactly catches these combinations is most fortunate, especially if he is an artist or writer.

In this sense Bunin was a very fortunate writer. He saw everything with the same sharp-sightedness: the Central-Russian summer, the sullen winter, and the "barren, leaden, and tranquil days of late fall," and the sea, "which from behind the wild wooded hills suddenly looked at me with all its immense dark waste."

In Bunin's notes there is a short phrase which refers to the beginning of the summer of 1906. "The season of lovely clouds is beginning," Bunin noted, and by this he seems to reveal to us one of the "secrets" of his life as a writer. These are words about the approach of inevitable and pleasant work, which in Bunin is connected with summer, "the season of clouds," the "season of rains," and "the season of flowering."

With these words Bunin marks the beginning of his work on the observation of the sky and the study of the clouds, always mysterious and attractive.

Not without reason did all our best poets so concisely and colorfully write about clouds. Let's at least take two of our contemporaries. In Yury Olesha, a light cloud, similar to the outlines of South America, hangs over Moscow. Zabolotsky, in particular, has many clouds. "In a soft sky is a cloud of unusual beauty, like a lump of silver. On the sides it is misty lilac, and in the middle — threatening and bright — the wing of a wounded swan slowly swimming somewhere."

Every time you read Bunin's lines about summer, you remember this note. His words about summer are always full of anguish, even if they occupy only two lines.

"The garden had finished blooming and was covered with leaves, the whole day the nightingale sang, and the whole day the lower windows were raised."

Bunin just as keenly and subtly saw everything that chanced to catch his attention in life. And he saw very much. Since his youth he had been afflicted with traveling, restlessness, and the desire to see without fail everything he hadn't yet seen.

He confessed that he never felt so fine as in the minutes when a highway stretched before him.

There is a strong connection between such phenomena as light, smell, sound, and color.

What does this connection consist of? While looking at unknown flowers similar to the huge crocuses in Van Gogh's picture, or while looking at dense light which recalls the transparent juice of some strange fruit, it consists, at the very least, in unexpectedly in-haling the sweet and stimulating smell of this fruit and the fresh and weak breath of the wet sand of the sea. A steady wind from foreign islands seems to bring this smell to the picture hall. While reading Bunin you often catch yourself in a sensation of this kind. Color gives rise to a smell, light inspires a color, and sound recalls a series of amazingly exact pictures. All this together engenders a peculiar mental state which alternates between concentration and sorrow, between lightness and life with its warm winds, the sound of trees, the endless drone of the ocean, and the pleasant laughter of women and children.

In *The Life of Arsen'ev* Bunin says this about his feeling for colors in nature:

"At the mere sight of a box of paints I shook all over, I smeared paper from morning to evening, stood for hours, looking at the marvelous blue of the sky which turns into lilac and which, on a hot day, opposite the sun, can be seen through the tops of trees which appear to be bathing in this blue — and I was always imbued with a very deep feeling of the truly divine sense and meaning of the colors of the earth and sky. When I sum up what life has given me, I see that this is one of its most important results. I will re-member this lilac blue, coming through the branches and leaves, even when I am dying . . ."

The slightly deadened colors characteristic of Central Russia immediately acquire heat and richness when Bunin speaks about the South, the tropics, Asia Minor, Egypt, or about Palestine.

"The bright void of the tropical sky looked into the door of the deck-house. The glassy waves more and more slowly rolled past the sides of the ship, illuminating the cabin."

In the fall of 1912 Bunin lived on Capri and during this time he talked with his nephew Nikolai Alekseevich Pusheshnikov. Pusheshnikov's notes about these talks have been preserved. They are very simple notes. They show us Bunin — a very restrained man — during times of rare candidness.

These notes all speak about Bunin's intense love for life. Looking out the window of a train at the shadow of the steam engine's smoke melting in the transparent air, Bunin said:

What a joy it is to be alive! And to be able to see, to see just this smoke and this light. If I had no arms and legs, and I could only sit on a bench and look at the setting sun, I would be happy. This is what's necessary — to see and to breathe. Nothing gives the kind of enjoyment colors give. I am used to looking. Painters taught me this art . . . Poets don't know how to describe autumn because they don't describe colors and the sky. The French — Heredia and Leconte de Lisle — achieved extraordinary perfection in descriptions.

In Pusheshnikov's notes is an amazing spot which reveals the "secret" of Bunin's mastery.

Bunin said that no matter what he begins to write about, he first of all has to "find a sound." "As soon as I have found it, everything else comes by itself."

What does "to find a sound" mean? Obviously Bunin put much more meaning into these words than appears at first sight.

"To find a sound" is to find the rhythm of prose and to find its basic intonation, for prose possesses the same inner melody as poetry and music.

This feeling for the rhythm of prose and its musical intonation is obviously also organically enrooted in an excellent knowledge and sensitive feeling for one's native language.

Even in childhood Bunin keenly felt this rhythm. While still a boy he noticed the light circular movements of the lines in the prologue to Pushkin's "Ruslan": "The sorcery of ceaseless circular motions."

"And night — and day — the cat — kept walking — on a chain — around."

In the realm of the Russian language Bunin was an unsurpassed master.

Out of an immense number of words he unfailingly chose for each story the most powerful and picturesque words, which were connected by some unseen and almost mysterious bond with the narration and were necessary for this narration alone.

Each story and each poem of Bunin's is like a magnet which attracts all the particles needed for this story from the most varied places.

If a fairy-tale writer like Christian Andersen lived now, perhaps he would have written a fairy tale about how all kinds of unexpected things, including a ray of the sun in a bush covered with hoarfrost, scraps of clouds, and gray mourning robes, come flying to a writer who possesses a magic magnet, and about how the writer arranges them in a special order known to him alone, sprinkles them with spring water, and then — a new work is already living in the world — a narrative poem, lyric, or a story — and nothing can kill it. It is immortal as long as man is alive on the earth.

Bunin's language is simple, almost laconic, pure, and picturesque. But it is also unusually rich in imagery and sound — from the singing of cymbals to the ring of spring water, from measured clarity to amazingly delicate intonations, from a light melody to thundering Biblical curses, and from them — to the pointed and striking language of Orlov peasants.

I have referred to *The Life of Arsen'ev* only in passing. This story, however, demands careful reading.

I called *The Life of Arsen'ev* a story. This, of course, is not true. It is neither a story, nor a novella, nor a novel. It is a work of a new, still unnamed genre. It is a unique and astounding genre which takes the human heart into poignant and at the same time serene captivity.

It is generally considered that *The Life of Arsen'ev* is autobiography. Bunin denied this. *The Life of Arsen'ev* is written too freely for autobiography.

It is not autobiography. It is a fusion of all earthly sorrows, pleasures, reflections, and joys. It is an amazing compilation of the events of one human life, journeys, countries, cities, and seas, but, in the midst of all this variety of the world, our Central Russia is always in the foreground. "In the winter there is a boundless sea of snow, and in the summer — a sea of grain, grasses and flowers . . .

And the eternal quiet of these fields, and their mysterious silence . . ."

In *The Life of Arsen'ev* Bunin succeeded in collecting his life in a magic crystal, but, in distinction from Pushkin's crystal, the breadth of this story and the breadth of a writer's life is sharply outlined and is transparent to the very core.

I continue to call *The Life of Arsen'ev* a story, although with equal right I could call it a poem or a legend.

The Life of Arsen'ev is one of the most remarkable phenomena of world literature. To our great fortune it belongs first to Russian literature.

In this astounding book poetry and prose are fused into one, fused organically, and they have created a wonderful new genre.

There is something austere and at times severe in this fusion of a poetical perception of the world with its extremely prosaic appearance. There is something Biblical in the very style of this work.

In this book it is no longer possible to distinguish poetry from prose, and many of its words leave a lasting impression on the heart.

It is enough to read several lines about the North in order to understand that Bunin found the only necessary and the only possible expressions for everything he wanted to say.

These lines cannot be read without a strong emotional reaction:

In her distant native land, alone, forgotten forever by the whole world, let her rest in peace and let her beloved name for ever and ever be blessed. Can she whose eyeless skull, whose gray bones lie now somewhere there in the cemetery grove of an impoverished Russian city, on the bottom of an already nameless grave, can she really be the one who once rocked me in her arms?

The strength of the language and the strength of the exact imagery in *The Life of Arsen'ev* are the kind that engender sadness, agitation, and even tears. The rare tears which only something beautiful arouses.

The newness of *The Life of Arsen'ev* consists just in the fact that in no other of Bunin's works was the phenomenon revealed with such simplicity which we, in the poverty of our language, call a person's "inner world." Is there really a clear boundary between the inner and outer world? Is the outer world really not one whole with the inner world?

Everything Bunin speaks about in this book is very visible, audible, tangible, and material, and it cheers or saddens us for a long time. I will quote several passages from this book. Here, for example, is a little boy's first encounter with the city:

Shoe polish turned out to be the most astounding thing in the city. In my whole life I haven't experienced the kind of enthusiasm and joy from things I have seen on earth – and I have seen many! – as at the bazaar in this city, when I held a small box of shoe polish in my hand. This round box was made of simple bast, but what bast it was and what incomparable artistry this box had been made with! And the polish itself! Black, tightly packed, with a dull sheen, and with the elating smell of alcohol.

In this book there is a spot about the "loneliness" of the moon. This passage is written with a kind of piercing sorrow, even though Bunin writes it in the person of the same little boy:

I remember: once on a fall night for some reason I woke up and noticed a soft and mysterious twilight in my room, and through the big uncurtained window – a pale and sad fall moon, standing high-high above the empty yard of the estate, a moon so sad and so filled with such an unearthly charm from its melancholy and loneliness that some ineffably sweet and bitter feelings gripped my heart, the same feelings that it, this pale fall moon, also seemed to experience.

Bunin made this description of his poor native land with terse forcefulness:

Where was I born, where did I grow up, and what did I see there? Neither mountains, nor rivers, nor lakes, nor forests – only brush in the hollows, here and there small groves, and only rarely the likeness of a forest, a Zakaz or Dubovka, and always the fields, the fields, and the boundless ocean of grain . . . This is the Podstep'e, where the fields are like waves, where everything is gullies and small hills, shallow meadows, most often stony, and where the villages and their bast-shod inhabitants seem forgotten by God – this is why they are modest, naturally simple, and kindred to their willow branches and straw.

Writers use a term borrowed from sculptors – "the modeling of people." Few writers have the unerringly accurate and at times unmerciful or touching ability to "model people" which Bunin has. Here, for example, is a shepherd boy:

The urchin shepherd boy was extremely interesting: his coarse linen shirt and small short pants were nothing but holes; his legs, arms, and face were dried out, peeled and burned by the sun; his lips hurt because he eternally chewed either a crust of sour rye bread, or burdock, or "goat's beard," which made real sores on his lips; but his sharp eyes roguishly roved from side to side — you see, he well understood all the criminal nature of our friendship and the fact that he incited us to eat lord knows what. But how sweet this forbidden friendship was! How enticing everything was that he told us about, disconnectedly, on the sly, glancing around every minute. Besides this, he cracked and snapped his long whip surprisingly well and laughed impishly when we tried to crack it and painfully scorched our ears with the end of the whip.

The Russian landscape, with its softness, timid springs, and its plainness, which in a short time proved to have a quiet beauty and aroused even pity, had found, at last, its spokesman, a spokesman who never attempted to embellish it. In the Russian landscape there wasn't the smallest trifle which Bunin would not have noticed and described:

We passed a clayey pond whose surface, spread out in a hollow among hillsides trampled by livestock, glistened hotly and despondently. Here and there on the open hillsides shelterless crows sat in meditation.

In *The Life of Arsen'ev* a small chapter begins with the words: "Everything that surrounded me in my boyhood years was very Russian." Further on, Bunin speaks about the highway near the village "Stanovy," about robbers, terror, and the nights, and what an amazing picture of recent Russia he sketched there:

The highway beside Stanovy descended into a deep ravine, which we called the "Head," and this spot always inspired an almost superstitious terror. Many times in my youth, riding past it near Stanovy, I myself experienced this purely Russian terror . . . This is how everything arose in my imagination: look, it's them — there they are! With hatchets in their hands, with clothes drawn tightly and low down on their hips, with fur caps pushed down over their watchful eyes, not hurrying they are walking to cut you off. And suddenly they stop, and quietly and with exaggerated calmness they order: "Why don't you stop for a minute, merchant . . ."

This book has a large multitude of magnificent places. Nowhere in our prose do I recall the kind of description of winter which I quote below:

I still remember many gray and harsh winter days, many dark and muddy thaws when Russian rural life became especially oppressive, when the faces of all became bored and malevolent — Russian man primevally subjected to natural influences! — and everything on the earth, one's own existence as well, wearied you with its unnecessariness. I remember how the bell towers of the cities' churches were scarcely visible through the impenetrable Asiatic blizzards which sometimes blew for whole weeks. I remember the Epiphany frosts, which brought to mind the deep antiquity of Old Russia and the hard frosts which "split the earth a yard wide." Then over the snow-white city, completely submerged in snow drifts, the white constellation of Orion burned menacingly at night in the steel-blue sky, and in the morning, mirrorlike, two dull suns gleamed ominously, and in the taut and resonant immobility of the burning air the whole city slowly and wildly emitted scarlet smoke from the chimneys, and the city crunched and squeaked from the steps of passersby and from sled runners.

When speaking about Bunin, you unintentionally become an annoying person. All the time you want to point out the beautiful spots one after the other to the reader. Always it seems that this one here is the best. But it turns out that farther on is an even better spot, and you can't remain silent about it. Here, for example, are some words about youth and an almost childlike love:

Everyone thinks about his lost youth with sadness. Then we loved love and everything it brought us, both "the star of many colors, quietly shimmering in the East, far beyond the garden, beyond the village, beyond the summer fields, from where the distant beat of quail came sometimes barely audible and for this reason particularly entrancing," and the breathing of the girl I loved — how can I communicate the feelings with which I looked at Liza, in my mind seeing her there in that room, sleeping to the murmur of leaves streaming with a quiet rain outside the open windows, through which now and then entered and blew a warm wind from the fields, tenderly fondling her young sleep, which, it seemed, was purer and more beautiful than any one on the earth.

In 1917 by chance I came to the estate Kropotovo to the south of Efremov. The estate at one time had belonged to Lermontov's father. Lermontov once dropped in to see his father here on the way to the Caucasus.

The old and mournful house was closed and boarded up, I sat near it on a log for a while.

Low, fragile, dark clouds endlessly crept from behind the clay hills. The rain started now and then and beat on the torn leaves of the burdock.

And only recently, reading *The Life of Arsen'ev*, I learned that Bunin had often visited Kropotovka and that this village had always aroused thoughts in him about the great poetry of our provinces.

"Everything all round was poor, squalid, and deserted. I rode along the highway and was surprised at its neglect and barrenness. I rode along country roads, and I passed small villages and estates: not only in the fields and on the muddy roads, but also in the equally muddy streets of the villages and in the deserted court-yards of the estates everything was empty . . . Here is Kropo-tovka, the nailed-up house, which I never can look at without endlessly sad and inexplicable feelings. This was Lermontov's poor home . . . What a life, what a fate! Only twenty-seven years, but what infinitely rich and beautiful years, right up to the last day, to that dark evening on a side road at the foot of the Mashuk, when, as out of a cannon, the shot of some Martynov roared from an enormous pistol and '*Lermontov fell, as though cut down.*'"

The more I read Bunin, the clearer it becomes, that Bunin is al-most inexhaustible.

In any case, it requires much time to become familiar with everything Bunin wrote and to learn all about his life, restless and impetuous in its motion, and stormy in spite of the author's elegiac style.

Bunin himself told part of his life in *The Life of Arsen'ev* and in numerous stories which are almost all connected with his biography in some degree; and part of his life his wife, Vera Nikolaevna Murom – Bunin, told in her book *The Life of Bunin* which she published in 1958 in Paris — a very valuable collection of reminiscences and material about Bunin.

All Bunin's life to the last day was devoted to traveling and creation. It was not without significance that Bunin wrote the story about the sailor, Bernard, from Maupassant's yacht *Dear Friend*.

Bernard, a splendid sailor, dying, says, "It seems, I wasn't a bad sailor." Bunin wrote about himself that he would be happy if, in the hour of his death, he could rightfully repeat Bernard's words and say, "It seems, I wasn't a bad writer."

Bunin was bold and honest in his convictions. In his "The Village" he was one of the first to uncrown the sugary myth about the Russian peasant God-bearer, which armchair populists had created.

Besides his brilliant and completely classical stories, Bunin wrote travel sketches about Judaea, Asia Minor, Turkey, Greece, and Egypt which are extraordinary in the purity of their description, in their magnificent power of observation, and in their feeling for distant lands.

Bunin was a first-class poet of the pure, if one can put it this way, "Parnassian" school. His poetry still hasn't been appreciated. In it are genuine masterpieces of expressiveness and of the conveyance of difficult-to-catch things.

All his life Bunin waited for happiness; he wrote about human happiness, and he sought paths toward it. He found it in his poetry and prose, in his love for life and his homeland, and he spoke great words about how happiness is given only to the experienced.

Bunin lived a complex and sometimes contradictory life. He saw and knew much, loved and hated much, worked much, and sometimes made mistakes, but all his life his greatest, most tender, and invariable love was for his native land, Russia.

> *And the flowers, bumblebees, grass, and grain,*
> *And the azure, and midday heat . . .*
> *The Lord will ask the prodigal son again:*
> *"Were you happy in earthly life?"*
> *And I shall forget all — I will remember only these*
> *Paths here among the fields of grain and tares.*
> *I will fall on merciful knees,*
> *And not answer, so full of tears.*

II. A MEETING WITH OLESHA

I HAD many meetings with Yury Karlovich Olesha. Each has remained in my memory for a long time.

I will speak about one of these meetings now. It took place in the very beginning of the war, in June, 1941. I came to Odessa from the front near Tiraspol' on a military truck; I jumped off near the railroad station, and started walking to the Hotel London.

I walked along deserted Pushkin street. It was beginning to dawn. It was pouring.

In the first days of the war, the people of Odessa had painted their white southern houses with heavily diluted soot. They thought that black houses were not as visible from the air as white ones.

The complicated house painting enterprise, which bore the high-sounding name "camouflage," was completely useless. The summer happened to be a rainy one and after the first rain the houses peeled and became covered with streams of filth.

I walked along Pushkin Street and didn't recognize a city which had long been familiar and close to me. It was Odessa, and, at the same time, it was not Odessa. It was as though I saw the city in reality and in a dream at the same time.

Ominous water gushed out of the drainpipes. Except for the hurried beating of the rain on the sheet-iron roofs, there was not a sound all around. Only the smell of the soaked leaves of the acacia trees recalled the recent summer days.

At that time I was for some reason sure that the war had brought a new atmosphere with it. It tore the old layer of atmosphere — mild, warm, and at times foggy — away from the earth and replaced it with harsh and empty air, which changed the appearance of all places and objects. The new air was like liquid nitroglycerin. It smelled as if something mixed with a very strong medicine was burning.

Probably from this strange air, from the lifeless streets, and from the dampness of the rain I felt a complete loneliness, just as though I had come to an absolutely deserted city.

I therefore sighed with relief when I saw an unshaven old man in purple suspenders and a crumpled shirt in the dark vestibule of the Hotel London.

He was sitting at a desk and reading Alexandre Dumas's *Queen Margot*.

The stub of a yellow candle burned motionlessly in front of him. Barely perceptible blue smoke curled like a strand of hemp over the flame.

"Are you the doorman?" I asked uncertainly.

"Let's assume I am."

"May I stay here for the night?"

"What a strange question!" the old man said angrily. "There's not a soul in the hotel. Take any room. With or without an alcove. If you have a broad nature, you can have two rooms to yourself. Or three. And with all this it's completely free. Gratis!"

The doorman used an old-fashioned word of merchants and traveling salesmen, "gratis," which meant that goods were let go free.

"Gratis!" repeated the old man. "There's absolutely no one to take your money. Intourist has been evacuated. I'm here as a watchman."

"Isn't there really a single soul in the hotel?" I asked, listening intently to the sound of breaking glass in the hallways.

"What do you mean not a single soul!" exclaimed the old man indignantly. "Don't you count Yury Karlovich Olesha?"

"He's here?"

"No doubt about it. Tell me where he'd be if not in Odessa. I've known Yury Karlovich for a long time. He grew up here and lived here when Odessa whirled for days on end like a merry-go-round. Everything galloped before your eyes: ships, famous fliers, chic women, fast talkers, captains, thieves, Italian prima donnas, famous doctors, and violinists. And you ask if I know who's still here! Bad times have fallen on Odessa now. Olesha was here then, and he is here now. He's a pure Odessan, understand? Right now he's sitting in a room alone. After an illness. Every time an air raid alarm starts, I go to try to talk him into coming down to the cellar. But he won't go for anything and right off begins joking. 'Solomon Shaevich,' he says, 'see that the Fritzes during the bombing don't smash the street lights I wrote about in my fairy tale *The Three*

Fat Men.' What can I say to that? I also like to joke you know. I say that if I had my way, I would plate those lights with silver so that Odessa would always remember this book."

I went up to Olesha's room. He was sitting sullenly at the desk and was writing something in his big and rather free handwriting.

We kissed. Olesha was hopelessly unshaven, and he was terribly thin; he had had dysentery. A dry yellowness covered his cheeks. But his eyes, as always, were penetrating and had a kind smile in them. And as always, they were ready to blaze instantly with the flame of fancy and inspiration seized on the spur of the moment, and with the brilliance of well-put and unexpected comparisons. When he began to speak, life immediately became interesting and seemed radiant. Just how did he do this? He did it with the liveliness of his humor, his poetry, and his instant and exact understanding of human hearts.

It always seemed to me (and perhaps this truly was so), that Yury Karlovich all his life conversed quietly with geniuses and children, with vivacious women and good-hearted eccentrics.

He argued boldly and impetuously. He mercilessly and triumphantly thrust his words into the person he was talking with.

A special life, carefully selected by him from the reality surrounding him and decorated with his colorful expressions, existed about him, in turn growing and lessening in intensity. This life around him had a sound like that of the tree branch full of flowers and leaves which he described in *Envy*.

There was something stormy, and powerful, like Beethoven, in Olesha. Even in his voice. His sharp eyes saw many splendid and comforting things around him. He wrote about them succinctly and precisely, well knowing the law that two words can be incredibly strong and that four words are four times weaker.

A homemade cane stood in the corner of the room. A checkered knapsack hung on the head of the cane.

"Yes," said Olesha and nodded at the cane and knapsack, "when the final hour, and then the final minute comes, I'll leave on foot for Nikolaev, and then for Kherson. To get there, you mustn't think about anything. You just walk, walk, and walk, as long as your legs hold out . . . By the way, get me some kind of a map, even one from a school atlas. It'll be bad for me to go without a map."

I was listening to him and falling asleep sitting up. I had to lie down and rest for at least an hour. Olesha went with me along the empty hotel corridors to pick out the best room.

A bomb explosion had knocked out almost all the windows. Draughts rushed about the hotel and swelled out the dusty, dark-red curtains. Behind them rustled the dried leaves of palm trees.

My sleepiness passed. We decided to be hard to please and walked from room to room, opening one room after another. One we rejected because it smelled like strawberry soap, a second because it had a broken mirror, and a third because of the picture *A Boyars Feast*, which a recent explosion had covered with plaster dust. Finally, we chose the smallest and darkest room. Its windows opened onto a little inside courtyard. Aged plane trees were growing in it.

"A bomb shelter," said Olesha. "The safest room in the hotel."

I at once fell asleep with my clothes on. I woke up to the distant drone of departing bombers. The glass of an open window, grown scaly from age, reflected a golden sunset. I jumped up and went to Olesha. He wasn't in his room. I found him in the narrow and dark hall of the hotel restaurant.

This was a historic restaurant. As is usually said in newspaper accounts, "its walls had seen many famous people." Until not long ago, this hall still glittered with crystal, silver, china, and silver plate. The hard, bluish tablecloths on the small tables were as crisp as parchment. Chandeliers resembling clusters of grapes burned under an intricately modeled ceiling. Cracked ice grated in silver buckets, and the menu was mysterious and lavish.

Now the hall was empty and dark, a single wartime light burned sickly under the ceiling. No one ever turned it off. Two waiters — friends of Olesha — old as Odessa and in rumpled white jackets wandered around the hall and served the rare visitors plain tea and slippery black vermicelli.

Olesha was sitting at a table with a sad, silent Negro actor from the Odessa film studio.

"There was just a raid," said Olesha. "You slept through it. Well, what do you have to say for Odessa?"

I said that the city had changed since the beginning of the war, it had grown quiet, and the Odessans seemed to have lost their traditional liveliness.

"Ba – lo – ney!" said Olesha clearly and distinctly. "Odessans don't surrender and don't die. Their wit is crossed with fearlessness. Their bravery flourishes on sharp remarks. You have a preconceived idea about Odessans. The same kind, as, let's say, about Diogenes."

I, of course, understood that this had nothing to do with me, that I had never expressed an opinion about Diogenes in Olesha's presence, at the very least because I simply didn't have one. Diogenes was the excuse for some witty fabrication.

"Everyone here," said Olesha, "including you, considers Diogenes the head of the Cynics. But what kind of Cynic was he! He was a timid, stupid, old man. He lived, by the way, in a barrel. Because of his stupidity. Even though the barrel was just another barrel, it was living space. It had to be paid for. Diogenes, understandably enough, never had either a kopeck or a drachma. The owner of the barrel constantly threatened to throw the old man out on the street for debts. Then Diogenes would go to his friends and, blushing, would begin to mutter, 'Give me some money for the barrel.' Good lord what a clamor and uproar were raised then. 'Money for a barrel?' 'Smart aleck!' 'Money-grabber!' 'Cynic!' "

The silent Negro suddenly broke out laughing. Olesha cast a quick glance at him and said, "Even now, during the war, Odessans are just as brave, cheerful, and funny as ever. Let's go walk around the city, and I can guarantee that somewhere we will see old Odessans who yield to nothing. To a certain extent this also is heroism."

We left the restaurant. The clear air was red from the sunset. The boulevard was full of commotion.

Fascist squadrons were moving over the sea toward Ochakov. The naval anti-aircraft guns were shelling them heavily and loudly.

We started for the Greek market. There, according to Olesha, a tea room, where they served real Moldavian "Brynza," a sheep-milk cheese, was still living out its last hours. But we didn't reach the Greek market. An air raid alarm caught us. The policeman opened up fierce pistol firing in the air — obviously for those who hadn't heard the alarm on the radio. They also were herding all passersby into courtyards.

We went into the first yard. It was a typical Greek courtyard. One can't describe this kind of yard, you have to see it or even lie in it several days to understand all its charm. I doubt that a reader will receive anything from a dry description. But nevertheless, I'll try.

They are rectangular courtyards, surrounded on all sides by old two-storied houses. The gates on the streets are the only exits from these yards. All the rooms and apartments of all the floors of these Greek houses open onto old outside wooden terraces and onto just as old stairways.

The terraces extend along all the walls of a house, and they shake and creak. They serve as a very well-liked and lively addition to the rooms and apartments.

On the terraces people fry mackerel or flounder on kerosene stoves, cook their famous caviar, bathe their children, wash, quarrel (one floor with another), listen to record players, and even dance.

This was the kind of courtyard we entered. It was deserted.

The German bombers were dive-bombing with an iron screech and howl. Explosions rumbled. The fragments of anti-aircraft shells clicked on the stones of the courtyard.

To take cover from the fragments, we stood under the roof of an upper terrace. An old yardman with a torn gas mask on his shoulder sat beside us on a box and slept. In spite of the rumbling, whistling, and dust which was blown into the yard in whole salvos from the street, he didn't wake up.

Opposite us we noticed a porch with a massive door. It led, apparently, to a separate apartment. A bronze plaque engraved with the letters *I. S. Weintraub, Dentist* was screwed to the door.

The old orthography testified that Weintraub had been settled here since time immemorial.

"Before the revolution!" remarked Olesha. "That sounds like 'Before Christ' or 'Before the Deluge.' "

Next to the porch was a Venetian window with drawn curtains. Behind them could be seen the black leaves of fig plants.

An airplane began to whine. Explosions and the salvos of the anti-aircraft guns started roaring like iron avalanches.

Then we saw a simple and not at all remarkable scene. I, by the way, still don't understand why Olesha and I laughed so long when we remembered it later.

Someone angrily jerked back the curtains on the Venetian window, struck the frame of the middle window with the palm of his hand and flung it open with a crash. The side windows flew away to the wall.

An old, badly shaved Jew with lowered suspenders and in a creased shirt leaned out the window. It was obviously Dr. Weintraub himself. He held a newspaper in his hand. He probably had been sleeping and had covered himself with this newspaper because of the flies. The explosions and whine of the planes had awakened him.

Resting his hands on the windowsill, he leaned out the window. With sclerous eyes, red from irritation, he looked at a plane which had blundered low over the courtyard with a satanic whine.

"What? Again? Tramps! !" he shouted indignantly.

He spit furiously after the plane, slammed the window with a crash, and jerked the curtain shut.

Then the yardman, who hadn't awakened even with the explosions, immediately came to, yawned, and said sadly, "The most desperate tenant in our whole yard. Napoleon!"

The raid ended. We went out on the street. It was already dark.

"You see," said Olesha, "I was right. There it is, the old Odessa that never surrenders."

"You were just lucky," I answered.

We started walking to the Hotel London. Near the Opera Theater was an acacia tree which had been torn out by the roots. Its roots were caught on the second floor of an old-fashioned house and were entangled in the balcony railing.

Near the entrance stood an ambulance. From the windowsill on the second floor very bright blood slowly dropped onto the sidewalk.

Smoke spread out in layers over the sea. Something was burning in the suburb Peresyp'. And perhaps there, beyond the estuary, the moon was rising.

The street lights from *The Three Fat Men* were intact and I was not less glad of this than Olesha.

I could say much more about Olesha, but it is still too difficult now. He died recently, and it is quite impossible to forget the little red rose in the buttonhole of his old coat. I saw this coat on him for many years.

III.   ALEKSANDR BLOK

THERE is no task more difficult than talking about the smell of river water and the quietness of a field. And at the same time telling it so that a listener will distinctly sense this smell and feel the quietness.

How can you convey "the crystal ring," as Blok said, of Pushkin's lines which in the most varied circumstances emerge completely unexpectedly in your mind.

There are hundreds of remarkable phenomena in the world. We still have no words or expressions for them. The more wonderful and the more splendid a phenomenon is, the more difficult it is to speak about it in our lifeless words.

Aleksandr Blok's poetry and life are one of the beautiful and in many ways inexplicable phenomena of our Russian reality.

The more time passes since the day of Blok's tragic death, the more improbable seems the very fact of the existence among us of this man of genius.

For many of us he has merged with extraordinary people, with the poets of the Renaissance and with the legendary heroes of all humanity. For me, Blok in particular stands among such unbelievable and almost fantastic figures as Orlando, Petrarch, Abelard, Tristan, Leopardi, Shelley, or the still misunderstood Lermontov, the boy who during his short life succeeded in speaking about the ardor of a soul wasted in the wilderness.

Blok took Lermontov's place. He said these sorrowful and concise words about him: "In his frenzied torments is the anguish of an unprecedented spring."

I consider the circumstance that I didn't see and hear Blok one of the greatest misfortunes of my life.

I did not hear Blok, and I do not know how he recited his poetry, but I believe the poet Pyast, who wrote a small article about it.

The timbre of Blok's voice was subdued, distant, and uniformly calm. His voice reached even his contemporaries as though it were a voice from a near distance. There was something magical and insistent in it, like the hum of a string slowly falling silent.

The Blok I am talking about firmly exists in my consciousness and in my life, and I never will be able to think about him otherwise. I have spent many nights in silence with him, my heart has often fallen from each randomly spoken line of his singing verse. "This voice is yours, and I will give life and grief to its incomprehensible sound." Even now, when, according to the words of Esenin, "It is time to gather my mortal belongings for the road," Blok has remained the same as when he entered my life in my distant and arduous youth.

Blok's poetry can never be counted as among his "mortal belongings," because they are not subject to the laws of mortality and the laws of decay, and they will exist while man is alive on our earth and until "God's miracle of miracles" — the free Russian word — disappears.

Perhaps our somewhat oversensitive and intensely sad attitude toward Blok can be explained by the hydrogen death which lurks beside us. All some madman or good-for-nothing has to do is press a button, and everything worthwhile in human life, and man himself, will be destroyed. And because there are so many good-for-nothings and because they are forward, insolent, and vicious, their presence fills all peaceful humanity with great anxiety. And in the confusion this anxiety causes, we, with particular anguish, feel the sublimity and clarity of Blok's poetry.

But this is our particular misfortune and particular theme.

Yes, I am sorry I did not know Blok. In one place he said: "The consciousness that something miraculous is beside us comes too late."

A life cut short is irreversible. We cannot revive Blok, and we can never see him in our daily life. But there is one phenomenon in the world which is equal to a miracle and which defies all natural laws, and, for this reason, is consoling. This phenomenon is art.

In our consciousness it can create everything and revive everything! Reread *War and Peace*, and I guarantee that you will clearly hear the laugh of Natasha Rostova who has hidden behind your back, and you will fall in love with her as with a living and real person.

I am certain that the love for Blok and the longing for Blok are so great that sooner or later he will appear in a long narrative poem or story, completely alive, complex, captivating, and experiencing the miracle of his second birth. I have faith in this because our country has no scarcity of talents and because the complexity of the human spirit still has not been reduced to one common denominator.

Forgive me, but I shall have to say a few words about myself.

I have begun to write an autobiographical narrative and in it have reached the middle of my life. It is not a memoir, it is just a story where the author is free in its composition. But in the main, I more or less adhere to real events.

In this autobiographical narrative I am writing about my life as it actually was. But each person, including me, must have a second life, a second biography. It, as one says, "has not emerged" in real life and has not really taken place. It exists only in my desires and in my imagination.

And it is precisely this second life which I want to write about, to write about it as it would have been, if I had created it by my will, without depending on any chance occurrences.

In my second "autobiography" I want to and can meet closely with Blok, even become friends with him, and write everything I think about him with the great appreciation and tenderness I feel for him. It is as though I, in this way, want to continue Blok's life in myself.

You are right in asking me why this is necessary.

It is necessary so that my life will be harmoniously concluded and so that the power of Blok's poetry will be shown in the example of my life. I did not see Blok. In the last years of his life I was far from Petersburg. But now I am trying to compensate, at least indirectly, for this loss.

Perhaps this appears somewhat naïve, but I want to see everything connected with Blok — people, surroundings, and the Petersburg landscape which has hardly changed since the poet's death.

Even a long time ago the incomprehensible desire to find the house in Leningrad where Blok lived and died began to torment me, but I had to find it alone, without the help of anyone else at all, without any questions, and without studying a map of Leningrad. And not clearly knowing where the river Pryazhka was (Blok lived on the bank of this river on the corner of the present-day Decembrists' Street), I walked to the Pryazhka and did not ask anyone the way. I myself don't completely understand why I acted like this. I was certain that I would find the way by intuition and that the power of my attachment to Blok, like a blind man's guide, would lead me by the hand to the threshold of his home.

The first time I did not reach the Pryazhka. It was beginning to flood, and the bridges were closed.

I shivered and just looked into the dull slate mist in the west, where the Pryazhka was. A wet wind blowing from there struck my face and brought in the fog, and huge vague forms of houses rose in the fog like stone ships in a storm.

I knew that Blok's home stood on the shore and, obviously, was the first to receive the blows of a Baltic storm.

And only on the second try did I reach the house on the Pryazhka. I did not go alone. With me was my nineteen-year-old daughter, a youngster beaming with sorrow because we were seeking Blok's home.

We walked along the river bank. I somehow recall the whole way with unusual clarity.

It was a misty October day with swirling, fallen leaves. On such days it seems as if a thin fog had long lain over the earth. It was sprinkling lightly, filling one's chest with fresh air and covering the iron railings with fine drops of water.

Blok used the expression "the shadow of fall days." So here was a day filled with this shadow — slightly dark and cold. The windows of large old homes which had been riddled by shell fragments during the blockade flashed blindingly. It smelled of hard-coal smoke, which must have been carried from the port.

We walked very slowly, stopped often, and for a long time looked at everything that was open to view all around. Somehow I was sure that Blok more often had returned home by this route and not by the depressing Officers' Street route.

It smelled strongly of slimy water and sawdust. Right here in this spot on the bank of the open Neva some girls in wadded jackets were using a buzz saw to cut up birch trees for firewood. The sawdust flew out like a fireworks display, but for some reason the usually irritating screech of the saw sounded soft and muted here.

Beyond the dark canal where the Pryazhka was, loomed ship-ways, smokestacks, smoke, and soot-covered factory buildings.

I knew that the windows of Blok's apartment opened on the West, on this factory landscape, on this sea coast.

We came out on the Pryazhka and I immediately saw, behind some low stone buildings, the only large house — brick and very ordinary. This was Blok's home.

"Well, we have arrived," I said to my daughter.

She stopped. Her eyes flashed with joy, but a gleam of tears was immediately added to this joyful radiance. She tried to restrain herself, but the tears did not obey her and kept accumulating in small drops and rolled off her eyelashes. Then she took hold of my shoulder and pressed her face on my sleeve in order to hide her tears.

The windows of the house reflected Leningrad's hazy light. For both of us this spot, and this light seemed sacred.

I thought about how fortunate a poet is who receives life's first love, shy and grateful, in his youth. Youth acknowledges a young poet. That is why Blok always was and always will remain young in our conception of him. Such is the fate of almost all poets who have lived tragically and perished tragically.

Even in the last years before his death, Blok, exhausted by an inner torment which he revealed to no one and which, therefore, remained unsolved, preserved the outward features of his youth.

Here I must make a small digression.

It is widely known that the works of some writers and poets possess a great infecting power.

When their prose and verse happens to enter our consciousness even in the smallest doses, they disturb us, arouse a torrent of thoughts and a swarm of images, and infect us with an insur-mountable desire to fix all this on paper.

In this sense Blok unmistakably had an effect on many poets and writers. Not only did his poetry influence them, but so too did the events of his life. I will quote here an example which perhaps is not very characteristic, but right now I do not remember another.

The writer Aleksandr Grin has a posthumous and still unpublished novel, *Touch-Me-Not*. The setting of this novel coin-cides with Blok's stories about his life in Brittany in the small port of l'Aberwrach.

There Blok for the first time became acquainted with the life of the sea. It provoked an almost childlike admiration in him. Every-thing became terribly interesting.

He wrote his mother: "We live surrounded by marine signals. The main lighthouse flashes every five seconds and illuminates our walls. In the port stands a disarmed frigate of the twenties (of the last century) which was in the Mexican War and now rests at anchor. Its name is *Melpomene*. On its bow a white statue yearns for the sea."

Here is another characteristic place from a letter which must be quoted: "Recently the old keeper at one of the rotating lighthouses died before he had readied the beacon for the evening. Then his wife and their two little children rotated the beacon all night by hand. For this she received the Order of the Legion of Honor."

"I think," Blok remarked, "Russians would have done the same."

The old Fort Cezon was located on an island near l'Aberwrach. Because of the fort's complete decay and obsoleteness the French government was trying to sell it very cheaply.

Blok apparently wanted to buy the fort very much. He even calculated that the purchase, improvement of the land, laying out of a garden, and repairs would cost twenty-five thousand francs.

Everything in this fort was romantic: the half-ruined draw-bridge, the casemates, the powder magazines, and the old-fashioned cannons.

The members of Blok's family talked him out of this purchase. But he talked to his friends and acquaintances about this fort a lot — the dream did not easily yield to sober considerations.

Grin heard this story of Blok's and wrote a novel in which an old man and his beautiful young daughter, who is nicknamed "Touch-Me-Not," buy an old fort from the government, settle in it, and convert the ramparts into fragrant flower gardens and un-dergrowth.

All kinds of events take place in the novel. But perhaps the fort — friendly looking, long since in ruins, peaceful, and romantically old — is drawn best of all. Also beautiful are the descriptions of the gardens and the picturesque attributes of the trees, bushes, and flowers.

I must confess that Blok's poetry suggested to me an idea which at first glance seemed strange — writing several stories connected by a common mood with Blok's poetry. This thought has not left me even now. For the time being I have written the story "Rainy Dawn," which in its entirety is derived from Blok's poem "Russia."

> *And the impossible is possible,*
> *And the long road is easy,*
> *When in the road's distance*
> *A short glance flashes from under a kerchief . . .*

I do not want to give and I cannot give my interpretation of Blok's life and poetry. I do not believe very much in Blok's prophetic and mystical horror before the coming tribulations of Russia and humanity, in the fatal desert surrounding the poet, in a certain oversimplified perception of the revolution, and in his hopeless doubts and catastrophic falls.

We have a large number of Blok's so-called "conceptions" and riddles. It seems to me that everything in Blok is clearer and simpler than his critics make it.

It is only the concrete side of the poetry of Blok's verse and of his life that attracts me and holds my attention. The fogs of symbolism, deliberate, deprived of living images and live blood, and incorporeal, are only the prolonged inclination of a young man.

Sometimes I think that much in Blok cannot be understood by the people of the last generation and by the new youth.

His love for impoverished Russia cannot be understood. From the point of view of today's youth, how could one love this country where "it is impossible to count or measure with the eye the mean, poor villages; and a fire in a distant meadow shines in the darkened day."

It is difficult for today's youth to understand because this Russia no longer exists. It is just this no longer existent quality that Blok knew and loved in it. If some remote villages, log roads, and wilds have still remained, then the man in these villages and wilds is already different. A generation has been replaced and the grandsons no longer understand the grandfathers; nor, at times, the sons, the fathers.

The grandsons do not understand and do not want to understand the poverty wept over in songs, adorned with legends and fairy tales, with the eyes of timid mute children, and with the lowered eyelashes of girls, and agitated by the tales of wanderers and cripples, by the constant feeling of an unbearable mystery living alongside one in the forests, in the lakes, in rotten logs, and in boarded-up peasants' houses, and the always present sense of a miracle. "I slumber and behind my slumber is a mystery, and in the mystery you sleep, Russia."

A broad and strong heart and a great love for one's people are needed to fall in love with these gray houses, the smell of ashes, weeds, and lamentations, and to see behind all this poverty the pale beauty of Russia, girded by forests and surrounded by thickets. This Russia is dead. Blok mourned it and sang a dirge over it:

> *Not in a rich grave*
> *Do you rest, poor Finnish Russia!*

A new Russia, "A new America," rises for Blok in the southern steppes.

> *No, Cossack tufts don't wave in the wind.*
> *The hetman's standards don't color the steppes . . .*
> *There rise black factory chimneys,*
> *There plant whistles shriek.*

For the people of the last generation old and new Russia are familiar to an almost equal degree. In this vast knowledge of Russia lies the wealth of this generation.

You cannot know the new Russia without knowing the old, without knowing all "the strange things the Chuds did and the Merya intended," without knowing the old villages, without knowing the enchanted wanderers who roamed about the whole land, and without seeing the sunset in blood over the field of Kulikovo.

Blok's poems about love are magic. Like all magic, they are inexplicable and poignant. It is almost impossible to speak about them. You must read them over and over, repeat them, each time experiencing a quickening of your heart; you must be overcome by their agonizing melodies and be endlessly amazed that they enter your mind suddenly and forever.

In this poetry, especially in "The Stranger," and "In a Restaurant," his mastery reaches its height. It is terrifying and seems unattainable. Probably thinking about these poems, Blok said, addressing his muse:

> *And more insidious than the northern night,*
> *And more intoxicating than golden champagne,*
> *And shorter than Gypsy love*
> *Were your terrible caresses . . .*

Blok's poems about love are growing stronger with time; their images envelope one: *"And her resilient silk breathes ancient beliefs"; "I see an enchanted shore and an enchanted distance"; "And bottomless dark blue eyes bloom on the distant shore."*

These are not so much poems about the eternally feminine as they are an outburst of an enormous poetic force which captures both tempted and untempted hearts.

An "unknown power" transforms Blok's poetry into something higher than just poetry alone, into an organic fusion of poetry, music, and thought, into an accord with the beating of each human heart, and into a phenomenon of art which still has not found its definition.

It is sufficient to read one stanza known all over Russia to be convinced of this:

> *You darted away like a frightened bird.*
> *You passed by, light, like my sleep . . .*
> *And you breathed perfumes, your eyelashes slumbered.*
> *Your silk whispered anxiously . . .*

In his poetry and prose Blok passed along the enormous path of Russian history from the stagnation of the nineties to World War I, to the most complicated interweavings of philosophical, poetic, political, and religious schools, and, finally, to the October Revolution "in a white wreath of roses." He was poetry's guardian, its minstrel, its slave, and its genius.

Blok said that genius casts light on the immeasurable expanses of time. These words, in their entirety, refer to him. His influence on the fate of each of us, writer and poet, perhaps, is not immediately apparent, but it is significant.

Already in my youth I understood the meaning of his greatest words and believed them:

> *Erase the accidental features*
> *And you will see — life is beautiful . . .*

I strove to follow Blok's advice. And I am deeply grateful to him. We live in the resplendent radiance of his genius, and it will reach, perhaps only more clearly, the future generations of our country.

translated by JAMES BAILEY

Biographical Notes

BORIS BALTER graduated from military school in the late 1930's and saw action in the Russo-Finnish War, where he was wounded three times. "Three from a Town" is the first portion of a longer work, *Goodbye, Boys,* which appeared serially in the journal *Youth* in 1962 (Aug.–Sept.) and, subsequently, as a separate book. He has published numerous short stories.

MELVILLE CANE, one of America's most eminent poets, has, since 1926, published eight books of poetry, including *A Wider Arc, And Pastures New* and *Bullet Hunting.* Mr. Cane is also widely known as the author of the book, *Making a Poem.*

ANDREI DOSTAL' has written numerous books of poetry, including *Poems and Songs, A Song Will Find the Way, The Pines Rustle* and *Morning.* His poems have won several Soviet poetry awards.

VSEVOLOD IVANOV, who in his youth was a protégé of Maksim Gor'ky, is known for his colorful and ornate prose of the twenties. His most famous work is the novel, *Armored Train 14–69.* He died in August, 1963.

YURY KAZAKOV is thirty-six years old and has published six collections of short stories, among them: *On the Road, At the Waystation* and *Man'ka.* He has also written a long nonfiction sketch entitled *Northern Diary.* A volume of his stories in English has been published by Houghton Mifflin.

VLADIMIR KORNILOV is a poet who, although a member of the Soviet Writers' Union and held in high regard as a promising young talent, has to date appeared in print relatively infrequently. A first book of poems, entitled *The Pier,* has, however, been announced for publication in 1964.

GALINA KORNILOVA is the wife of Vladimir Kornilov. Born in 1928, she is a literary critic and journalist by profession.

VLADIMIR KOBLIKOV is the author of a book of short stories, *Open Windows,* and a novella, *Dar'ya.* Koblikov served as one of the editors of *Pages from Tarusa.*

NAUM KORZHAVIN is the pseudonym of Lev Mandal'. Although his first published poetry dates from 1941, Korzhavin's first book of poems, *Years*, appeared in 1963.

LEV KRIVENKO was born in 1920 and fought in the front lines during World War II. He is the author of numerous short stories, many of which deal with the war.

STANLEY KUNITZ is the author of three books of poetry: *Intellectual Things*, *Passport to War* and *Selected Poems — 1928–1958*. For the latter collection Mr. Kunitz was awarded the Pulitzer Prize. His translations of the Soviet poet Andrei Voznesensky have appeared in the magazine *Encounter* (April, 1963).

DENISE LEVERTOV, one of America's outstanding younger poets, has published four books of poetry: *Here and Now*, *Overland to the Islands*, *With Eyes at the Back of Our Heads* and *The Jacob's Ladder*. Those interested in questions of poetry translation will want to read her article "Boris Pasternak in English" in the magazine *Jubilee* (June, 1962).

VSEVOLOD MEYERHOL'D began his career as a student of Stanislavsky but became famous for his highly stylized productions of Symbolist plays by poets such as Aleksandr Blok and Fyodor Sologub. After 1917 Meyerhol'd remained active in the theater. He was arrested in 1939 and died in a Stalinist concentration camp.

BULAT OKUDZHAVA is of Armenian and Georgian descent, although he himself speaks neither language. Okudzhava is the author of two books of poetry, *Lyric* and *Islands*. He enjoys great popularity among Russian youth for his café poetry which he sings, accompanying himself on the guitar. "Lots of Luck, Kid!" is Okudzhava's first story.

KONSTANTIN PAUSTOVSKY, now in his seventies, has been a professional writer since 1925 and is one of the most popular authors in the Soviet Union. His works include *A Novel about Forests*, *The Black Sea* and an autobiography, *A Life's Tale*.

F. D. REEVE, who teaches Russian literature at Wesleyan University, was the companion and translator for Robert Frost on the poet's trip to the Soviet Union, and he is the author of *Robert Frost in Russia* (Atlantic-Little, Brown). He has published poetry in numerous journals including *The New Yorker* and *Hudson Review*.

BORIS SLUTSKY is forty-five years old. He has published three books of poetry: *Memory*, *Today and Yesterday* and *Time*. A short essay on Slutsky's poetry may be found in Il'ya Ehrenburg's book, *Chekhov, Stendhal and Other Essays* (Knopf, 1963).

NIKOLAI STEPANOV is a well-known critic who has written extensively on a score of important Russian writers and poets, including Radishchev, Krylov, Pushkin, Gogol and Mayakovsky.

ANNE STEVENSON is a new poet whose poems have appeared in *Poetry, Audience, Saturday Review, Paris Review* and other journals.

YURY TRIFONOV is thirty-four years old. He is known as the author of the novel, *The Students*, and a book of short stories, *Under the Sun*. Another of Trifonov's short stories is included in the anthology, *Short Stories of Russia Today*, edited by Yvonne Kapp (Houghton Mifflin, 1958).

MARINA TSVETAEVA was born in 1892; her first poetry was published in 1911. Among her many books of poetry are *Poems to Blok, Separation* and *Craft*. After the 1917 Revolution, Tsvetaeva went into emigration and lived for many years in Paris. In 1939 however she returned to Russia, and, shortly thereafter, she hanged herself under circumstances which have never been fully explained.

FRIDA VIGDOROVA is the author of several novels which deal mainly with school life: *This Is My Home, The Road To Life* and *Family Happiness*. Her book, *My Class*, has been published in English under the title *Diary of a Russian Schoolteacher* (Grove, 1960).

EVGENY VINOKUROV was born in 1925. He is the author of seven books of poetry, among them *The Word, The Human Face* and *Confessions*. A book of his collected poems was published in 1962.

NIKOLAI ZABOLOTSKY was born in 1903. He and Boris Pasternak are widely recognized as being the finest poets in Russia in the difficult period from 1930 to the death of Stalin. Zabolotsky served seven years in a Stalinist concentration camp. He died in Tarusa in 1958.

THE EDITOR, Andrew Field, was born in 1938 in New Jersey and studied at Columbia and Harvard, where he has also taught. Presently he is serving as an exchange scholar from Harvard at Moscow University. Mr. Field's scholarly articles and critical essays have appeared in *Partisan Review, The New Leader, Slavonic Review, Columbia University Forum, Russian Review* and other journals.